Mathematics for the Multitude?

A History of the Mathematical Association

Prepared for the Mathematical Association by

Michael Price
University of Leicester

The Mathematical Association

First published in 1994 by
The Mathematical Association
259 London Road
Leicester LE2 3BE
England

ISBN 0 906 588 324

Publication sponsored by
The London Mathematical Society

Research supported by the University of Leicester

Cover designed by
Leicester University Audio-Visual Services

Printed and bound in Great Britain at
J.W. Arrowsmith Ltd, Bristol

CONTENTS

Contents

TABLES AND FIGURES

PLATES

ABBREVIATIONS

AIGT   Association for the Improvement of Geometrical Teaching
AMET   Association of Mathematics Education Teachers
APSSM   Association of Public School Science Masters
ASE   Association for Science Education
ATAM   Association for Teaching Aids in Mathematics
ATCDE   Association of Teachers in Colleges and Departments of Education
ATM   Association of Teachers of Mathematics
AUMET   Association of University Mathematics Education Teachers

BAAS   British Association for the Advancement of Science
B Ed   Bachelor of Education
BNCM   British National Committee for Mathematics

CNAA   Council for National Academic Awards
CSE   Certificate of Secondary Education
CSM   Contemporary School Mathematics

DES   Department of Education and Science
DSA   Department of Science and Art

FRS   Fellow of the Royal Society

GCE   General Certificate of Education
GCSE   General Certificate of Secondary Education

HMC   Headmasters' Conference
HMI   Her/His Majesty's Inspectorate/Inspector

IAAM   Incorporated Association of Assistant Masters
ICM   International Congress of Mathematicians
ICME   International Congress on Mathematical Education
ICMI   International Commission on Mathematical Instruction

ICSITM	International Commission for the Study and Improvement of the Teaching of Mathematics
IMA	Institute of Mathematics and its Applications
INSET	In-service Education and Training
JMC	Joint Mathematical Council
LEA	Local Education Authority
LMS	London Mathematical Society
MA	Mathematical Association
MEI	Mathematics in Education and Industry
MG	*Mathematical Gazette*
MIS	Mathematical Instruction Subcommittee
MME	Midlands Mathematical Experiment
NAMA	National Association of Mathematics Advisers
NATE	National Association for the Teaching of English
NATFHE	National Association of Teachers in Further and Higher Education
NCC	National Curriculum Council
NCTM	National Council of Teachers of Mathematics
NU(E)T	National Union of (Elementary) Teachers
NUJMB	Northern Universities Joint Matriculation Board
OEEC	Organization for European Economic Co-operation
SCAMES	Standing Conference of Associations concerned with Mathematics Education in Schools
SCDC	School Curriculum Development Committee
SEAC	School Examinations and Assessment Council
SEC	Secondary Examinations Council
SMP	School Mathematics Project
SSEC	Secondary School Examinations Council
TGAT	Task Group on Assessment and Testing
UDE	University Department of Education
UDEMSG	University Departments of Education Mathematics Study Group

ACKNOWLEDGEMENTS

Since 1987, when I started to pursue the possibility of writing a history of English mathematics education focused on the Mathematical Association, a number of people and institutions have helped, over a period of six years, to bring all the work on this project to fruition.

For providing oral, written or documentary evidence, my thanks are due to the following:

B.G. Atwood, C.A.R. Bailey, C.C.H. Barker, W.M. Brookes, L. Brown, P.B. Coaker, R.H. Collins, J.T. Combridge (1979 correspondence), B. Cooper, W.A. Dodd (1985 correspondence), B.J.F. Dorrington, R. Fielding, W. Flemming, T.J. Fletcher, R. Gowing, J.W. Hersee, A.G. Howson, F.W. Land, W.J. Langford, D. Layton, A.P. Penfold, D.A. Quadling, P.H. Ransom, P. Reynolds, J.M. Rollett, H.B. Shuard, F. Smithies, D. Tahta, J.A. Thurston, R.K. Tobias, J.M. Truran, H. Whitby, F.A. Wood.

The **Mathematical Association**, through its officers and headquarters staff, has given me all possible support, in spite of financial stringency. Particular thanks are due to the former treasurer John Hersee, the executive secretaries F. Alan Wood and Heather Whitby, and the Publications Committee and its chairman Bud Winteridge.

The **University of Leicester** has supported the project in various ways and particular thanks are due to the following:

The Research Board for a grant in aid of the fieldwork; the Establishment Board for the award of a term's study leave in 1990; the staffs of the University Library, which holds the Association's collection, and the School of Education Library; the secretarial staff of the School of Education's Research Office; Angela Chorley and Julie Bowles of Audio-Visual Services; and the staff of the Central Photographic Unit.

Thanks are also due to the **London Mathematical Society** for a grant in aid of publication and to the **Association of Teachers of Mathematics** for permission to reproduce Plate 8.3 from *Mathematics Teaching*.

The writing of this book owes much to the critical scrutiny provided by readers of my drafts. Specifically, I must thank Bill Brookes, Roland Collins and Jeremy Kilpatrick for help with particular chapters; and Trevor Fletcher, Geoffrey Howson, Douglas Quadling and Eva Searl for providing much help and encouragement throughout the writing phase. The weaknesses which remain are my own.

Finally, thanks are due to my wife, Jackie Price, for her secretarial support, and to my son, Stephen Price, for all his help in making the most of my word-processing facilities and for producing all the camera-ready copy.

To bring about a better understanding between the high and the low, the few and the many, is, in my opinion, the mission of this Association. There is still work for it to do; it has to make the extremes meet. It has to bring the higher knowledge to the multitude.

(Richard Wormell, Presidential address, 1893)

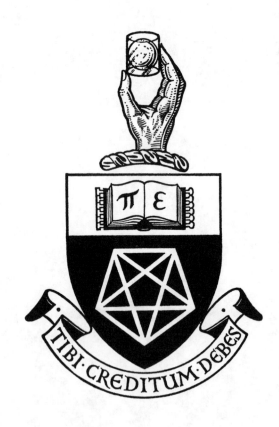

Plate 1.1   Coat of Arms

CHAPTER ONE

INTRODUCTION: PERSPECTIVES ON THE MATHEMATICAL ASSOCIATION

I hold every man a debtor to his profession; from the which as men of course do seek to receive countenance and profit, so ought they of duty to endeavour themselves, by way of amends, to be a help and an ornament thereunto.

(Francis Bacon (1561–1626), preface to *Maxims of the Law*)

It is essential that the voice of professionals should be heard. If it is not, then our claim to be professionals will cease – the Association's motto, 'I hold every man a debtor to his profession', will have become outdated.

(Geoffrey Howson, Presidential address, 1989)

There are many ways of writing history, and institutional histories are no exception. The opening quotation from Bacon, which became the motto of the Mathematical Association at the start of this century, provides a convenient starting-point, both for establishing the purposes of the present book and for clarifying the kind of history to be found within it. Clearly, any history of the MA should at least be informative regarding the internal growth and developing characteristics of this institution since 1870. In this connection, the motto and its links with the MA's coat of arms have a history which can be simply and straightforwardly told.

The motto was adopted by the MA on the suggestion of W.J. Greenstreet (1861–1930), who was then editor of the Association's organ, the *Mathematical Gazette*. The motto first appeared in the *Gazette* of March 1901 and has featured ever since. It propounds a spirit of service by individual members to their professional body, and Greenstreet was himself a notable servant of the MA, both as editor of the *Gazette* for just over thirty years and through his major contribution to the growth of the MA's library. (1)

The link between the Bacon quotation and the MA's coat of arms is to be found in the Latin inscription on the latter: *Tibi creditum debes*. This was taken from a Horace Ode on Virgil and a ship, and the link is clear in translation: 'What has been entrusted to you, you owe.' The assignment of a coat of arms was suggested by Walter Langford, MA President 1957–8, and taken up by the Council of the MA in 1962. Langford also carried through the detailed negotiations with the College of Arms, which were not fully completed until 1965. (2)

The adoption of a motto and coat of arms constitutes a significant but very small part of the MA's historical development. Inevitably, individual members have already featured in the narrative and it would be very hard to construct an institutional history which was not shot through with the contributions of individuals along the way. But already questions of selection, emphasis and attention to detail have arisen. The problem of doing justice to individual contributions in an institutional biography has been well delineated in an apologia which concludes a jubilee history of the Historical Association, 1906–56:

> The study of the genesis of institutions, policies and ideas may discover the dates of resolutions put to the meeting and controversies that have come out into the open; but it can never recover, and never do justice to, the perpetual play of thought, the constant interchange of suggestion and counter-suggestion, out of which concrete proposals eventually arise. Nor can it do justice to the perennial labours of a central office, or of committees which carry on within their terms of reference year in and year out, or of individuals who for a great portion of a lifetime may serve an organization in one capacity and another. (3)

In the present study, individual contributions will force their way in where they relate to what are judged to be significant features in the MA's own history. In order not to break the flow of the narrative and argument, much of the material concerning individual biographies will be confined to the notes and references for each chapter. To do justice to the contributions of many individuals, now deceased, reference may be made to their obituaries. But in relation to post-war developments and the contributions of members who are still alive, and in many cases still very actively involved in the MA's affairs, the problem may appear to be compounded. Here the opening quotation from Geoffrey Howson's Presidential address points to wider considerations which will dictate the kind of history to be found in the later chapters of this book. (4)

In the educational climate of the late 1980s, as Howson points out, 'the mathematics curriculum is now very much a political issue'. (5) What is more, his Presidential address is very much a political statement in the field of mathematics education. What has become increasingly clear as the research for this book has progressed is that, as we move forward in time, so it becomes increasingly important to look outside the confines of the MA in order to make sense of what is happening within this organization. Thus, the focus necessarily shifts towards the wider educational, political, economic and social context, and away from the contributions of individual 'actors' in the day-to-day work of the MA itself. It is hoped that the need for such a shift of emphasis in constructing a history of the MA will provide some consolation to members whose contributions have received scant justice or been overlooked. It must also be admitted that personal motives have played an important part in the shaping of this present book.

Until comparatively recently, little serious work had been done on the history of mathematics education, and, more generally, historians of education had largely neglected the curriculum field as an area for detailed enquiry, preferring to leave it to social scientists or subject specialists. Exceptionally in mathematics, Geoffrey Howson has produced a wide-ranging and ambitious study: *A History of Mathematics Education in England* (1982). (6) Remarkably, he uses the medium of individual biographies – nine in total – to capture general developments in mathematics education over more than four centuries up to *circa* 1960. (7) Three individuals – J.M. Wilson (1836–1931), Charles Godfrey (1873–1924) and Elizabeth Williams (1895–1986) – cover the period of the MA's history. Given the growing complexity, over the past 120 years, of both the educational system and the place of mathematics within it, it became clear that a complementary study to Howson's, in the form of an institutional biography, was worth undertaking. Howson's choice of Wilson, Godfrey and Mrs Williams to serve his historiographical purposes was shrewd but necessarily limiting in scope. For an institutional biography, the MA was an obvious choice – or rather there was no serious alternative – and the focus is less obviously limiting where a principal aim is also to present a view of English mathematics education over the same period.

Interests in institutional history may also spring from within the membership of an institution, and subject associations are no exception. In addition to the jubilee volume of the Historical Association, (8) a scholarly and comprehensive history of the now large and influential Association for Science Education has been produced by David Layton. (9) Less ambitious but obviously historical material is also to be found in the journals of subject associations and particularly at times of major historical significance. A very recent example here concerns the amalgamation of the Modern Language Association (1892–1989) and the British Association for Language Learning (1961–89) within the all-embracing Association for Language Learning (ALL) from 1990. The final issues of both journals contain historical sections to mark the demise. (10)

In the case of the MA, the *Mathematical Gazette* first appeared in 1894, and historical material, sometimes of a more or less anecdotal nature, has continued to feature within its pages ever since. Contributions both on the history of the development of mathematics and mathematics education have appeared over the years, including occasional articles relating to the history of the MA itself. (11) Even before the first appearance of the *Gazette*, the reports of the Association for the Improvement of Geometrical Teaching (the MA's predecessor) included a brief foreign perspective on the AIGT's first twenty years, from Professor G. Loria. (12) Commemorative numbers of the *Gazette* provide a useful secondary source of material on the MA's historical development, including reprints of notable contributions to the *Gazette* and photographs of leading members. (13)

Presidential addresses to the MA are also quite commonly taken as an opportunity to pursue some historical interest, which may focus on the development either of aspects of mathematics itself or of its place in education. In the latter case, some appraisal of the work of the MA, with possible pointers for the future, may or may not also feature. Effectively the first Presidential address, to the AIGT, was given by R.B. Hayward (1829–1903), in 1881. (14) He concentrated squarely on the progress of the AIGT over its first ten years and the potential for extending its operations. Forty years later the MA celebrated its golden jubilee and the Presidential address was fittingly given by a founder member of the AIGT, who had become *Canon* Wilson. The title of his address warrants quoting in full: 'The early history of the Association, or the passing of Euclid from our schools and universities, and how it came about. A story of fifty years ago.' (15) This title holds the dubious distinction of being the longest for Presidential addresses up to 1993. And, for shortness, the title chosen by A.W. Siddons (1876–1959), the first 'mere assistant master' President of the MA, can hardly be bettered: 'Progress'. (16) His address of 1936 provides a useful sketch of the development of public school mathematics teaching over the previous hundred years, with frequent references to the contribution of the AIGT and the MA. (17)

However, many Presidential addresses concentrate on the significance and beauty of mathematics itself, from the standpoint of the creative mathematician. The Presidential address of Professor E.H. Neville (1889–1961) in 1935, 'The food of the gods', is a paradigm in this respect and was justifiably reprinted in the centenary number of the *Gazette*. (18) Addresses since 1980 clearly reflect the rapidly changing educational climate, both in their titles and their substance: Douglas Quadling, 'Pressures and priorities' (1981); Geoffrey Howson, 'New challenges' (1989); and Peter Reynolds, 'Full circle' (1990), which is far from being a discourse on the circle! (19) These contributions return us firmly to the historical and political context of mathematics education and to the place of the MA within it.

The MA celebrated its centenary year in 1971 and this was naturally a time for looking back on past achievements. For this purpose, Theodore Combridge (1897–1986) acted as the unofficial historian of the MA, a position which Siddons's contributions to the *Gazette* suggest that he had previously occupied. (20) To mark the centenary, Combridge gave historical talks on the MA and produced some short articles, including a contribution in two parts to what was then a new journal of the MA, *Mathematics in School*. (21) His most detailed work on the MA's history was never published, including a substantial paper given at the Shell Centre for Mathematical Education in the University of Nottingham. However, this paper has a surprising connection with the work of Margaret Thatcher, who was Secretary of State for Education and Science at the time of the centenary celebrations. Mrs Thatcher had been invited to open the centenary conference and deliver a suitable address. To this end, a request for relevant briefing material was directed to Combridge, who, in the time available, could only provide the draft typescript for his Shell lecture. The story is best taken up by Combridge at this point:

> So I passed the much-corrected and rather scruffy-looking copy of this address . . . to the channel nearest to me . . . The day for the opening ceremony came, and the speech was duly delivered, free from any blemish that might suggest inadequate briefing.
>
> On May 6 the typescript was returned to me through the nearest channel. To my delight, various marks of annotation adorned the

copy, and in a blank space at the end was written (in true blue and in the lady's own handwriting): 'Returned (that is to say the lecture left my desk on 17 April). If it is printed, please may I have a copy? I thoroughly enjoyed reading it. M. Thatcher.' (22)

This lecture and related correspondence have been deposited in the archives of the MA, at its headquarters in Leicester.

The historical writing of leading members of the AIGT and MA – notably Wilson, Siddons and Combridge – provides a useful secondary source for the historian, who must, however, guard against possible errors of fact or judgement. Such contributions, including occasional Presidential addresses, typically present a view of the MA from within and one constructed mainly for an audience of MA members. In writing for *Mathematics in School*, Combridge was well aware of the difficulties and clearly declared his own position in response: 'No appraisal of its work is attempted – that would need a writer much less biased than the present author.' (23) By contrast, in writing this present book the intention is to provide a view of over 120 years of the MA from without, which sets major developments in context and includes some appraisal of them. Obviously, the MA membership still provides a principal target audience but the appeal is not intended to be of a straightforward, self-congratulatory kind. Rather, the aim is to provide a history of mathematics education which is relevant to the interests of those who work in the general field of mathematics education, and to others who have an interest in the curriculum and its historical determinants.

Combridge's work on the history of the MA was not confined to the period of the centenary celebrations. A centenary appeal was launched in 1971, and in 1975 the MA acquired new headquarters at 259 London Road, Leicester. The library of the MA had already been transferred, to what was the University College, Leicester, some twenty years earlier. The MA's library is a valuable resource for historians of mathematics and education. (24) Books, pamphlets and periodicals are largely shelved in an open stack system but material of a more archival nature cannot be readily accommodated in the library of the University. It was Combridge who took the lead in getting the growing amount of archival material – principally journals, reports, minutes, correspondence and other papers – suitably accommodated at the new headquarters, originally in a converted bathroom on the first floor. The archives have since been transferred to a converted adjoining garage – the Joan Marshall Room – along with the growing collection of back numbers of periodicals and copies of reports of the MA. (25) Combridge was responsible for some of the early sorting and classification in the archives and quite a lot of his own material has since been incorporated. He also produced a very detailed although unpublished set of notes on records and sources for the MA's history, which necessitated a careful search of all the reports of the AIGT and the issues of the *Gazette*, up to the late 1970s. Taken together with the comprehensive *Index to the Mathematical Gazette*, up to 1931, this work provides much useful ground-clearance for the present author and a particular debt to Combridge must be acknowledged. (26)

For the period from the turn of the century, the minute books of the Council and various committees of the MA, and notably of the Teaching Committee since 1902, are an important primary source for detailing internal initiatives, major deliberations and policy making, including responses to external developments. No minute books of the AIGT survive but the early general reports, in nineteen volumes (1871–93) are an informative primary source. (27) The archives now lack only one twentieth-century minute book, that of the Other Secondary Schools Special Committee, 1912–22. (28)ʼ For post-war developments one other source of evidence – first-hand accounts, both oral and written – deserves mention.

There are obvious difficulties in writing relatively recent or contemporary history and the curriculum field is no exception, particularly where the focus is on major developments and the leading figures identified in an historical account. Sins of omission and errors of fact or judgement will all invite the criticism of the participants who were principally involved. Where an institutional history is concerned, some depersonalization of the account may partly alleviate the difficulties but the importance of individual human motives and actions must be given due recognition. A recent book by Barry Cooper on the modern mathematics reform movement of the 1950s and 1960s has understandably not escaped criticism and at least one lesson can be learned from Cooper's valuable efforts, which are largely based upon published reports. (29) Individual reminiscences and judgements, which can be cross-checked and compared with other evidence, can help significantly in constructing and filling out an historical picture. Personal correspondence and individual interviews have provided an important source of evidence for the post-war period and helped in making some assessment of the MA's place within it.

It remains in this introduction to raise some key questions about the nature, functions and structure of an institution such as the MA. The two quotations which opened this chapter – the MA's motto and Howson's comment on it – were chosen to provide a suitable entry point for this purpose. To what extent is it appropriate to refer to the MA as a professional body, analogous to the legal profession in Bacon's context, and to its members as 'professionals'? As Howson implies, the answer to this question may vary over time, given changing educational and political circumstances. But the implied link with professions warrants at least some investigation. A wide-ranging and seminal study of the professions was undertaken by Carr-Saunders and Wilson in the 1930s. (30) Their coverage includes scientific societies – representing chemistry, physics and engineering – industrial institutes and a range of teachers' professional organizations. Perhaps surprisingly, mathematics is nowhere mentioned and yet the London Mathematical Society was founded in 1865, a few years before the AIGT. (31) However, the promotion of aspects such as communication, investigation or research, and the medium of publication, is only one aspect of professionalism in the sense of Carr-Saunders and Wilson and it is not regarded as sufficient for a 'professional' body, which should also exercise an important degree of regulation both on membership and the maintenance of standards, and, in addition, seek to promote the status of a profession and represent its wider social and political interests. The position of the MA, which is a voluntary organization and largely run on a part-time basis as an unincorporated charity, is further complicated by the fact that it is not a straightforward academic study society but is principally concerned with the place and shape of an academic subject in education. Thus its position within the complex world of teachers' organizations needs also to be considered.

Throughout the history of English education over the past two centuries, the concept of teaching as a profession in the general sense has been problematic, and, with the nineteenth-century rise of the examination system, the related influence of the universities, and the growing involvement of the state in educational provision, the aspirations for full professional status and a self-contained profession of teaching have remained far from realization. The recent development of a statutory National Curriculum also impinges on the concept of professionalism in English education. Sectional interests and individual organizations catering for them mushroomed in the nineteenth century, and, in all this, trade-union functions loomed large. The variety and complexity in teachers' professional organization were well demonstrated in an early survey by Webb, who pointed to the 'chaos of specialism' by the time of the First World War. (32) The MA and a number of other academic subject associations with teaching interests had been created by this time and Webb sought to disentangle their distinctive functions from those of the mainstream teacher organizations or unions:

> It seems open to question how far a professional association should regard itself as the main organ for advancing technique; this is the duty of the scientific society or 'subject association' which can unite the teacher, the executant, the researcher, the dilettante amateur, and, finally, the expert representative of the user or 'consumer' of the product or subject-matter. (33)

The conclusion was that

> the advancement of the technique of classics, history, English or mathematics is not exclusively, or even primarily the duty of the Head Masters' Conference or the N.U.T., but of the Classical Association, the History Association, the English Association and the Mathematical Association respectively . . . (34)

A chronological table (Table 1.1) will help to place the formation of the MA and its forerunner the AIGT within the wider context of academic and educational organization in the nineteenth century. The table is arranged in three columns with a vertical linear time scale from 1870. Down the left column are listed a small number of examples of associations with a principal concern for the advancement of an area or areas of specialist knowledge. Down the right column are listed again only a selection of associations with a principal concern for or self-interest in some aspect of the general English educational system. A third, central column, and central for the purposes of this book, represents the middle ground between knowledge advancement and educational politics. Here are included all the

Table 1.1
Institutional Developments in Knowledge, Education and Pedagogy

ADVANCEMENT OF SUBJECT KNOWLEDGE	SUBJECT TEACHING	EDUCATION
Royal Society (1660) British Association for the Advancement of Science (1831) Royal Geographical Society (1831) Chemical Society (1841) *1860*		Society for the Diffusion of Useful Knowledge (1826) Central Society of Education (1837) College of Preceptors (1846) *1860*
London Mathematical Society (1865)		
		Headmasters' Conference (1869)
1870	Association for the Improvement of Geometrical Teaching (1871)	National Union of *1870* Elementary Teachers (1870)
		Association of Head Mistresses (1874)
Institute of Chemistry (1878) *1880*		*1880*
		Association of Assistant Mistresses (1884)
1890		Association of Head *1890* Masters (1890)
	Modern Language Association (1892) Geographical Association (1893)	Association of Assistant Masters (1891)
	Mathematical Association (1897)	
1900	Association of Public School Science Masters (1901) Classical Association (1903)	*1900*
	Historical Association (1906) English Association (1907)	
1910		*1910*
	Association of (Women) Science Teachers (1912)	

major academic subject teaching associations having a particular concern for secondary education. All these associations were formed in the period 1870–1914, and the AIGT conspicuously earlier than the rest. The reasons for this first for mathematics will be explored in the next chapter. But a little more still needs to be said about the links between the three columns of the table.

In the case of mathematics, the distinction between the first and second columns was exemplified by Alan Broadbent (1903–73), who edited the *Gazette* for nearly twenty-five years:

> The line of distinction between the Association and the London Mathematical Society . . . is clear: the London Mathematical Society is primarily interested in mathematical research, in the discovery and publication of new mathematics, particularly of recent years in pure rather than applied mathematics, and it is our premier research society. Here the association does not compete . . . Our field is not that of mathematics alone, nor that of teaching alone; it is the combination, the *teaching* of *mathematics*. (35)

However, scholarly societies did also venture into the middle ground, to influence either a subject's general status in education or its shape, i.e. details of curriculum content and pedagogy. This was certainly so in the cases of the British Association for the Advancement of Science, from around 1850, and the Royal Geographical Society, from around 1870, both of which were particularly concerned with the issue of the educational status of science and geography respectively. But notice that the subject teaching association for geography, the Geographical Association, was not formed until 1893 and the first science teaching association, for public school science masters, did not emerge until 1901, with women forming a separate organization in 1912.

Furthermore, general educational organizations or teachers' unions also became involved in the middle ground concerning aspects of school curricula, both in principle and practice, and in details of specific subjects. Examples here are provided by the socially dissimilar cases of the Headmasters' Conference, representing the élite public schools, and the National Union of Elementary Teachers (NUET), representing the much larger and socially inferior body of elementary school teachers. Although both these associations were from 1870 much concerned with the general politics of education in their separate spheres, and with the self-interests of their members, they did also, from time to time, address specific curriculum issues. In the case of the NUET, their work penetrated the details of government requirements under the period of centralized curriculum control administered through payment based on the results of tests taken by elementary school pupils. (36)

The exceptional College of Preceptors, an association of private school teachers, was formed as early as 1846 and had very wide-ranging aspirations. These embraced the ideals of a self-regulating teaching profession to be realized through the mechanisms of examination and certification, provision of training facilities, registration for teachers, and also research, study and dissemination functions. Given the growing involvement of the state in education from the mid-nineteenth century, the College's wider professional aspirations went largely unfulfilled. However, it was the first professional association of teachers in England and, perhaps surprisingly, its journal from 1847, the *Educational Times*, is included in Archibald's survey of minor English mathematical serials. (37) Its long-running series of mathematical questions and solutions, from the 1840s, included many contributions from eminent mathematicians such as A. Cayley (1821–95), J.J. Sylvester (1814–97), T.A. Hirst (1830–92), the first President of the AIGT, and W.K. Clifford (1845–79). By comparison, the *Mathematical Gazette*, which included questions and solutions as an early feature, did not start until 1894. (38) The College's journal provides an example of a general educational association crossing over the middle ground of curriculum and pedagogy and making a contribution, albeit a minor one, to the advancement of specialist subject knowledge.

Similar societies were developing in the USA. The New York Mathematical Society – an American counterpart for the LMS – was formed in 1888 and it became the American Mathematical Society from 1894. Around this time it was a general educational organization – the National Education Association, founded in 1870 – which first turned its attention to national concerns in mathematics education. The Mathematical Association of America (MAA) – an association principally concerned with undergraduate curricula in the colleges – was not formed until 1915, and, partly as a reaction to the relatively limited range of the MAA's membership, the National Council of Teachers of Mathematics was founded in 1920 to cater for and represent the interests of high school teachers on a national scale. (39) However, there is no evidence of any significant links at an institutional level between the MA and these American organizations.

The discussion thus far has aimed to locate the MA as an institution within a wide scenario of institutional developments in the fields of knowledge and education. This viewpoint also suggests the need to consider not only the MA's internal development but also its shifting place, external influence and relationships in the world of mathematics education. Drawing inspiration from Layton's study of the ASE, the constitutional, social and political dimensions can be briefly summarized and related to the internal and external aspects of a subject teaching association's development (as in Table 1.2).

In relation to the constitutional dimension, a general management perspective is pertinent and has recently been provided, fittingly, by the present executive secretary of the MA, Heather Whitby. (40) Before taking up this appointment she had made a study of nine voluntary organizations: three medical, two from the general voluntary service and four subject teaching associations. The four comprise the MA, the Association of Teachers of Mathematics (ATM), the ASE and the National Association for the Teaching of English (NATE). Institutional comparisons can be illuminating and will be utilized implicitly and explicitly in the view of the MA's history presented in the chapters which follow. (41) As the first of the academic subject teaching associations, however, the AIGT cannot be directly compared with any close contemporaries. Furthermore, for over twenty years it had no obvious model upon which to build, from small

Table 1.2
Constitutional, Social and Political Dimensions of Institutional Growth

INTERNAL DEVELOPMENTS	
CONSTITUTIONAL	**SOCIAL**
Organization and Management (Central and Local)	**Professional Development Strategies**
Membership and Hierarchy	**(Central and Local)**
Rules and Regulations	Meetings and Courses
Administration and Accommodation	Committees and Working Groups
Finance	Periodicals and Publications
	Library and Study Facilities
	Examinations and Accreditation
EXTERNAL DEVELOPMENTS (POLITICAL)	
Representation, Consultation, Advice and Direct Involvement	Institutional Developments
Teacher Supply and Training	Other Organizations
Curriculum Development and Examinations	Institutional Relationships
Central and Local Government Initiatives	
Links with Industry and Commerce	
Public Image and Public Relations	

beginnings in 1870. Why and how did the AIGT come into existence? What were its objectives and achievements in the nineteenth century? Was it a political force in mathematics education? How did it develop constitutionally and socially, in the context of Layton's model? These are the key questions to be pursued in the next chapter.

CHAPTER TWO

ASSOCIATION FOR THE IMPROVEMENT OF GEOMETRICAL TEACHING

... these heretics, meeting at Rugby in 1870, founded an Association for the Reform of Geometrical Teaching, and thereby struck the first blow in the revolution in the teaching of school mathematics, a revolution still going on. (1)

(T.A.A. Broadbent, 1946)

There is a society for the Improvement of Geometrical Teaching. I have no knowledge of its work; but as to the need of improvement there can be no question whilst the reign of Euclid continues ... Euclid for children is barbarous. (2)

(O. Heaviside, 1893)

INFLUENCE OF EXAMINATIONS

By 1870, examinations had become established as a linchpin of the English educational system. From the pinnacle of the tripos examinations at the University of Cambridge, where the mathematical tripos had acted as a paradigm for competitive examinations generally, down to the system of 'payment by results' involving examinations in the rudiments of reading, writing and arithmetic for working-class pupils in elementary schools seeking the support of grants from the state, the system which developed was differentiated to serve all classes of Victorian society. What is more, such a system had grown up in a piecemeal and largely unco-ordinated way. (3)

The Victorian predilection for examining as a means of reducing educational and social deficiencies and injustices developed rapidly from the mid-nineteenth century. Examinations came to be widely valued for the administrative purposes of certification and selection as well as for the maintenance or raising of educational standards. At the higher levels, examinations contributed to the undermining of patronage in various forms, they promoted open competition, and were generally valued for their intrinsic competitive potential. The competitive edge built into the arrangements for the widely influential Cambridge mathematical tripos

13

with its order of merit for honours in three classes – wranglers, senior optimes and junior optimes – has been well captured in the following cameo:

> The system obviously involved great confidence in the accuracy of marking attainable; and its prevalence and popularity might be ascribed in part to the general British interest in sport. University studies were reduced as far as possible to the semblance of a race; the candidates were the horses, their teachers the trainers, the examiners the judges. In Cambridge great interest was always felt in these competitions, especially in the Mathematical Tripos, large crowds always attending when the list was read out. Even the general public, usually little interested in University matters, were involved; the lists were telegraphed to the newspapers, short biographies of the Senior Wrangler and other high wranglers were published . . . (4)

The principles and practices of the Cambridge model were widely exported to other fields of examining through the influence of Cambridge graduates, particularly those who entered the field of education as administrators or teachers.

Different parts of the English educational system were served by different examining bodies. Two departments of state – the Education and the Science and Art Departments – acted as major examining bodies. The former not only administered the system of payment by results in elementary schools but also conducted examinations and inspections, linked to grants, for the elementary teacher training colleges. The latter department administered a system of examinations and related grants for various 'science and art' subjects, including pure mathematics and practical (plane and solid) geometry, intended principally for artisans studying on a part-time evening basis.

The Civil Service Commission not only conducted the examinations for competitive entry to the various grades of the Civil Service but also administered the examinations for entry to the military academies of Sandhurst and Woolwich. Certain leading secondary schools, such as Eton, Rugby, Cheltenham and Wellington, included army 'sides', alongside the classical and modern divisions within the school. Such schools competed with private 'cramming' establishments in preparing for the army examinations, which included papers in mathematics as a major component.

In referring to 'secondary schools' it is important to recognize the differentiated nature of the system, which had developed without any major intervention from the state. The top stratum included the old-established public boarding schools, which traditionally served the landed and professional classes, and enjoyed close links with the two ancient universities at Oxford and Cambridge, whose entrance and scholarship examinations served to strengthen these ties from the mid-1850s. For all Oxbridge degrees a prescribed minimum of mathematics was required for matriculation: Responsions ('Smalls') at Oxford and the Previous ('Little-go') at Cambridge. The public schools' identity was further strengthened by the establishment of the Headmasters' Conference (HMC) in 1869, and, in 1873, a new examining body – the Oxford and Cambridge Schools

Examination Board (the Joint Board) – was established specifically to provide inspection and examinations for the HMC schools.

Following the industrial revolution, some new high-status schools had also been established to serve the needs of the upper echelons of the new bourgeoisie who were in the vanguard of industrial and commercial enterprise. The new leading proprietary schools and colleges, such as Marlborough, Rossall, Radley, Haileybury and Clifton, developed more modern curricula than the classics-dominated older public schools. To serve the needs of schools for the middle classes generally – proprietary, endowed and private schools – a system of 'local' examinations was established from 1858. Again it was the Universities of Oxford and Cambridge which took the lead in establishing the Oxford Local Examinations Delegacy and the Cambridge Local Examinations Syndicate. The aim was to stimulate middle-class education along broadly 'liberal' lines and to give parents some guarantee of general standards from an impartial and respected authority. (5)

The lowest grade of 'secondary' education was provided by the weakest endowed schools and the great mass of private schools, many of which were run as individually owned businesses. Such schools and some of the smaller proprietary schools came under the early influence of the College of Preceptors, which provided its own examinations. Arithmetic was compulsory for a certificate and these examinations proved to be particularly attractive to an increasing number of girls' schools in the late nineteenth century. Indeed, until the turn of the century, the College's examinations were conducted on a scale greater than the Oxbridge locals but they remained inferior in terms of status. The Cambridge tripos model was closely followed: three classes of certificate were awarded with class lists in order of merit and special awards published regularly in the College's journal, the *Educational Times*.

Thus the character of English school and college curricula at all levels become very much bound up with the requirements of an examination system over which the state had a relatively restricted hold. Essentially, the important examinations for all grades of secondary school were in private hands. (6) This situation was to prove important in relation to the early tactics of the AIGT. But to make an informed assessment of the AIGT's early progress it is also necessary to have some picture of the baseline for mathematics – both its place and shape – as a feature of the English educational landscape.

MATHEMATICS IN ENGLISH EDUCATION

Although state involvement in the examination system was limited in scope, growing state interest in its general educational responsibilities is evidenced by the establishment and outcomes of the work of various royal commissions in the 1850s and 1860s which paved the way for a number of related Acts of Parliament, including the Elementary Education Act of 1870. This Act established a framework for a national system of elementary education up to the age of thirteen, to be administered on a local basis by school boards, the principal aim being to fill out the existing patchy provision for education in the voluntary schools. By this time elementary schools were already feeling strongly the effects of the Revised Code of 1862, which had introduced the system of payment by results in examinations at, initially, six standards in the '3Rs'. The various Codes and Instructions to Inspectors (HMI) exerted a powerful and dominant influence on the curriculum in elementary schools, producing what has been aptly referred to as an 'instrumentary education' for the children of the working classes in the late nineteenth century. (7)

In the case of arithmetic, one of the three nineteenth-century core subjects, criticisms of the harmful side-effects of the centralized system implemented by HMI were beginning to emerge by 1870, and such criticisms were articulated in uncompromising terms by Matthew Arnold, a leading HMI. In his annual report for 1869 Arnold commented:

> The object being to ensure that on a given day a child shall be able to turn out, worked right, two out of three sums of a certain sort, he [*sic*] is taught the mechanical rule by which sums of this sort are worked, and sedulously practised all the year round in working them; arithmetical principles he is not taught, or introduced into the science of arithmetic. (8)

He went on to quote the general judgement of one of his HMI colleagues:

> Unless a vigorous effort is made to infuse more intelligence into its teaching, Government arithmetic will soon be known as a modification of the science peculiar to inspected schools, and remarkable chiefly for its meagreness and sterility. (9)

Furthermore, in the Victorian educational climate of the 1860s, there was a growing interest in continental practices and performance, and sometimes unfavourable comparisons surfaced. Arnold had visited France, Prussia and Italy on a fact-finding mission for the Schools Inquiry (Taunton) Commission, 1864–8. In the case of elementary arithmetic, he pointed to the exemplary performance of Prussia, as measured by the intelligence and mental power demonstrated by the children. In addition, French superiority was shortly and sharply highlighted by the quoted experience of one French schoolmaster, who had visited a number of English schools: 'Your boys do not learn arithmetic, the science of numbers; they learn to reckon (le calcul).' (10)

In the case of secondary schools of all types, the reports of two royal commissions in the 1860s – the Public Schools (Clarendon) Commission (1861–4) and the Taunton Commission – provide much valuable evidence concerning curricular thinking and practices, including the specific claims and provision for mathematics. The Clarendon Commission considered only nine 'public' schools – those with ancient foundations – Eton, Winchester, Westminster, Charterhouse, St. Paul's, Merchant Taylors', Harrow, Rugby and Shrewsbury. The Taunton Commission ranged widely to consider all kinds of schools between the Clarendon nine and the elementary schools, which themselves had been the subject of a full investigation by the Newcastle Commission (1858–61). (11)

The 'fight for recognition' in connection with mathematics in the curriculum of the classics-dominated Clarendon schools, with their ancient foundations, has been highlighted by other writers, drawing on the evidence of the Clarendon Commission itself, and the developments in individual schools need not be detailed here. (12) Suffice it to say that gradual recognition came, by the 1860s, and it was embodied in such developments as: the change in status of mathematics from a subject taught only as an 'optional extra', probably by a writing master, to a subject allocated a secure place on the timetable; the increasing independence of the arrangements for teaching mathematics from those for teaching classics; the appointment of masters specifically for mathematics; and a slow improvement both in the status of the subject – judging by indicators such as pupils' esteem and the provision of prizes – and in the teachers' remuneration. These developments are bound up with the growth of the examination system, which generally demanded at least the elements of arithmetic, and the competing claims of newer schools with more modern curricula, including a secure place for mathematics from the outset.

But the Clarendon Commission found that classics still constituted the dominant study at these exceptional nine schools, and this subject was intrinsically more attractive than mathematics to the great majority of boys. Somewhat grudgingly the Commission concluded:

> But mathematics at least have established a title to respect as an instrument of mental discipline; they are recognised and honoured at the Universities, and it is easy to obtain Mathematical Masters of high ability who have had a University education. (13)

The scope of the mathematics taught obviously depended upon the abilities and aspirations of the pupils. The range here was fairly summarized by Siddons:

> the few best mathematicians in various schools did trigonometry, mechanics, conic sections and in some schools differential calculus; but the majority of boys seem to have done nothing beyond about four books of Euclid, some Algebra and Arithmetic, and the work was generally very mechanical. (14)

In geometry the majority of boys did not get as far as the study of similarity, which is not treated until Euclid Book 6, after a rigorous and difficult general treatment of proportional magnitudes in Book 5. What is more, there was plenty to occupy and mystify the average boy in just a couple of Euclid's Books. Books 1 and 2 cover angles, parallels, triangles, quadrilaterals and areas, and this amount of geometry was sufficient for Responsions (matriculation) at Oxford University or it could be avoided altogether by taking 'algebra to simple equations' instead! In general, the Clarendon Commission pointed to some unfavourable comparisons in mathematics between the nine public schools and some other leading secondary schools, and quoted one university tutor's remarks on the pupils' examination performance: 'the answers to the questions in arithmetic do not encourage us to examine them in Euclid or algebra'. (15)

The picture of mathematics in the mass of secondary schools surveyed for the Taunton Commission is more variable but concerns about standards of provision and teaching are still much in evidence. In addition, what also begins to come to the surface in the detail of these reports is a significant measure of dissatisfaction with the *status quo* in school mathematics with its staple diet in the three elementary branches: arithmetic, algebra, and geometry as presented in the various editions of the early Books of Euclid's Elements. (16) The briefest of summaries of the general picture for secondary schools of all types, including some girls' schools, has been provided by Bushell:

> A very small amount of Mathematics, easy Arithmetic, some earlier propositions in Euclid, and perhaps the very elements of Algebra are being attempted; very occasionally some Trigonometry. In the better schools, no doubt the few boys were going further, but in general masters could not cope themselves with anything but the elements. (17)

Arithmetic was the dominant branch in the small number of girls' schools surveyed by the Commission. In the private schools arithmetic also featured prominently and it was generally more successfully taught than the other branches. In some schools which claimed to teach geometry no more was attempted than the substance of Euclid Book 1 but, in some cases, 'Boys scarcely seemed to know the first twenty propositions.' (18)

Generally, the performance of pupils in geometry based on Euclid was judged to be markedly inferior to that in arithmetic. The Commissioners provided an interesting summary of the prevailing attitude to the place of mathematics in English secondary education in the 1860s:

> The importance of the branches of mathematics which follow arithmetic was rather generally admitted than earnestly pressed upon us by the witnesses whom we examined. No one can doubt the value of geometry as an exercise in severe reasoning; and algebra, though inferior to geometry in this respect, yet is needed to give perfect completeness to the knowledge of arithmetic, and affords admirable examples of ingenuity. There were a few indeed who would put mathematics distinctly above all other subjects as a means of general education; but on the whole there appeared to be no general desire to push the cultivation of mathematics very far. (19)

This somewhat lukewarm attitude partly relates to the general standard of mathematics teaching found in the schools: 'We cannot but ascribe this [attitude] in some degree to the fact, generally noticed by our Assistant Commissioners, that the teaching of mathematics in English schools is rarely satisfactory.' Yet the place of mathematics was bolstered on value grounds by 'its undeniable utility, both for mental discipline and on many occasions for practical application'. (20)

EUCLID: 'A VERY ENGLISH SUBJECT'

There is no doubt that the principal concern at this time was with school and college geometry teaching, based as it was on various editions of the Books of Euclid. During the period of the Taunton Inquiry a number of individuals expressed their concerns and Arnold, an Assistant Taunton Commissioner, was quick to point to unfavourable continental judgements:

> In general, the respect professed in France for the mathematical and scientific teaching of our secondary schools is as low as that professed for our classical teaching is high . . . our geometry teaching was in foreign eyes sufficiently condemned when it was said that we still used *Euclid*. One of the great sins of Cambridge was her retention of *Euclid*. I am bound to say that the Germans and the Swiss entirely agree with the French on this point. *Euclid*, they all said, was quite out of date, and was a thoroughly unfit text-book to teach geometry from. I was, of course, astounded; and when I asked why *Euclid* was an unfit text-book to teach geometry from, I was told that Euclid's propositions were drawn out with a view to meeting all possible cavils, and not with a view of developing geometrical ideas in the most lucid and natural manner. This to me, in my ignorance, sounded plausible; but at any rate the foreign *consensus* against the use of *Euclid* is something striking . . . (21)

Arnold, the eldest son of Thomas Arnold, the famous headmaster of Rugby School, was himself a respected man of letters and an influential educationist through his writings and work both as an HMI and as an educational commissioner. On his own admission he was a relative stranger in the world of mathematics but he was nonetheless an educational force to be reckoned with. His conclusions concerning English mathematics teaching were partly based on the evidence of two Frenchmen, Jacques Demogeot and Henry Montucci, who visited England during the period of the Taunton Inquiry and produced a wide-ranging report on the state of English secondary education, for the benefit of the French education ministry. In particular, the Frenchmen's criticism of Euclid as a school textbook was unequivocal: learning Euclid merely exercised the memory and not the intelligence of pupils; the logic might be cast-iron but the treatment was prolix and tedious; there were serious alternatives, such as the geometry of Legendre, which had been widely adopted in France. (22)

Other notable critics included G. Griffith, the Secretary of the British Association for the Advancement of Science (BAAS), who opined that too much time was spent on Euclid and 'many boys had read six books of it who knew nothing of geometry'. (23) T.H. Key, Professor of Comparative Grammar at University College London, 'went so far as to express a wish to get rid of Euclid altogether as a most illogical book'. (24) It was Frederick Temple, one of the leading Taunton Commissioners, who saw a clear opportunity in the summary report of the Commission boldly to question the *status quo* in English school geometry:

> Euclid is almost the only text book now used in England for teaching geometry . . . But we think that it is well worth consideration whether

> Euclid be a proper text book for beginners, and whether boys should
> not commence with something easier and less abstract. (25)

Temple, who later became Archbishop of Canterbury, was at the time
the headmaster of Rugby School. He was a contemporary and friend of
Matthew Arnold but also had some mathematical credibility: a double first
in classics and mathematics from Oxford University, where he had also
lectured for a short time before entering the church. J.M. Wilson, a founder
member of the AIGT, was on Temple's staff at Rugby, teaching science and
mathematics. His judgement over fifty years later is undoubtedly sound in
pointing to the publication of the Taunton Report as 'the important and
decisive event' which:

> made plain to all a fact, in which schoolmasters had hitherto acquiesced
> as a decree of fate, that boys might have worked for years at Euclid,
> and even know Euclid perfectly, and yet know nothing of the spirit
> or method or the results of Geometry. Time was in fact wasted
> over Euclid: and time was of importance. A better method was
> wanted. (26)

By 1870 other pressures were also mounting and experimentation to
find a 'better method' was already under way. But on practical and
ideological grounds Euclid had become, in the words of Augustus De
Morgan (1806–71), 'a very English subject'. (27)

The specification of geometry in terms of the Books of Euclid was
the norm at this time. The fact that precise communication in relation
to mathematics education was possible in such simple descriptive terms
demonstrates the strength of the hold of Euclid on English practice,
and the convenience of this was not lost on the framers of examination
syllabuses. For example, a syllabus for geometry might be defined as 'the
substance of Euclid Book 1': what could be simpler? Over the first half of
the nineteenth century there was a remarkable growth in the number of new
editions of Euclid published in England, with a staggering seventy-three in
the decade up to 1850. (28) By this time Euclid had already become big
business in publishing terms and this business was to grow further with
the expansion of the educational system and the spreading influence of
examination requirements.

It is important to note that Euclid's deductive treatment of the science of
geometry was not the only form of geometry for which competing textbooks
catered in the nineteenth century. Practical geometry, both plane and solid,
which utilized the results of geometry and involved the practice or art
of geometrical drawing and construction, also provided a market for the
educational publishers. But in the 1860s this vocational market – geometry
for its utility – was much more limited in scope than the market for 'liberal'
geometries based on Euclid, which were generally in demand for use in the
universities, particularly at Cambridge, as well as in the mass of secondary
schools. (29)

The place of Euclid was further secured at the level of principle by
frequently repeated arguments concerning its suitability in relation to the
dominant nineteenth-century educational *Zeitgeist*. Broadbent's eloquently

expressed view of Euclid's extraordinary success as a nineteenth-century school textbook is suggestive:

> The Elements, with its orderly system, its brilliant logical triumphs in the theory of parallels and the theory of proportion . . . was a peak of Greek culture. How quite it came to be inferred from this that the book was one pre-eminently suited for the education of small boys in Victorian England, how it came to pass that the small boy learned his Euclid as he learned his list of the Kings of Israel and Judah, how it became accepted as incontrovertible that immense mental and spiritual benefits must result from these exercises, forms a curious chapter in the history of education in this country. (30)

There were two distinguishable grounds for the use of Euclid as an educational instrument. On the one hand, Euclid was a classical text – 'a peak of Greek culture' – from which spiritual or moral benefits were presumed to spring. The use of Euclid fitted comfortably within a classics-dominated education and could be defended on the basis of its humanistic value. This rhetoric also fitted the reality of Euclid in the hands of teachers who might themselves have been classics-trained and who were dealing with many pupils for whom mathematics was a distinctly inferior subject within a predominantly classical curriculum. For such pupils and their teachers the rote memorization of Euclidean propositions was a practically convenient way of treating one necessary and important branch of the subject.

On the other hand, the more strongly articulated ground for Euclid was its claimed value as a mental discipline. Both the Clarendon and Taunton Commissions deployed this argument with the latter referring to the study of Euclid as 'an exercise in severe reasoning'. Essentially it was claimed that the systematic ordering of propositions and logical rigour of Euclid's treatment, followed to the letter, had the potential to make a distinctive contribution to the development of pupils' minds as a necessary part of a liberal education. To maximize the formal strength of Euclid it was regarded as imperative to follow closely his pure geometrical reasoning and to exclude algebraic methods at all costs. Algebra was treated as a wholly separate branch of mathematics and it was, as the Taunton Commission pointed out, inferior to geometry. Thus, when the Taunton Commission reported in 1868, Euclid's hold on Victorian mathematics education was a very secure one both in principle and in practice. But, perhaps surprisingly, in the same year, English alternatives to Euclid began to appear on the market and to compete with the numerous editions of the classical text.

ALTERNATIVES TO EUCLID

Some of the earliest 'new geometries', as they were called, were produced by Wilson, on the advice and encouragement of his headmaster, Temple, by Richard Wright, following the inspiration of Hirst's teaching at Queenwood College, Hampshire, and University College School, and by Richard Wormell (1838–1914), another founder member of the AIGT, who became a schoolmaster-President in 1893. In his early academic studies Wormell also came under the direct influence of Hirst. (31) New geometry textbooks were reviewed in the journal of the College of Preceptors, the *Educational Times*, which also included some correspondence concerning the new possibilities. Wilson claimed in 1868:

> Many good teachers depart very widely from Euclid and in fact teach geometry to a great extent independently and then teach Euclid. But there are scores of schools where boys learn and say their Euclid like declensions. (32)

Wilson's geometry, initially covering only the substance of Euclid Books 1 and 2, was not developed from scratch but drew upon foreign textbooks from France, Germany, Italy and the USA. Obviously it was put to immediate use at Rugby School but it also made a swift and significant impact on the work of a small number of girls' schools. (33) It was a theoretical treatment of geometry, and, to accompany it, Wilson also produced, with a teacher colleague, F.E. Kitchener, a separate small textbook on 'experimental geometry', to provide an introduction involving the use of simple geometrical instruments. (34) Wilson's and other alternatives to Euclid commonly employed 'hypothetical constructions', to simplify the early deductive development, and various other tactics such as a freer use of superposition, the introduction of newer geometrical ideas such as locus and projection, more direct proofs of certain theorems, the separation of construction problems from the principal theorems, a reduction in the number of theorems and their regrouping by subject. Such tactics were adopted to overcome, in Wilson's words, Euclid's 'artificiality, the invariably syllogistic form of his reasoning, the length of his demonstrations, and his unsuggestiveness'. (35) Such criticisms were not just confined to the prefaces of textbooks but were openly expressed by Wilson and others in what became a lively public debate on Euclid's strengths and weaknesses as an educational instrument.

The London Mathematical Society was founded in 1865, six years before the AIGT. Hirst featured prominently in the foundation of both institutions and De Morgan was a prime mover in the case of the LMS, the roots of which were located in University College. Hirst's range of influence was considerable. He moved to University College in 1865 and subsequently took over from De Morgan as professor of mathematics. He was trained on the continent and was held in high regard there for his work in the comparatively new field of geometrical transformations. He was actively involved with the BAAS and the Royal Society, as well as the LMS and the AIGT. (36)

The LMS clearly fulfilled a strong need within the mathematical community of the 1860s, and, to quote one assessment:

> in a little over two years from its inauguration, the Society had enlisted among its members all the leading mathematicians of the country, and had become, in effect, what it has since remained: the national mathematical society. (37)

Its aim was simple: the promotion and extension of mathematical knowledge. In addition to De Morgan and Hirst, its early members in the 1860s included Cayley, Sylvester, Clifford and the Oxford mathematician H.J.S. Smith (1826–83). Before the end of the decade such eminent mathematicians also became peripherally drawn into the educational arena in connection with the special case of elementary geometry in English education. In particular, and somewhat surprisingly, in 1868 it was Wilson, a public schoolmaster, who was offered the platform of the LMS to publicize his heretical views.

Wilson began his address somewhat deferentially: 'It will not, I hope, be thought beyond the province of a Mathematical Society to discuss the merits and demerits of so distinguished a text-book of Geometry as Euclid's Elements.' (38) He then delivered the substance of his address: a strong critique of Euclid and a defence of his own treatment of geometry, as expressed in the preface of his textbook and subsequently published in the *Educational Times*. Wilson later recalled that he was 'well "heckled"' at the LMS meeting and that his textbook was also 'severely handled' by De Morgan in a review for the *Athenaeum*. (39) The debate was continued in letters from the two opponents which were also published in this same journal.

As Joan Richards has admirably demonstrated in a recent book, the theoretical arguments exemplified by the De Morgan-Wilson exchanges 'continued to echo in the textbook discussions of the subsequent decades'. (40) Both were agreed that the essential purpose of the study of geometry was to develop reasoning power but De Morgan took a more austere and conservative view of the educational means to this end: Euclid, in spite of some minor logical imperfections, was still the best treatment of geometry largely because of its difficulty. The upshot was that the LMS in effect played no further part in the matter of reform in geometry teaching. This also seems to have set an important precedent for the LMS of non-involvement in mathematics education and of exclusive concern for the advancement of the subject. In 1869, however, the subject of geometry teaching also attracted the attention of the mathematical community within the context of the annual meeting of the BAAS.

The rhetoric from Sylvester, professor of mathematics at the Royal Military Academy, Woolwich, was typically forceful, in his Presidential address to the mathematics and physics section of the BAAS: 'I should rejoice to see . . . Euclid honourably shelved or buried "deeper than did ever plummet sound" out of the schoolboy's reach.' (41) By way of apology, he added:

> The early study of Euclid made me a hater of geometry, which I hope
> may plead my excuse if I have shocked the opinions of any in this room
> (and I know there are some who rank Euclid as second in sacredness
> to the Bible alone, and as one of the advanced outposts of the British
> Constitution) by the tone in which I have previously alluded to it as a
> school-book. (42)

The BAAS responded in 1869 by setting up a committee 'for the purpose of considering the possibility of improving the methods of instruction in elementary geometry'. (43) The committee included seven professors, among them Sylvester, and also Wilson as a schoolmaster representative, along with Hayward of Harrow. Exceptionally for a schoolmaster, Hayward was elected a Fellow of the Royal Society in 1876, and he became the second President of the AIGT.

Within the committee there was some support for the liberalization of geometry teaching, to accommodate more flexible and inductive methods of reasoning along the lines of the natural sciences, whose position in education was beginning to gain strength through the individual advocacy of Thomas Huxley, Herbert Spencer and others, and the institutional championing of the BAAS. Hirst was also a sympathetic committee member, but two other professors, Cayley and Kelland, were closely aligned with the Cambridge school of mathematics and would therefore have strongly supported De Morgan's stance in favour of retaining pure Euclid as a paradigm of formal deductive reasoning. (44) Significantly, the committee of the BAAS did not report until 1873, which may partly reflect its *modus operandi*. (45) But, more importantly, English mathematicians were clearly divided on the question of Euclid's retention. In these circumstances the schoolmasters themselves took the initiative.

BIRTH OF THE ASSOCIATION

To quote Wilson, the situation in 1870 was as follows:

> correspondence took place among mathematicians and mathematical masters with the aim of securing sufficient uniformity of treatment to make possible the conducting of Examinations. That was the real difficulty. Some of us, including myself, had hoped that either the British Association, or an association of University Professors would draw up for us an authoritative Syllabus to which text-books might be written. But those august bodies made no sign. We therefore resolved to form an Association for ourselves, since the need was urgent . . . (46)

The new scientific journal, *Nature*, provided an important means of communication for the schoolmasters. (47) Robert Tucker, a master at University College School, an associate of Hirst and secretary of the LMS, pointed out in *Nature*'s columns that the London matriculation requirements – Euclid Books 1–4 – essentially prohibited the use of alternative geometries. Rawdon Levett (1843–1923) of King Edward's School, Birmingham, took the matter further by calling for the formation of an 'Anti-Euclid Association' and, together with Tucker and Wormell, he invited interested readers of *Nature* to forward their names to him. (48) Wilson was drawn in and also the Reverend E.F.M. MacCarthy, second master at Levett's school. Funds were raised and a circular went out in October 1870, from Levett and MacCarthy, announcing a first conference to organize an 'Association for the Reform of Geometrical Teaching', to be held on 17 January 1871 at University College. (49) The circular

ASSOCIATION FOR THE REFORM OF GEOMETRICAL TEACHING.*

CONFERENCE, JANUARY 17TH, 1871.

The Association will first be organised.

The following Resolutions will then be proposed—

(1) That the main object of this Association is to induce all Conductors of Examinations, at which pupils who have been trained under different systems present themselves, to frame their questions independently of any particular text book ; and that with a view to this object, the members present at this meeting do pledge themselves to use every effort to increase the numbers, and extend the influence of the Association.

(2) That with a further view of extending the influence of the Association, Local Secretaries be appointed for different parts of the kingdom, whose office it shall be to collect information, to make the objects of the Association more generally known in their immediate neighbourhood, and to communicate on all matters of interest with the Central Committee.

(3) That the Local Secretaries, *ipso facto*, be Members of the Committee of Management.

(4) That all Members of the Association shall collect information with regard to text books and methods of teaching Geometry in England and other countries, and that such information shall be forwarded to any Secretary or Local Secretary of the Association.

(5) That the Committee of Management shall, from time to time, print and circulate among members and others, such information as they may consider valuable.

(6) That this meeting is of opinion that in any new text book—

    (*a*) the following principles, only partially or not at all recognised by Euclid, should be adopted :—

        (i) Hypothetical constructions.

        (ii) The arithmetical definition of proportion.

        (iii) Superposition.

        (iv) The conception of a moving point, and of a revolving line.

    (*b*) the following limitations should be removed :—

        (i) The restriction of the number of axioms to those only which admit of no proof.

        (ii) The restriction which excludes all angles not less than two right angles.

    (*c*) modern terms, such as locus, projection, &c., should be introduced.

These points will be voted upon in detail.

Plate 2.1   Summons to First Conference 1871

was sent chiefly to head and mathematical masters with 'the canvass of mathematicians at the Universities being postponed until the Association should be more completely organized'. (50) A first list of twenty-eight members was compiled and published in October. With Hirst of London and W.H. Laverty of Oxford as the only two university members, the AIGT started life as a ginger group of schoolmasters. (51)

At its second annual meeting, in 1870, the HMC also considered the question of geometry teaching. It was resolved to communicate with government departments, the universities and other examining bodies, urging greater freedom in examination requirements. However, given the involvement of the BAAS and subsequently the AIGT, the HMC decided not to pursue the matter in any detail and adopted a waiting attitude. (52)

Hirst chaired the meeting of twenty-six members, plus a few gentlemen non-members, and, at his suggestion, the name was changed to the Association for the *Improvement* of Geometrical Teaching, on the ground that this implied longer-term objectives than those immediately pressing. Apart from Hirst and three others, the members attending the January meeting were either mathematical or senior masters, and women were not yet represented. (53) In an address to the BAAS in 1873, Professor Smith from Oxford University, who was a sympathetic member of the unproductive committee on geometry teaching, commented on the AIGT's formation:

> For some years past this Section [mathematics and physics] has appointed a Committee to aid in the improvement of Geometrical teaching in this country . . . we have advanced at least one step in the direction of an important and long-needed reform. The action of this Section led to the formation of an Association for the improvement of Geometrical teaching. (54)

Smith's remark should be qualified by adding that it was the action of the BAAS and the subsequent inaction of its committee, reflecting major differences of opinion among mathematicians, which led to the formation of the AIGT. It was the very special circumstances associated with English mathematics education around 1870 which partly explains why the AIGT was formed over twenty years before another secondary subject teaching association was to emerge (for modern languages) in 1892.

The committee of the BAAS, the HMC headmasters and the founder members of the AIGT all recognized that examination requirements held the key to progress in geometry teaching. Alternatives to Euclid were growing in number, with reviews and correspondence in both the *Educational Times* and *Nature*, and various competing treatments were becoming available to those teachers who wished to depart from the Euclidean order in deductive geometry. The AIGT's early major objective, therefore, was 'to unify the teaching on the new lines' and thereby overcome the problems of examining proofs in alternative geometries. (55) The first publicity leaflet of the AIGT well summarized the case for the Association's existence, and its early strategy.

SIR,

We beg to call your attention to the existence of an ASSOCIATION FOR THE IMPROVEMENT OF GEOMETRICAL TEACHING.

The movement is already supported by a large number of the leading mathematical teachers in the best schools of the country, and our list of members is increasing steadily. It will thus be seen that the dissatisfaction with the present state of Geometrical Teaching is widely spread. The causes of dissatisfaction are not far to seek. Looking at results only, it is generally admitted that the average boy is capable of nothing further than the reproduction of a number of propositions in the words of his text-book : he breaks down altogether when he is asked to do the simplest deduction. The comparative worthlessness of such a result is at once evident when we compare the average knowledge of Geometry with that of other branches of Mathematical Science, Arithmetic or Algebra for instance ; far more boys can do a problem in Arithmetic or Algebra than a deduction in Geometry.

The opinion is prevalent among the members of the Association that the defective instruction in Geometry is chiefly due to the retention of Euclid as a text-book. Euclid has become fossilized by age. It wants all the improvements and simplifications, both of matter and manner, of the last two thousand years. It contains many useless propositions ; it is an unsuitable preparation, as well for the higher mathematical training as for the mechanical wants of the present day ; and, worst of all, it wants life and freshness. These last are qualities which cannot be imparted to it, even by the best of teachers, so long as the exact order and words of the book are demanded in examinations.

Euclid is seldom, if ever, adopted as the Geometrical text-book in continental schools. The opinion of French Mathematicians on this question is plainly expressed in the Report of MM. Demogeot and Montucci, and is referred to in the Report of Mr. Arnold to the Endowed School Inquiry Commissioners. The universal rejection or modification of Euclid abroad ought, we think, to throw the *onus probandi* on those who desire to retain it in England ; nor is the disadvantage of severing English elementary study from European practice a thing to be overlooked.

The means by which the Association proposes to bring about the desired improvement are two-fold ; first, by bringing the direct influence of a large number of eminent mathematical teachers to bear upon examining bodies to induce them to frame their questions without reference to any particular text-book ; secondly, to make it easier thus to frame questions and to assign the proper amount of credit to the answers, by putting forward, or by inducing some body of greater authority to put forward, a syllabus or programme of Geometry in accordance with which all future text-books should be written.

Feeling strongly that students of moderate ability whose formal education ends with the school will gain everything by the proposed change, while those who continue their mathematical reading with a view of obtaining honours at the University, or of qualifying themselves for the scientific professions, will gain much through economy of time and the advantage of modern lights, we venture to solicit your support in our endeavour to bring about this improvement in an important branch of education.

We forward to you a copy of the First Annual Report of the Association, including an account of the proceedings at a General Meeting, held at University College, London, on January 17th, 1871, under the presidency of Dr. HIRST, F.R.S.

The Subscription (10/- annually) will be received by the Treasurer, Mr. R. WORMELL, Albion Villa, Loughborough Road, S.W.

We are, Sir,

Yours faithfully,

R. LEVETT, M.A.

E. F. M. MACCARTHY, M.A.
Honorary Secretaries.

KING EDWARD'S SCHOOL, BIRMINGHAM.

Plate 2.2   First Publicity Leaflet

PRESSURE AND RESISTANCE

To achieve a new consensus the AIGT chose the tactic of syllabus construction and not the production of yet another textbook which might have the necessary rigour and authority to replace the various editions of Euclid. Hirst was convinced that 'no really valuable text-book would ever be produced by a committee or an association', and the BAAS committee concurred when it eventually reported in 1873. (56) The first priority was to produce a syllabus, backed by the authority of the BAAS, which could then be submitted to the various examining bodies. But it was inevitably a slow and painstaking business to produce a new consensus from members' proposals, and a syllabus to replace Euclid Books 1–4 was not published until 1873. The committee of the BAAS judged it to be 'decidedly good so far as it goes' but chose to wait for the AIGT's extension of the syllabus to Book 6 before deciding on 'the advisability of giving to it the authority of the British Association'. (57)

The AIGT laboured with understandable difficulty and at great length over Euclid Book 5 (ratio and proportion) and its complete syllabus for plane geometry up to Euclid Book 6 was not published until 1875. The committee of the BAAS reported again in 1876 and judged that the AIGT's syllabus 'should be considered in detail by authorized representatives of the Universities and other great examining bodies of the United Kingdom with a view to its adoption'. (58) It was not until early in 1877 that the AIGT was in a position to persuade the various examining bodies to adopt its alternative syllabus, supported by the carefully worded testimonial from the BAAS. (59)

The AIGT approached all the major examining bodies in the United Kingdom: the Universities of Oxford, Cambridge, London, Durham, Aberdeen, St Andrews, Glasgow and Edinburgh; Trinity College Dublin and Queen's College Belfast; the Civil Service Commissioners, the India Office, the Education Department and the Department of Science and Art; the College of Preceptors, the Incorporated Law Society, the Pharmaceutical Society, the Royal College of Surgeons and the Royal Veterinary College. In their report for 1877 the secretaries Levett and MacCarthy summarized the general response in plain and simple terms: 'The direct result of these applications has been very small.' (60)

Of the universities, only London had made any concessions and the matriculation paper for 1876 'deviated from the old Euclidic Type so far as to provoke a spirited controversy in the columns of *The Times*'. (61) But the other bodies were unmoved, and, what is more, the officers of the government departments felt that 'the Government should, in this matter, rather follow than attempt to lead public opinion'. (62) After six years of painstaking work the AIGT as a political force in mathematics education had made little headway. The Euclidean order in the teaching and examining of geometry remained strong and secure.

In seeking to explain the AIGT's failure to achieve a breakthrough in the 1870s it is necessary to consider not only its own tactics but also the mathematical and educational context within which its early work was located. In the production of a new syllabus for Euclid Books 1–6,

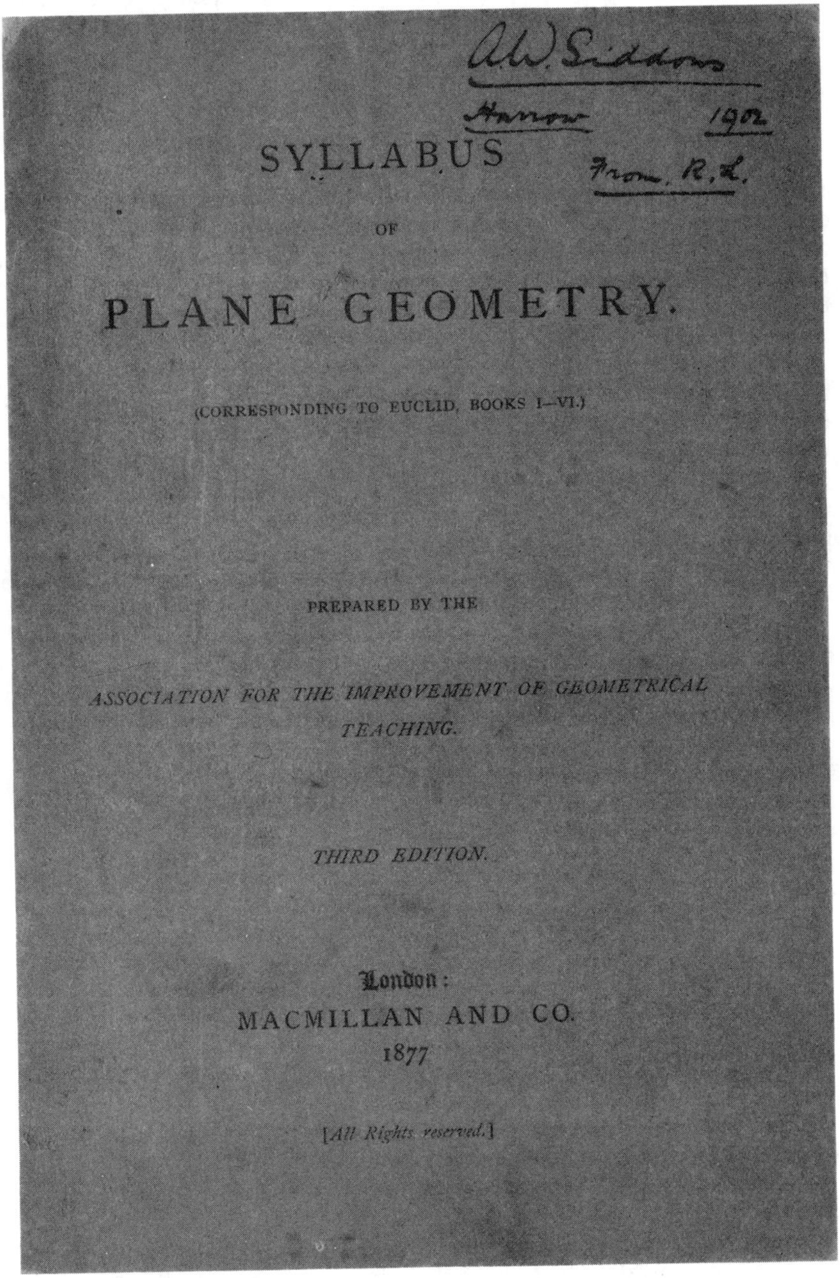

A.W. Siddons
Harrow 1902
From R.L.

SYLLABUS

OF

PLANE GEOMETRY.

(CORRESPONDING TO EUCLID, BOOKS I—VI.)

PREPARED BY THE

ASSOCIATION FOR THE IMPROVEMENT OF GEOMETRICAL TEACHING.

THIRD EDITION.

London:
MACMILLAN AND CO.
1877

[*All Rights reserved.*]

Plate 2.3 First Syllabus of Plane Geometry

the processes of drafting, printing, circulating, discussing at the annual meeting, and redrafting, were inevitably time-consuming. In order first to achieve a consensus amongst the writers, and then to hope to satisfy the critical scrutiny of the BAAS committee, many compromises had to be made along the way. In addition, the nature of the English examination system presented the AIGT with a major practical barrier to large-scale curriculum change.

This examination system was uniquely complicated, comprising a large number of autonomous bodies each of which had to be independently approached. No mechanism existed for imposing a new uniformity for examining in geometry. Euclid was already a well-established and convenient standard for all examining bodies. Such bodies were generally conservative and sought to cater for the prevailing practices of the majority of teachers, who still accepted the *status quo*. (63) The AIGT was at this time a small and sectional group; its syllabus was largely untried and unfamiliar to the majority of schools for which the examining bodies catered. At Cambridge, which was at the power centre in terms of curriculum control, Howson has clearly shown that the distinctive internal organization for teaching and examining, within a collegiate structure, was such that Euclid was particularly convenient for teaching and examining in geometry at all levels. (64) In addition, some leading university mathematicians were strong in their defence of Euclid on value grounds.

Hayward underlined the importance of Cambridge in a Presidential address to the AIGT: 'Most of the Mathematical Teachers of this country derive the knowledge of Mathematics which they possess either directly or indirectly from the Cambridge school.' (65) Early and outspoken opponents of reform included the influential textbook writer Isaac Todhunter of Cambridge, Charles Dodgson (alias Lewis Carroll) of Oxford, and the first Sadleirian professor at Cambridge, Cayley. Todhunter included a chapter on elementary geometry in a book of educational essays published in 1873. (66) In tone it strongly reflected the view he had expressed to Tucker in a letter of 1871:

> I am indebted to you for a copy of the report of the Society for geometrical reform. I fear I am a conservative. When Rugby [Wilson's school] does 1/1000 part as well in mathematics at Cambridge as the City of London School I shall think more favourably than at present of the new methods. (67)

Dodgson's *Euclid and his Modern Rivals* was first published in 1879, and, in the form of a play, he stylishly exposed the inferiority of various alternative geometries including Wilson's. (68) Cayley was a staunch admirer of Euclid and an uncompromising opponent of reform until his death in 1895. His influence within and outside Cambridge was considerable and the following anecdote from E.M. Langley (1851–1933) well captures the extent of Cayley's conservatism:

> One or two uncompromising opponents had been met with. Professor Cayley was the most formidable . . . In the course of the discussion he

(Mr Langley) having drawn attention to the fact that the authorised treatise was an inconsistent one, – a mixture of Euclid and Simson, – in which use was not made of the corollaries introduced by Simson in proving subsequent propositions, Professor Cayley suggested striking out Simson's additions and keeping strictly to the original treatise; · upon which a member of Senate whispered that perhaps to study it in the original Greek would be better still. (69)

Bushell later remarked, 'Cayley, of course, was out of touch with realities', but until his death in 1895 he personified the influential Cambridge school. (70)

In the 1880s, the AIGT adopted the alternative tactic of textbook production. The bulk of the work was undertaken by Levett and Hayward and it was again a slow and difficult task spanning some five years. *The Elements of Plane Geometry* was published in two parts, in 1884 and 1886, and covered the substance of Euclid Books 1–2 and 3–6 respectively. (71) There was no possibility of the various examining bodies 'adopting' such a textbook, albeit one approved by an association of mathematics teachers. But these bodies were again approached and requested to modify their requirements at least to accommodate the examination of students who had followed the AIGT's syllabus and textbook. Predictably, the general response was merely along the following lines: 'Euclid's sequence and axioms being retained, any proof will be admitted.' (72) This did lead to the publication of new editions of Euclid by popular textbook writers such as Hamblin Smith and the partnership of Hall and Stevens. To quote one reviewer, such editions were 'cleared to a great extent of [Euclid's] cumbrous verbiage and well supplied with exercises and addenda'. In terms of pedagogy, this was an improvement on the older popular editions such as those of Potts or Todhunter. (73) However, Miss Beale of Cheltenham Ladies' College pointed out in a letter to the AIGT:

The alteration in the regulations is quite unsatisfactory. Still no candidate who had substituted our syllabus for Euclid could pass. Euclid's order is not good in many ways, and that is insisted on still, and the regulations prevent the use of loci and limits in any demonstration. I see no concession at all. If we want our girls to pass, we must give up the syllabus. (74)

In Hayward's words, the AIGT's mission in the 1870s and 1880s was:

to remedy certain long recognised and widely felt defects in Euclid's Elements as a text book for a beginner. This it has done by putting forth a syllabus following in the main the same lines, but indicating a more systematic treatment of the subject, and a more natural sequence of propositions, while in the proofs . . . it has been an object to maintain in all its essentials that severity of form to which the great value of Euclid as a mental training for the young student is doubtless to be attributed. (75)

In making a full appraisal of the AIGT's work in elementary geometry it is also important to consider the values held by its leading members and the relationship between these values and the general 'climate' of educational thought in the late nineteenth century.

By comparison with the very rapid progress in geometrical reform from around 1900, it can be fairly argued that the AIGT became involved in an impossible mission. Essentially its members were seeking to overthrow Euclid but the implicit rules of the contest were still largely dependent on Euclidean ideals. Thus, Godfrey, a pupil of Levett, later commented on the AIGT's textbook in terms which mirror the earlier remarks of Hayward:

> The whole treatment is severely logical and scholarly; for instance, there is a careful exposition of Euclid, Book V., an essential link unless a fundamentally different educational standpoint is adopted. The AIGT advocated no such fundamental change.
>
> In the two first pages of the book there is a list of elementary constructions to be made with ruler and compass . . . I do not remember that we used ruler and compass in Levett's class room.
>
> Perhaps the best illustration of 30 years' change of standpoint is that the first theorem in the *Elements of Plane Geometry* is 'All right angles are equal to one another'; the proof occupies a page and a half. (76)

In terms of pure mathematics, Euclid remained unassailable until rigorous axiomatizations of geometry were developed in the 1890s. But, in the same decade, the emphasis in school geometry started to shift, away from the mathematical foundations and mental discipline and towards wider questions of educational purpose and pedagogy. Late-nineteenth-century geometry teaching in practice comprised two wholly independent streams: practical geometry, i.e. geometrical drawing; and theoretical or deductive geometry, i.e. Euclid. The thinking and work of the AIGT did little to undermine this binary tradition. Both socially and in terms of educational ideals the AIGT did not associate itself with the practical tradition and its utilitarian values. The latter was aligned with the movement for technical education which had working-class associations. Only when the relationship between the two streams began to loom large on educational grounds, as part of the much wider Perry movement from 1900, did a confluence become possible. (77) Hirst was an important early influence in relation to the AIGT's pedagogical conservatism, which not only marginalized the potential of practical geometry but also reinforced the strict separation of deductive geometry from the other two basic branches of mathematics: arithmetic and algebra. (78) When the ideals and tactics of the AIGT are placed in context it is not unreasonable to conclude that its frustrations as a curriculum pressure group in the 1870s and 1880s were inevitable.

The discussion thus far has focused on the work of the AIGT in the context of the politics and ideology of Victorian mathematics education. The AIGT's origins and much of its early work were firmly located within the political arena. But to complete the picture up to 1900 it is necessary also to consider major aspects of the constitutional and social development of the Association which, by the turn of the century, had become the Mathematical Association, along with the Modern Language (1892) and Geographical (1893) Associations. The formation of subject teaching associations for science, classics, history and English was soon to follow. The AIGT is of particular interest as a pioneering association of this type.

CONSTITUTIONAL AND SOCIAL DEVELOPMENTS

In 1871 the AIGT started with a Committee of Management comprising a president (Hirst), two vice-presidents (Wilson and the Reverend J. Jones), a treasurer (Wormell), two honorary secretaries (Levett and MacCarthy) and twelve local secretaries, including two from London (Tucker and Merrifield). (79) The existence of a local network from the outset is notable, though a system of branches involving formal local association was not established until the twentieth century. The initial resolutions of 1871 made explicit the AIGT's principal role as a pressure group on examining bodies in geometry, with lines of communication for members through the local secretaries and Committee of Management. (80) Annual meetings were held in January at University College and the proceedings subsequently recorded in the published annual reports, along with lists of the officers, members and resolutions in force. In the 1870s, the business at the annual meetings was wholly concerned with the various subcommittees' work on syllabus construction, the strategies for achieving the Association's objectives, and the outcomes. Before the end of the first decade, the work of subcommittees in geometry extended beyond Euclid Book 6 to include solid geometry, higher plane geometry and geometrical conics. (81) Hayward, a Harrow schoolmaster, replaced Hirst as President in 1878. Under the new presidency there were some notable constitutional and social developments in the 1880s.

In 1881, at a special Easter meeting of the AIGT, the question of widening the scope of its work beyond pure geometry was debated and in the following year a comprehensive set of rules was adopted. (82) The Association retained its name, in the interests of historical continuity, but the object was now 'to effect improvements in the teaching of Elementary Mathematics and Mathematical Physics, and especially of Geometry'. The governing body was now called a Council, comprising the officers and eight other elected members. In addition, a membership hierarchy was established, with two classes, 'ordinary' and 'honorary', the latter to be 'distinguished mathematicians or mathematical teachers' nominated by the Council for election. The two classes were listed separately in the annual reports. The first such list of twelve honorary members included six from Oxbridge, plus W. Spottiswoode, who was then President of the Royal Society, and Wilson was the only schoolmaster in this category. (83) It seems clear that the AIGT was seeking to enhance its status in relation to the mathematical community and thereby to strengthen its political influence.

In 1884 the legal and financial basis of the AIGT was strengthened by rules governing the appointment and duties of trustees and an auditor, to deal with matters of property and funds. (84) By this time four committees were working on geometry, three on syllabuses and one on the textbook; one committee had started work on arithmetic and one on mechanics.

(85) Two years later, another institutional development was the establishment of a special Cambridge Committee, following a summer conference at Cambridge involving the AIGT and some 'influential members of the University'. (86) The first such committee, comprising nine AIGT members, was listed in the annual report for 1886. (87) This was clearly another strategy adopted by the AIGT to strengthen its political position through gaining an organizational foothold at the centre of power itself. However, this appears to have achieved little in the short term and a Cambridge Committee is not listed after 1888. By this time the AIGT's textbook had been generally rejected as a possible alternative geometry for examination purposes.

When membership and its growth are surveyed, the graph for the MA's first sixty years (Figure 2.1) clearly shows the relatively limited gains up to 1900 by comparison with the next thirty years. The first list of sixty-one members in January 1871 comprised around 60 per cent mathematical masters, 20 per cent senior or head masters, three members from Oxbridge and no women. In subsequent January listings Miss Beale is the first woman to appear, in 1875, followed by Misses Cooper and Wood in 1877, and Miss Buss and Mrs Bryant in 1878. (88) Dorothea Beale (1831–1906), Frances Buss (1827–94), who founded the North London Collegiate School for Girls, and Sophie Bryant (1850–1922), who succeeded her in the headship, were all prominent figures in the general late-Victorian movement to advance the status of and opportunities for girls' and women's education.

The provision of secondary teacher training for women developed alongside the growth of secondary schooling for girls. In the development of professional training for secondary teaching women were in the vanguard and this gender difference is partly explained by the fact that university opportunities for women were restricted in the nineteenth century, particularly at Oxbridge. In the case of the Cambridge mathematical tripos, women could not compete as equals, or be awarded degrees, in spite of the fact that Philippa Fawcett (1868–1948) was placed above the senior wrangler in 1890, nine years after women were first allowed at least to sit the examinations. (89)

It is interesting to find women such as Miss Buss and Miss Beale starting to play a small part in the male-dominated world of the AIGT from the 1870s. (90) But progress here was slow: women comprised only 7 per cent of a total membership of 242 in the list for January 1900 and were then represented by only one Council member. (91) In total size the membership doubled through the 1880s, which suggests that the appeal of the AIGT widened significantly during the period of Hayward's presidency (1878–89).

FROM GEOMETRY TO MATHEMATICS

At an early stage Hayward clearly saw a need to extend the mathematical range of the AIGT's work, with a view to enhancing the Association's status, appeal and influence in mathematics education. Addressing the January meeting of 1881, he paved the way for a detailed review at

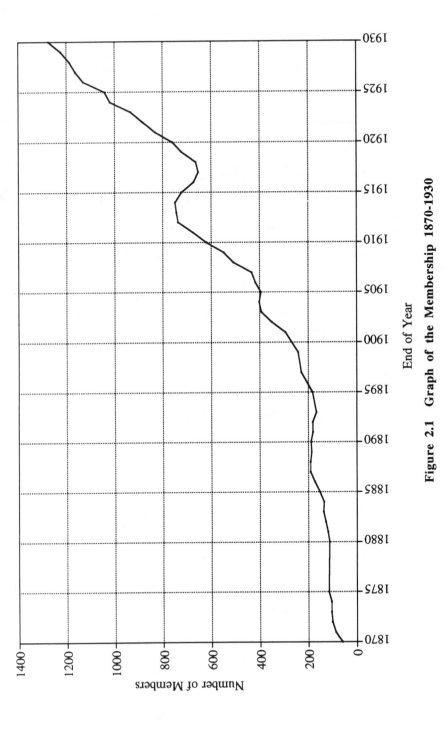

Figure 2.1 Graph of the Membership 1870-1930

the special general meeting in April of the same year. Significantly, he remarked:

> I cannot doubt but that we have to some extent suffered from the restriction of the field within which we have hitherto worked. Elementary Geometry is essentially a *school* subject . . . which . . . is not a subject of *real teaching* in our Universities or higher Colleges at all. (92)

He continued:

> It is reasonable to expect therefore that, by extending the scope of our work to other subjects, of which only the elements can (in general) be taught in schools and which will afterwards be more fully studied at the Universities, we shall enlist the sympathies of a wider circle of Mathematical Teachers, extend the list of our members, and connect ourselves more intimately with the living Mathematical teaching of our Universities, and thus we shall, I believe, greatly promote the recognition of the work which we have already done. (93)

The main thrust of Hayward's argument was towards extending the AIGT's mathematical range upwards for obvious strategic reasons. But he also pointed to the possibility of extending the range downwards to embrace arithmetic, which was 'at the base of our educational system'. He suggested potential links with teachers in preparatory and 'even in primary schools', as well as HMI. Thus, very tentatively, he proposed a vision for the future:

> our organisation might become a means of linking together all grades of Mathematical Teachers, from the humblest to the highest, in an association which could not fail, if heartily supported, to become a powerful influence for good on the whole education of the country. (94)

Twelve years later, in a Presidential address from Wormell, who confessed he was 'only a schoolmaster and teacher of the multitude', similar sentiments were expressed but the tone was distinctly less optimistic in the case of 'mathematics for the multitude'. (95) However, the possibility of a comprehensive association embracing mathematics for all kinds of purposes, and attracting teachers from the full range of educational settings, was at least envisaged by individual members of the AIGT. The extent to which this vision became a reality will be pursued in the subsequent chapters of this book.

In the context of the AIGT's work in the 1880s, Hayward could point to some significant broadening in the range of its mathematical concerns. Apart from the work in higher geometry, a committee had also considered arithmetic and produced a set of principles which had been closely followed in at least one textbook. Another committee was working on linear dynamics and a syllabus was published in 1890. (96) In the case of algebra, 'they had taken no direct step' beyond reprinting and circulating a powerful critique of the teaching of this branch produced by Professor G. Chrystal of the University of Edinburgh, in his Presidential address to the BAAS in 1885. (97) In general the teaching of algebra attracted very little

PUBLICATIONS ISSUED BY THE
Association for the Improvement of Geometrical Teaching.

Syllabus of Elementary Plane Geometry, corresponding to Euclid, Books I. to VI. Macmillan & Co. 1s.

The Elements of Plane Geometry, in which the Syllabus has been revised and proofs of the propositions, and exercises on them supplied. Swan Sonnenschein & Co. Part I. (corresponding to Euclid I. and II.), price, 2s. 6d. Part II. (corresponding to Euclid III., IV., V., and VI.), price, 2s. 6d. The complete work in one volume, price, 4s. 6d.

Syllabus of Elementary Geometrical Conics. Swan Sonnenschein & Co. Price, 1s. 6d.

Syllabus of Modern Plane Geometry. Macmillan & Co. Price, 1s.

Syllabus of Linear Dynamics. Macmillan & Co. Price, 1s.

General Reports of the Association. Nos. 1 to 16. Nos. 1, 3—5, 7—9, 13—17, may be obtained by application to the Honorary Secretaries, or of Messrs. Whittaker & Co., 2, White Hart Street, Paternoster Square.

Reprint of Addresses to Section A of the British Association, by Profs. HENRICI and CHRYSTAL.

THE FOLLOWING PAPERS APPEAR IN THE GENERAL REPORTS:

1883. *" The Teaching of Elementary Mechanics."* (W. H. BESANT, M.A., F.R.S.)
" Notes on the Teaching of Elementary Dynamics."
(Prof. G. M. MINCHIN, M.A.)
" The Basis of Statics." (Prof. H. LAMB, M.A.)

1884. *" The Discovery and the Geometrical Treatment of the Conic Sections."*
(Rev. C. TAYLOR, D.D.)

1885. *" Elementary Mechanics."* (Prof. R. W. GENESE, M.A.)

1886. *" The Correlation of the various branches of Elementary Mathematics."*
(R. B. HAYWARD, M.A., F.R.S.)

1887. *" The Teaching of Modern Geometry."* (Rev. G. RICHARDSON, M.A.)
" The Modern Treatment of Maxima and Minima."
(Rev. J. J. MILNE, M.A.)
" Geometry from an Artist's point of view." (G. A. STOREY, A.R.A.)
" Note on the Nine Point Circle." (E. M. LANGLEY, M.A.)

1888. *" The Recent Geometry of the Triangle."* (R. F. DAVIS, M.A.)
With notes by E. M. LANGLEY, M.A., and R. TUCKER, M.A.
" The Multiplication and Division of Concrete Quantities."
(Prof. A. LODGE, M.A.) With notes by Mrs. BRYANT, D.Sc.
" Some Principles of Arithmetic." (W. BELL, M.A.)

1889. *" The Vices of our Scientific Education."* (Prof. G. M. MINCHIN, M.A.)
" Horner's Method." (R. B. HAYWARD, M A., F.R.S.)

1890. *" A New Treatment of the Hyperbola."* (Rev. C. TAYLOR, D.D.)
" The Teaching of Trigonometry." (G. HEPPEL, M.A.)
" Some Geometrical Theorems." (E. M. LANGLEY, M.A.)
" Statics and Geometry." (Prof. G. M. MINCHIN, M.A.)
" Isoscelian Hexagrams." (R. TUCKER, M.A.)

1891. *" On the Use of the word 'Abstract' in Arithmetic."* Miss WOOD, B.Sc.)
" The Foundations of Geometry." (E. T. DIXON.)
" Some Notes on Statics and Geometry." (E. M. LANGLEY, M.A.)

1892. *" On Laguerre's Dictum Concerning Direction."* (Prof. R.W. GENESE, M.A.)
" The Geometrical Interpretation of Fallacy in Elimination."
(Prof. R. W. GENESE, M.A.)
" The Use of Horner's Method in Schools. (E. M. LANGLEY, M.A.)
" Note on the Theorem $\cosh u + \sinh u = e^u$*."* (R. LEVETT, M.A.)
" Theorems connected with I. 47." (Dr. J. S. MACKAY.)
" Geometrical Odds and Ends." (E. M. LANGLEY, M.A.)

Plate 2.4   Early Publications of the AIGT

attention until the turn of the century. It was an accepted, albeit inferior, part of mathematics in a liberal education, but, as Hayward pointed out, if it was to be 'worthy to take a place in the mental training of students' then it should not be treated as 'a bare piece of mechanism'. (98)

In addition to broadening the range of its mathematical concerns, the AIGT also extended the range of its professional and social functions in a small number of important ways, before it changed its name to the Mathematical Association. A new feature at the annual meetings, from 1883, was the reading of papers and the raising of discussions on various subjects, which were subsequently published in the AIGT's annual reports. Thus the annual report served as an organ of the AIGT for ten years before the appearance of the *Mathematical Gazette*.

These papers varied quite widely in terms of mathematical content and level as well as in the extent to which educational considerations featured. The publications list up to 1893 gives a good indication of the range of contributions. Clearly the aim was to cater for both mathematical and educational interests, and thereby to widen the AIGT's appeal. Early papers concerning general education and pedagogy were given by Hayward, on the correlation of the branches of elementary mathematics and by Professor G. Minchin of the Royal Indian Engineering College on 'The vices of our scientific education'. The first paper from a woman, not surprisingly on arithmetic teaching, was given by Miss Wood in 1891. Another leading woman member, Mrs Bryant, was responsible for an exceptional departure at the annual meeting in 1893.

The programme for the annual meeting in 1893 was atypical, with contributions on arithmetic teaching, the use of history of mathematics in teaching, and a demonstration lesson in geometry by Mrs Bryant. It is noteworthy but unexceptional to find a woman taking a distinctly 'progressive' educational lead, in the context of the AIGT's affairs, and the lesson consisted of work on three 'riders' (geometrical problems) on circles. It generated quite a lot of discussion and one observer was struck by 'the exceedingly ready way in which the young ladies had answered'. Hayward added that 'a vote of thanks was . . . due to the young ladies of Mrs. Bryant's class. Any teacher who had to deal with boys would envy her.' (99)

It was a natural extension of the policy of publishing papers for the AIGT to establish its own journal. As the first editor, Langley, of Bedford Modern School, subsequently emphasized:

> the reading of these papers, the discussions to which they gave rise, and the correspondence which ensued showed a widespread desire on the part of teachers to become acquainted with the methods of other teachers, and gave rise to the feeling that there was room for a journal . . . (100)

Members were circulated on the matter, adequate financial guarantees were secured, and the Council was gradually persuaded to act, with strong support coming from Wormell in particular. Langley initially had in mind a journal along the lines of Vuibert's *Journal des Mathématiques Elémentaires* and the first quarto number was published in April 1894. (101) The first

Association for the Improvement of Geometrical Teaching.

~~~~~~~

The General Meeting is to be held at University College, Gower Street, W.C., on Saturday, January 14, 1893.

At the Morning Sitting (11 a.m.), the Report of the Council will be read; the new officers will be elected; and the following will be proposed for election as members of the Association:—

> P. J. HEAWOOD, M.A., Durham.
>
> Prof. G. LORIA, Genoa.
>
> W. H. WAGSTAFF, M.A., Birmingham.

After the conclusion of the formal business, Mrs. BRYANT, D.Sc., will give '**A Model Lesson on Geometry, as a basis for discussion.**'

After an adjournment for luncheon at 1 p.m., members will reassemble (2 p.m.) to hear papers by Mr. G. HEPPEL, M.A. (**'The Use of History in teaching Mathematics'**), and Mr. F. E. MARSHALL, M.A. (**'The Teaching of Elementary Arithmetic'**).

All interested in the objects of the Association are invited to attend.

Members who wish to have any special matter brought forward at the General Meeting, but who are unable to attend, are requested to communicate with one of the Honorary Secretaries.

Plate 2.5   General Meeting 1893

THE
MATHEMATICAL GAZETTE
A TERMINAL JOURNAL FOR STUDENTS AND TEACHERS

Edited by E. M. LANGLEY, M.A.

No. 1.] APRIL 1894. [PRICE SIXPENCE NET.

ORIGIN OF THE MATHEMATICAL GAZETTE.

IN 1881 the Association for the Improvement of Geometrical Teaching widened its basis so as to include all branches of Elementary Mathematics and Mathematical Physics, though it retained its restricted name. The following means of carrying out the objects of the Association were indicated in the Report of the Council :—

The reading of Papers or raising Discussions at meetings of the Association.

The appointment of Committees to report on existing defects in the usual methods, order, range, etc., in teaching special subjects.

A glance through the titles of the papers read at the General Meetings will show that one part of the programme laid down in 1881 for future progress has been well carried out. But most of the work done in Committees has been that of one or two individuals, and would have been almost as valuable if it had at once been issued to the teaching world without the intervention of Committees, which has frequently been the cause of delay and expense. It is then, doubtless, to the widespread desire on the part of teachers of mathematics to become acquainted with the methods of other teachers that the Association owes its continued existence. In the hope of carrying out more fully that part of the 1881 programme which has been found most practicable the present journal has been published.

It cannot be doubted that many teachers are in possession of methods of their own which experience has shown to be better than those most in vogue. They are asked to let others have the advantage of knowing these special methods.

We hope to extract from desk and pigeon-hole many MSS. which have remained unpublished for want of a suitable organ for making them known. Our course must be *tentative*. We must find out from our readers on which of several possible lines it is best, in the general interest, to proceed. But we intend to keep strictly to "Elementary Mathematics": while not absolutely excluding Differential and Integral Calculus, our columns will, as a rule, be devoted to such school subjects as Arithmetic, Algebra, Geometry, Trigonometry, and Mechanics.

In conclusion we earnestly desire the co-operation of all who can from time to time help us with contributions or advice.

All communications should be addressed to THE EDITOR, 16 Adelaide Square, Bedford.

Plate 2.6   First *Mathematical Gazette* 1894

editorial clearly declared that the journal should keep strictly to 'elementary mathematics': arithmetic, algebra, geometry, trigonometry and mechanics, and, only exceptionally, calculus.

By 1890 the AIGT had also started to form a library of mathematical books, either presented by individuals or publishers, or purchased by the Council. Hirst, who died in 1892, made a significant early donation of English and foreign geometry texts and the gradually growing collection was made available for members' use. It was kept initially in the London home of C.V. Coates – the first 'librarian' – and such a facility provided another means of professional support. (102)

Finally, and appropriately, the AIGT changed its name in 1897 to the Mathematical Association: 'an association of teachers and students of elementary mathematics'. The Association by now exhibited many of the characteristics one might expect of a subject teaching association and indeed acted as a model for others. (103) It had made considerable gains in both status and professional scope, and bore little resemblance to the schoolmasters' pressure group of the 1870s. From around the turn of the century, the MA entered a new phase in its development at a time when the effects of the Perry movement were beginning to be strongly felt. The way in which the Association responded to the new twentieth-century circumstances is the principal subject of the next chapter.

CHAPTER THREE

THE MATHEMATICAL ASSOCIATION AND THE PERRY MOVEMENT

The impulse to reform came from the engineers, who found that their young men had learnt no mathematics that was of use, and little enough of any kind. In the person of Professor Perry, they raised public interest in the matter and induced the British Association to bestir itself. The Mathematical Association (descendant of the A.I.G.T.) awoke as one out of sleep. (1)

(Charles Godfrey, 1906)

We felt that during the period of rapid change it was undesirable that the Association should attempt to crystallise teaching. Until matters have settled down, it is for individuals to urge new ideas; an Association cannot easily do more than register the average opinion of sound teachers. (2)

(Charles Godfrey, 1920)

By 1900 the general context of English education, embracing its political, administrative, institutional and ideological aspects, had developed in a number of respects by comparison with the circumstances in the 1860s and 1870s. Furthermore, the AIGT's limited nineteenth-century achievements as a curriculum pressure group could now be placed alongside its coming of age as a subject teaching association. By 1900 the MA had become a significant agent for the professional support of mathematics in education, with a gradually growing membership which extended well beyond England to include addresses in Scotland, Wales, Ireland, India, South Africa, the West Indies, Australia, the USA, Japan, Italy and Egypt. (3) It had also grown in respectability as a *mathematical* association. In January 1900 the membership of ten from the USA included eight professors, one being an honorary member. Out of a total of thirteen honorary members, one was from Oxford and five were from Cambridge, including the MA President 1899–1901, Sir Robert Ball, the Lowndean professor of astronomy and geometry.

The MA's *Gazette*, under Greenstreet's editorship, had made a significant early impact, the number of issues increasing from three in 1899 to six in 1900 and the Council reporting: 'it has contained many important reviews written by mathematicians of high rank and is becoming very widely known and valued among teachers and students'. (4) But the pages of the *Gazette* around this time give no indication of the start of a renewed movement for major reform; and, unlike the geometrical reform movement around 1870, this new movement was not spearheaded by leading members of the MA. The opening quotation from Godfrey, who became a leading figure in the MA's development, is a somewhat harsh but nevertheless fair judgement in the light of the available evidence. It is necessary to look well beyond the confines of the MA in order to chart and explain the extraordinary initial success of what became widely known as the Perry movement in England, 'Perryismus' on the continent and the 'laboratory method' in the USA. (5)

In seeking to fill out the background to the reform movement's progress it is also necessary to consider much more than the specific demands of the engineering profession as personified by Professor John Perry (1850–1920). It is important to set the specific campaign in mathematics within a much broader context of educational advance, aspects of which have been well summarized by the historians Lawson and Silver:

> A range of new departures was becoming evident in English education in the 1890s. There were new schools and new interests in child study and child development . . . The constraints imposed by payment by results were being removed from the elementary schools, and new approaches in the infant school were beginning to have an influence on the higher classes. Technical subjects and science were not only finding a place in schools, but were also the focus of new thinking about methods and objectives in teaching. For most of the nineteenth century the major changes in education had been in terms of supply and structure. Under new pressures, changes in the final decades also began to focus on content and method, and on children. The search for a new understanding of children and of educational processes was closely related to the wider changes of emphasis in discussions of the individual, society and social policy. (6)

EDUCATIONAL DEVELOPMENTS

During the 1890s the policy for state involvement in the curriculum of the growing number of elementary schools was fundamentally altered, following the report of the Cross Commission (1886–8). The system of payment by results was gradually replaced by a system of block grants. The new arrangements provided encouragement for more breadth and variety in the curriculum, and more enlightenment in teaching methods. The mental and moral disciplinary value of the 'instrumentary' education of the masses was increasingly coming into question, as was the early Victorian cult of efficiency through the stimulus of annual external examinations throughout what had become seven standards for the elementary schools. The fundamental administrative policy shift from prescription and examination to inspection and suggestion was completed by the new Board of Education, which subsumed the work of the Education Department after the Board of Education Act of 1899. (7)

In the case of 'secondary' education in its various grades there had also been significant developments since the Clarendon and Taunton

Commissions of the 1860s. In terms of status, the public schools were still pre-eminent and the number of HMC schools had doubled to around one hundred between 1870 and 1900. (8) These prestigious schools were served by a developing system of boys' preparatory schools whose headmasters had formed an Association of Preparatory Schools in 1892. The HMC continued to act as a powerful lobby in the preservation of the public school system's independence from the state, though market forces and the requirements of examinations had promoted the modernization of curricula, which brought a choice of parallel routes through the classical, modern or army 'sides' of these schools. Modern subjects such as geography and modern languages, and to a lesser extent science, had begun to secure some place in the curriculum alongside the high-status classics, and mathematics had consolidated its position, though its character had changed little up to 1900. (9) But, by this time, the public school curriculum and some of its effects were coming into question.

The nature of the attack, with particular reference to mathematics, is well exemplified by the following sharp response in the journal *Engineer*:

> we in England have quite suddenly become convinced that we are really getting old and that we must wake up from a 'Rip Van Winkle' slumber in order to avoid Chinese decrepitude and rottenness. Professor John Perry's gallant crusade against orthodox mathematical method is one of the signs of these times . . . In England almost alone has there been solid refusal to budge with the times on the part of University mathematical examiners and public school head masters. They have stuck to the literal inspiration of their Euclid, and by their influential stolidity have retarded for more than a full generation the intellectual development of the British race. (10)

The unfavourable comparisons with China, which during this period, 1900–1, was struggling to cope with the Boxer Rebellion, were paralleled by growing concern in Britain over the handling of the Boer War, for which the products of the public schools were partly held responsible. Layton has drawn attention to the clear feeling that 'stout hearts and earnest sentiments were no substitute for intellectual efficiency in the maintenance of an Empire threatened from within by disaffection with British rule, and from without by the growth of industrial and military power in Europe and elsewhere'. (11) There is evidence at this time of a growing mood of 'declinism' in relation to Britain's military, industrial and commercial well-being, which was exploited by Perry and other reformers. In particular they pointed to the backward state of school mathematics, based on outmoded classical ideals and supported by the doctrine of mental discipline, as partly to blame for Britain's alleged decline. (12)

As well as in the elementary schools under the control of the Education Department, the state's influence on the provision and teaching of various 'science and art' subjects in a range of institutional settings developed greatly between the 1860s and the 1890s, through the work of the Department of Science and Art (DSA) and its examinations in a variety of science subjects, including pure mathematics and practical geometry. The DSA scheme, which was originally intended for the industrial classes and for part-time evening tuition, provided educational and financial incentives which increasingly attracted business from day technical schools or classes and from various providers of 'secondary' education: endowed grammar schools, the developing system of 'higher-grade' board schools, pupil-teacher centres and even elementary training colleges. (13) Technical instruction and aspects of its relationship with secondary education had been the subject of a Royal Commission (1881–4). Subsequent Acts of Parliament, between 1888 and 1890, released further funds from local government for the development of technical instruction, which was then very widely interpreted, and it expanded further with the continuing support of the DSA. These developments became a particular concern of the Bryce Commission (1894–5) on secondary education in England. (14)

The Bryce Commission pointed out that the DSA had become essentially the central authority for technical education, as well as a major examining body in the vaguely defined secondary field, where its operations had become educationally limiting and bureaucratically unwieldy. The Commission expressed concern over the 'warping' of curricula through the DSA's limited offering of examination subjects for secondary as opposed to part-time adult evening education. The Commission also pointed to a major curricular tension:

> More general in its nature . . . is that conflict which goes on in so many schools between the attempt to educate – to train the mind – and the attempt to teach something of immediate practical utility. (15)

This tension became a central one and particularly in the case of geometry teaching.

On the basis of experience and ideology, the educational benefits of practical work could now be set against the traditional claims of Euclid as an unrivalled mind trainer. During the first movement for geometrical reform, in the 1870s, Professor Olaus Henrici had pointed to the fact that 'Geometrical drawing belongs . . . to a branch of Geometry of which Euclid knew nothing, and where Euclid's propositions are of little use.' (16) Henrici deplored the divorce of the science and art of geometry but his was an isolated voice in this earlier period. One result, however, of the DSA's success in the examination business was the early dissemination of geometrical instruments for use in higher-grade schools, some grammar schools and even a few girls' schools, although the public schools remained untouched by such developments. (17) Bushell recalled that, as late as 1903, in his last term as a pupil at Charterhouse:

> Mr Tuckey produced a ruler with strange markings on it. It was, of course, a protractor. In those days, brought up on the purest Euclid, when protractors were banned and indeed unknown, I was dumbfounded at its appearance . . . (18)

Drawing exercises also gained considerable popularity in elementary schools with support from both the Education Department and the DSA. (19) This all contributed to a 'climate' for reform in mathematics education within which pure Euclid was at best uncomfortably accommodated.

Following the Bryce Commission, major changes in the administrative structure of English education were implemented through the Board of Education Act of 1899, which created a single central authority for all aspects of education involving the state, and the Education Act of 1902, which empowered newly established local education authorities (LEAs) to take over the work of the school boards in elementary education and also to develop the local provision for 'education other than elementary' in existing institutions and through the provision of new grant-aided secondary schools. (20) These steps were of enormous consequence for the development of a coherent national system of English education based on a concept of partnership between central and local authorities.

The establishment of the Board of Education brought together under one authority the hitherto unco-ordinated work of the Education Department, the DSA and the Charity Commission, whose involvement related to school endowments. The Board's administrative structure, which was hammered out at the end of the nineteenth century, was crucially important as it established parameters for the development of English elementary, secondary and technical education in the twentieth century. These categories had become blurred in the late nineteenth century, with the upward striving towards 'secondary' education of the higher-grade board schools and the spread of science schools and classes in a range of institutional settings under the DSA.

The public schools, however, still provided the paradigm for a 'secondary' education, which was closely linked with the requirements and values of the universities. Given social-class divisions and the association of the DSA with the industrial and working classes, the influential HMC schools were antipathetic to and remained uninfluenced by the DSA's work. But the HMC was a powerful lobby and within the new administration of the Board quite separate divisions were established for secondary and technical education. (21) Secondary education as developed by the Board and the new LEAs became aligned with a liberal education along public-school lines. Curricular breadth and balance were initially enforced by the Board's regulations which specified minimum hours for specific subjects. In the domain of science and art the Board's curricular control became limited to strictly vocational and predominantly part-time evening education. Through their examinations, the universities, particularly Cambridge, Oxford and London, shaped the whole curriculum of the developing system of secondary schools from the turn of the century. (22)

Administrative policies served also to sharpen the early-twentieth-century distinction between elementary and secondary education, and quasi-secondary developments out of the elementary system were inhibited. The Cockerton Judgement of 1901 seriously affected the future of the higher-grade schools, and the development of a 'higher elementary' system was discouraged by both the law and its administration. There were initially only two major options: to become a municipal secondary school under the Board or to work strictly within the regulations for elementary schools. The concept of 'two nations' in English non-vocational education persisted, linked only by the narrow ladder of, in practice, a competitive examination for entry to a secondary school, a route which excluded the majority of elementary school pupils, particularly given the limits in the provision of secondary places for such pupils. (23)

The legislative structure and administrative patterns of the English educational system were in a state of flux around the turn of the century and this, in turn, created institutional instability on a large scale. Such a system was likely to prove receptive to major curriculum development initiatives and to the Perry movement in particular. Receptivity to change also needs to be considered in the context of the prevailing educational values in the system and their relationship with the values held by the proponents of change. In the case of the Perry movement a distinctive pedagogy applicable to mathematics for the multitude was espoused and it gained strength from its associations and shared values with other late-nineteenth-century developments: the kindergarten movement, the development of technical education, manual training and workshops, and the growth of science teaching, with laboratory work.

PEDAGOGICAL DEVELOPMENTS

Perry was an important pioneer in the field of engineering and technical education in England, and he built upon his very early experience in Japan in the 1870s, where students were encouraged to use graphical methods, including the plotting of curves on squared paper. (24) This Japanese experience provided a foundation for the innovative development of curricula for technical students in England, at what became Finsbury Technical College, where Perry was appointed as a professor of mechanical engineering in 1882. This pioneering work placed much emphasis on empirical activity by the students themselves, with generous provision made for practical sessions in both the workshop and laboratory. (25) Essentially the pedagogy was based on 'learning by doing', and the associated values were shared by the kindergarten movement, which thrived in the late nineteenth century, its inspiration coming from the writings of Pestalozzi and Froebel. The teaching methods at Finsbury exemplified at an early stage aspects of what became a much wider and growing concern for 'practical education' in various forms, and the protagonists exploited the links with the infant educationists' arguments, especially their championship of the values of self-activity and the training of the senses. (26) Wormell, a founder member of the AIGT, was one such protagonist. As headmaster of the Cowper Street Middle-Class School, Finsbury, he became directly involved in the Technical College's affairs and shared much of Perry's educational idealism, including Froebelian sympathies:

> although the educational methods which are associated with the name of Froebel have been brought very near to perfection in the Kindergarten, they are to a great extent suspended when the pupil passes from the Infant School. They reappear, however, in the schools and colleges devoted to Technical and Experimental Science . . . It is very desirable that we should bridge over the gap . . . (27)

Both Wormell and Perry justified the value of workshop and laboratory methods in terms of 'hand and eye' (senses) training, heurism (learning by discovery) and motivation:

> The charm of these methods will always be, as in the Kindergarten, inherent in their nature. They give something to be done by the hand and followed by the eye, keeping pace with the course of thought and reasoning . . . the pupil . . . is constantly on a voyage of discovery, and has all the pleasure and stimulus of an original investigation. (28)

An extraordinary example of Wormell's pedagogy in action is to be found in the AIGT report for his Presidential year, 1893, when the AIGT's annual meeting included a demonstration lesson by Mrs Bryant. In concluding the discussion which followed, Wormell was prompted to give the following detailed illustration:

> suppose that it was necessary to use the fact referred to in the model lesson that the vertices of equal angles on the same base are cyclic, long before it had been reached in the order of Euclid. He would say:- take a piece of card-board or drawing paper twice as long as broad; from the middle of the long side draw a line obliquely to the opposite side, making thus two angles, one acute, the other supplementary to it, and cut the paper into two pieces along this line. Drive two pins through a sheet of paper on the drawing board at a distance not greater than the breadth of the original paper. Place the acute angle with its sides against the pins and rule lines on the paper below by means of the sides of the angle. Do this in many positions of the angle – say twelve – always placing the sides against the pins. Lay aside the acute angle and take the obtuse angle. Use it in the same way, but starting on the other side of the pins, that is to say, if the angular point was placed upwards between the pins before, place downwards between them now, he would then ask – what do you notice about the twenty-four angles which you have drawn? (29)

This striking example of practical work appears to have brought the morning meeting to an abrupt halt, and nothing quite like it is to be found anywhere else in the complete set of nineteen reports of the AIGT up to 1893. But, by 1900, Wormell would have been able to count on many other allies, as the Perry movement began to gain momentum and to draw strength from the general movement for a more 'practical' education, which embraced the promotion of newer subjects such as drawing, manual training, science and nature study, as well as the championship of a kindergarten-inspired and less 'bookish' pedagogy. (30)

The various components of the new pedagogy, applied to mathematics, were well summarized in a contribution to the *Educational Times* on 'impending reforms':

> Mathematical knowledge, like all other knowledge, has its foundation in the senses; abstract thought must be based on concrete experience, and in the immature mind must constantly revert to concrete experience as an aid to abstraction . . .

Self-activity. – By 'using' squared paper, by measuring, by plotting curves, etc.

Intuition. – Many mathematical truths can be apprehended and rationally employed long before they can be reduced to formal expression in a system of philosophic thought. (31)

As the contributor was quick to point out, 'We are not concerned with some new patent process, to be labelled the Perry Method. Heaven forbid!' What was important for the reform movement was the growing attention paid to the application of such principles in the debates concerning school mathematics, and geometry teaching in particular.

There is one further aspect to the pedagogical background of the Perry movement which remains to be considered. It is significant that Wormell taught mathematics and science, and produced a number of textbooks in both subject areas, all of which reflected the Froebelian influence. As the provision for science teaching developed, so the relationship with mathematics came to assume greater importance in two respects: the potential of the heuristic method in mathematics as well as science teaching; and the need for correlation between these two subjects.

Heurism as a method of teaching science is normally associated with the chemist and educationist H.E. Armstrong (1848–1937). A life-long friend of Perry and co-founder of Finsbury Technical College, he became 'the champion of the heuristic approach'. (32) In a contribution to the *Educational Times*, in 1900, Wormell pointed out that the method was 'applicable to other subjects – to art, to geometry, to algebra, etc.'. He described an interesting algebraic example of the method in practice. By employing a set of wooden cubes to build up progressively larger squares, and through carefully graded questioning, 'the mode of forming . . . successive additions was deduced, and the fact that $1+3+5+ \ldots + (2n-1)=n^2$ was established, and, it may be said, was discovered by the pupil'. In the case of geometry, he provided a rich example of the potential of the first proposition in Euclid Book 1 as a starting point for investigation:

> Having constructed the triangle ABC, construct equilateral triangles on each of the sides, and again on those sides, and so on. We thus learn the following:- (1) to construct a regular hexagon; (2) the hexagon is composed of six equilateral triangles; (3) the whole sheet of paper, that is to say, any plane area, may be completely covered with hexagons and therefore with equilateral triangles; (4) commencing with the side AB, if we construct ABC, then on AC, ACD, then on CD, CDE, and join EA, we see from the symmetry of the figure that we have erected a perpendicular to AB at its extremity; (5) to construct a square; (6) to cover the surface with squares, etc. (33)

W.D. Eggar (1865–1945), a master at Eton College and a founder member of the Association of Public School Science Masters (APSSM) in 1900, was another innovative physics and mathematics teacher. (34) He produced one of the new twentieth-century practical geometry textbooks, which he explained was

> an attempt to adapt the experimental method to the teaching of Geometry in schools. The main object of this method, sometimes

called 'heuristic', is to make the student think for himself, to give
him something to do with his hands for which the brain must be called
in as a fellow-worker. The plan has been tried with success in the
laboratory, and it seems to be equally well-suited to the Mathematical
class-room. (35)

But the links between mathematics and science teaching were not related
only to the heuristic method. The need for mathematical reform became
more evident with the growth in the scale of elementary science teaching,
which brought with it more pressing demands for correlation between these
two subjects.

As one commentator put it, the movement for correlation between
mathematics and science was 'the outcome of the desire to rank mathematics in its place as the handmaid of science . . . in close correlation with the
needs of the science syllabus right through the school'. (36) The gradual
development of science in education and the provision of laboratories
were advanced by the lobbying of the scientific community, particularly
acting through the BAAS, by the efforts of the practical educationists,
and, most importantly, through the arrangements for science schools
and classes under the DSA plus the funding permitted by the Technical
Instruction Acts. (37) One introductory course – 'elementary physical
measurements' – proved particularly popular and had obvious potential for correlation with work in arithmetic, mensuration, simple algebra
and graphs. Such links were being exploited in some schools, including
elementary and higher-grade board schools, but, as Eggar pointed out, the
older public schools were generally lagging behind. (38) Here the looming
crisis for mathematics teachers was well captured by Professor G.H. Bryan
(1864–1928), of University College Bangor, who subsequently became a
proactive President of the MA, 1907–9:

With the development of experimental science new teachers have been
appointed all over the country for physics, chemistry and biology, *but
next to nothing has been done to meet the greatly increased demand
for mathematical teaching thus produced* [Bryan's stress]. The same
teachers who provided efficiently for the teaching of mathematics on
the classical side have now thrust upon them an influx of new pupils
having quite different requirements. (39)

Thus the need for correlation with science emerged as yet another aspect
of the Perry movement's pedagogy.

The Perry movement's guiding principles were generally in accord with
the ideological 'climate' in English education around the turn of the
century. The movement was a timely one and Euclid's stranglehold on
geometry teaching was soon to be broken. One contributor to the *Educational Times* in 1903 went so far as to claim:

the change was inevitable . . . When teachers began to teach science
– as well as other subjects – scientifically and with more due regard
to the pupils' share in education, when the demands of the laboratory
and the workshop, of technical schools and colleges, made themselves
felt, reform was bound to come in the *teaching* of mathematics, as

of logic and languages and other subjects. It is part of a general movement. (40)

But nothing could be achieved without individual and collaborative action within the political context of mathematics education. It is to the tactics in the campaign for reform and its achievements in the short term that the discussion must now turn.

PRACTICAL MATHEMATICS

The work in science and art, supported by the examinations and grants of the DSA, saw an early breakthrough in 1899 when a new subject and syllabus, 'practical mathematics', was offered for the first time, and in the same year the DSA's operations were transferred to the newly created Board of Education. (41) The syllabus had been developed by Perry himself as part of his innovative contribution to the work at Finsbury Technical College. Practical plane and solid geometry had become separated from Euclid and the various other branches of pure mathematics at an early stage. But in relation to the developing needs of engineering and technical education there also developed the need for a much broader and more applicable treatment of mathematics than the conventional academic routine, and one which exploited a new pedagogy involving experimental, numerical and graphical methods. For example, the use of simple four-figure tables was a major innovation. Previously, mathematical tables had been regarded as suitable only for mathematical specialists, working to seven-figure accuracy. Perry could claim in 1901:

> since the Science and Art Department has distributed its tables of four-figure logarithms and functions of angles over the country as cheaply as grocers' advertisements, there has been a wonderful development in knowledge and use of such tables. (42)

What was required was rapid progress, to gain a working knowledge of a wide range of useful topics in mathematics, as opposed to the laborious academic treatment of the various separate branches of arithmetic, algebra etc., following rigorous pure mathematical lines, with utility neglected. Thus, while the DSA's requirements in pure mathematics still followed conventional academic lines, the new DSA syllabus embodied a radical alternative paradigm which served the needs of the practical users of the subject and also raised major new possibilities for school mathematics.

Perry's own introductory lectures on practical mathematics were first published by the DSA in 1899. (43) As he was quick to point out, the new scheme was 'exceedingly different from what used to be the study of the mere mathematician on the same subjects'. (44) The cutting reference to 'mere' mathematicians signifies a fundamental conflict between the practical users of mathematics and the high-status mathematicians of the Cambridge school. This conflict was to prove an important one in the context of the general movement to reform secondary school mathematics.

The elementary stage of practical mathematics as an examination subject was innovatory in a number of respects when compared with the traditional practice. In arithmetic emphasis was placed on decimals rather than fractions (including approximations) and on the use of both simple logarithmic tables and slide rules. In algebra the use of formulae featured prominently, as well as the study of functions and graphs, using squared paper, and leading to some early ideas in the calculus. The deductive ideals of a liberal geometry, based on Euclid, were largely ignored and replaced by a treatment based on measurement and drawing mixed with numerical and algebraic methods. Furthermore, the scheme encroached on some of the traditionally more advanced branches of mathematics by including some work in simple trigonometry, three-dimensional geometry and vector methods, as well as calculus. Overall, the scheme was notable for its breadth of subject matter and its mixing of hitherto separately treated branches of the subject. It was also permeated by the new practical pedagogy, as exemplified by Wormell and others. (45)

Under the new Board of Education's regulations for further education, the new examination subject enjoyed considerable success over the first decade of the twentieth century at the expense of the older-established stages of pure mathematics developed by the DSA. (46) New textbooks were produced which followed Perry's lead and reflected his influence, and in-service courses were provided at the Royal College of Science, South Kensington, where Perry was based as a professor of mathematics and mechanics, a post he had held since 1896. (47) A summary and fitting assessment of Perry's towering contribution to the development of mathematics in technical education has been provided by P.W.H. Abbott (1869–1954) of the Polytechnic School, Regent Street, who was a leading member of the Association of Teachers in Technical Institutions and did much to represent technical interests within the work of the MA also:

> It is probably correct to say that nobody has done more to influence the teaching of Mathematics in this country during the last 15 or 20 years than Professor Perry; and in no branch of the work has he brought about greater changes than in the teaching of Mathematics to technical students. Until the introduction of his 'Practical Mathematics', the mathematical teaching of students in Technical Institutions followed, for the most part, the ordinary conventional academic routine . . . But all this was changed by the introduction of Professor Perry's 'Practical Mathematics' . . . (48)

However, it is important to emphasize the limited scope of the achievements described thus far, in the context of mathematics for the multitude.

The subject of practical mathematics might have thrived in a range of institutional settings if it had been made available by the DSA in the 1890s, when 'secondary' education was, as a whole, ill-defined. But in the 1900s the scope of the direct influence of elementary practical mathematics as an examination subject became limited to strictly vocational and predominantly part-time evening education. This was a consequence of the general administrative policy and ideological assumptions of a new central authority which was also determined not to continue as an examining body for the work of secondary schools under its various regulations, following the Education Act of 1902. In terms of curriculum control, the universities remained firmly at the centre of power and were a key target in the renewed campaign for reform which again centred on the 'very English subject' of Euclid in geometry teaching.

PRESSURE FOR REFORM

Meetings, speeches and agitation in the educational and scientific press around 1900 were important precursors of more organized political activity. As well as attacking the *status quo* Perry could also now point to an alternative paradigm for school mathematics: his own scheme of elementary practical mathematics. As a correspondent in the journal *Engineering* indicated, Perry regarded his scheme as 'the best method of teaching children, for whatever life intended' and, what is more:

> it will be easily realised that the new system would from its very nature prove less startling to those who are trained to work hand-in-hand with Nature, and would therefore be easier to introduce to the engineering world than any other. Practical mathematics, in fact, is a system for teaching mathematics to all persons, of all kinds and all ages. (49)

Perry took the debate to the columns of *The Times* as well as *Nature*, which had also acted as an important mouthpiece for reform thirty years earlier. A new monthly journal from Macmillan, *School World,* also started to publish articles on the need for reform, as did the older *Journal of Education* and the *Educational Times*, both of which had published material of a relatively 'progressive' nature for many years, with particular stimulus coming from the work of the College of Preceptors. The columns of technical journals such as the *Electrician, Engineer* and *Engineering* also began to reflect the new climate, but the content of the *Mathematical Gazette* remained initially unaffected. (50) As one contemporary commentator judged, 'the time was ripe for stirring up both the scientific world and the teaching world on this subject', but more organized activity was a necessary prerequisite for the success of the campaign which had been initiated. (51)

The British Association (BAAS) had become involved in the geometrical reform movement in the 1870s, but very little was achieved in this earlier period. In 1900 Armstrong and Perry were instrumental in the establishment of a new section of the BAAS, for educational science, which in its first year, at Glasgow in 1901, co-operated in the arrangements for a joint discussion with the much older mathematics and physics section. The opening address to a widely representative audience of around two hundred was given by Perry, who launched a predictably strong attack on the existing state of school mathematics and the educational system which supported it. (52) In the interests of mathematics for the multitude he questioned the deductive ideals of the academic pure mathematician, which were embodied in the various school editions of Euclid – the establishment's mind trainer *par excellence* – and he advocated an alternative practical pedagogy for a broader and more outward-looking mathematics curriculum. He also proposed his own detailed scheme as a radical alternative which threw into sharp relief the general deficiencies in English school mathematics. Reactions to Perry's challenging proposals were multifarious. (53)

A three-hour discussion followed Perry's Glasgow address and it involved a wide range of interests in secondary, higher, technical and military education including, prominently, A.R. Forsyth (1858–1942), who had replaced Cayley as Sadleirian professor of mathematics at Cambridge in 1895. (54) Tensions between the liberal academic perspective and the technical or broadly vocational perspective, based on the utility of mathematics, rose clearly to the surface, with Perry exploiting declinist arguments and attacking the public schools and older universities 'where there is a deep-rooted scorn for all such scientific knowledge as may be useful to the nation'. (55) Perry was also a champion of the interests of the multitude and pleaded: 'I hold a brief in the interests of average boys and men; my strong language and possible excess of zeal are due to the fact that nearly all the clever men have briefs on the other side.' (56) Thus deeper-rooted issues of class, status and control were implicit in these early exchanges. But on pedagogical grounds there was much support for Perry, particularly concerning the values of practical work in geometry, and, in addition, 'general assent, even on the part of the "official" mathematicians, to the idea of "abandoning Euclid" – a notable fact'. (57) Other countries had long since abandoned Euclid and the position in England was becoming increasingly untenable. The need to pressurize examining bodies was now an imperative for, as Professor Love of Oxford pointed out, 'The future of mathematical teaching in this country is in their hands.' (58)

The immediate upshot at Glasgow was the establishment of a committee of the BAAS with Forsyth as chairman and Perry as secretary. Its terms of reference were straightforward:

> To report upon improvements that might be effected in the teaching of Mathematics, in the first instance in the teaching of Elementary Mathematics, and upon such means as they think likely to effect such improvements. (59)

Eggar of Eton was the only schoolmaster representative, but the strong representation of scientific, technical and military interests was clearly favourable to Perry's cause. The initiative taken by the BAAS and the substance of the Glasgow debate generated a further flurry of discussions and contributions to the educational and scientific press. The MA too became drawn into the campaign by the end of 1901. (60)

The new developments were first reported at a Council meeting in October 1901 by Professor A. Lodge (1854–1938) of the Royal Indian Engineering College. He and Professor Minchin were the only two members of Council who were also on the BAAS committee, and Forsyth was not involved with the MA at this time. The Council chose not to take an early lead, and indeed Dr F.S. Macaulay, who was involved with Greenstreet in the editing of the *Gazette*, felt that 'it would be better that suggestions should come from a higher quarter and be discussed by the Association' and, furthermore, that 'schoolmasters were not the best persons to suggest reforms in teaching'. (61) The MA chose initially to adopt a waiting attitude and defer to the BAAS committee. By the end of the year, however, the pages of the *Gazette* began to reflect the new developments.

The BAAS discussion was reported in the October 1901 number of the *Gazette* and the next number included contributions from three public schoolmasters, Langley, Siddons and Godfrey. (62) Godfrey, a pupil of Levett and a successful Cambridge product, who was appointed senior mathematical master at Winchester College in 1899, showed sympathy, opportunism and diplomacy in relation to the developing situation. In his first contribution to the *Gazette* he began: 'After Professor Perry's stimulating denunciation at Glasgow, many of us must be wondering how far are we really able to mend our ways at public schools?' (63) Godfrey went so far as to present his own 'compromise' syllabus, which he had developed over his first eighteen months at Winchester, within the limits still in force concerning Euclid's order of propositions for deductive geometry. He also led a collective initiative involving a number of younger public schoolmasters, before the MA took any organized steps.

Forsyth approached Godfrey independently to obtain some representation of public school interests to assist the work of the BAAS committee. Godfrey acted swiftly and compiled a letter which was signed by twenty-three schoolmasters who were predominantly under thirty, Levett and Langley excepted, and from nine leading public schools. (64) The letter was published early in 1902 in *Nature*, the *School World* and the *Gazette*, and it served to strengthen the hand of the BAAS committee by providing evidence of significant support for reform from within the public school sector, commonly presumed conservative. (65) The detail of the letter, which was based on Godfrey's Winchester 'compromise', did not go so far as to undermine deductive geometry based on Euclid's order but in other respects it was a sympathetic response in relation to Perry's scheme for elementary practical mathematics.

In the debates and representations at this time there was still some understandable concern that the abandonment of Euclid's order might lead to chaos in examinations and curricula, but the weight of opposition was mounting. Exceptionally, the *Gazette* of 1902 included a concise and stylish attack on Euclid from an advanced pure mathematical standpoint by Bertrand Russell, who had himself suffered under the severity of the Cambridge tripos system but subsequently become involved in work on the foundations of mathematics. He argued that the claim that Euclid was 'an invaluable training to the youthful powers of reasoning . . . vanishes on a close inspection'. At the foundations, Russell argued: 'His definitions do not always define, his axioms are not always indemonstrable, his demonstrations require many axioms of which he is quite unconscious.' (66)

It has been persuasively argued that the development of both non-Euclidean geometries and projective geometry introduced 'significant strains into the previously unified nature of geometry' in Victorian England. (67) Euclid's geometry was at the centre of the unified view, being a pinnacle in the logical organization of what were presumed to be geometrical facts concerning a physical reality. Mathematical and philosophical strains in this view were further felt with the development of formal axiomatics towards the end of the nineteenth century, within which new canons of rigour revealed logical imperfections in Euclid, and this stimulated the development of alternative treatments by David Hilbert and other mathematicians. However, in relation to the debates concerning Euclid as an educational instrument, these newer geometrical developments at the foundations were largely ignored. Rather, the tendency was to turn away from the foundations of geometry at school level and to allow greater freedom deductively. It was pedagogical and not mathematical or philosophical arguments which largely won the day.

The MA discussed the general question of reform at its annual meeting in January 1902. An introductory paper was given by Lodge, who argued decisively:

> I think this meeting should not conclude without appointing a strong committee to co-operate with the British Association Committee and assist it in every way possible. That Committee has already had a valuable communication signed by 23 schoolmasters, and has asked me to express to this Association its request for the fullest co-operation and advice. (68)

Thus the Council resolved that the first Teaching Committee should be established, to include Godfrey, a new member of Council, and the other Council members representing schools, including Levett, together with the BAAS committee members, Minchin and Lodge. (69) To facilitate meeting, the full committee of around thirty members of the MA was largely composed of public schoolmasters from the London area, with a significant younger element as well as a number of older members of the AIGT, but no women representatives. (70) The circumstances surrounding its formation confirm Siddons's subsequent judgement: 'The Letter from 23 Schoolmasters . . . was the main cause of the appointment of the Mathematical Association Teaching Committee.' (71)

The meetings of the new Teaching Committee, which were held at King's College, were normally chaired by Lodge or Minchin, with Siddons as secretary, and there was a much greater sense of urgency in its work during 1902 than had been the case with the AIGT in the 1870s. Two small subcommittees worked separately on drafts in geometry and arithmetic with algebra. After five meetings, the passing of various detailed resolutions, and redrafting, a first report on geometry was published in May of 1902 and circulated to all HMC schools. (72) Significantly the report did not propose a new order of theorems and still followed Euclid's, with some omissions and readjustments, but a course of geometrical drawing and measurement was proposed. Godfrey, writing in *Nature*, described the report as 'an attempt, on conservative lines, to simplify the study of geometry and make it interesting'. He added, 'If the attempt is judged to be successful, now is the time to make examiners unstop their ears.' (73) As it turned out examiners generally chose to go much further than this, which explains Godfrey's later judgement on the report's significance:

> On the eve of our liberation the M.A. published a report on Geometry teaching, a very conservative report, as it was considered impracticable

Members of the Committee

date of 1st meeting

Prof. M.J.M. Hill (University Coll.)   Mr H.J. Holmes (Merchant Taylors)

" A. Lodge (Cooper's Hill)   " E. M. Langley (Bedford Modern)

" G. M. Minchin (Cooper's Hill)   Dr F.S. Macaulay (St Pauls)

~~Mr S.J. MacKean (Watford Coll.)~~   Mr J.F. Moulton

Mr S. Barnard (Rugby)   " C. Pendlebury (St Pauls)

Mr J. M. Dyer (Eton)   " W. N. Roseveare (Harrow)

" W.J. Garstang (Bedales)   " C. A. Rumsey (Dulwich)

" C. Godfrey (Winchester)   " S. A. Saunder (Wellington)

" W.J. Greenstreet (Stroud)   " A. W. Siddons (Harrow)

" F.W. Hill (City of London)   (Hon. Sec.)

" R.W. Hogg (Christs Hospital)   " C. O. Tuckey (Charterhouse)

new members at date of 2nd meeting

Mr H.D. Ellis (Marlborough)   Dr H.C. Playne (Clifton)

Mr W.M. Baker (Cheltenham)   Dr H.A. Saunders (Haileybury)

Mr C. Hawkins (Haileybury)   Mr E.C. Sherwood (Westminster)

Elected at 3rd meeting   Mr H.J. Gossage (Wr. Coll. Re.) Prof. Hudson (King's Coll)

Mr E.J. Whittaker (Trin. Coll. Cambdg)

Elected at 5th meeting   Mr C C Lynam (Oxford Preparatory School)

Plate 3.1   First Teaching Committee 1902

to secure the abolition of the sequence. This report became obsolete in 1902. (74)

The work on arithmetic and algebra was less problematic and a first report was agreed by the Teaching Committee and published in the July number of the *Gazette*. (75) It recommended various omissions and simplifications, more emphasis on developing understanding, including links between the branches, and the extensive use of graphs. After ten meetings of the Teaching Committee a final version of its report on all three branches of elementary mathematics was agreed and published before the end of 1902. (76) By this time the BAAS committee had also reported to the educational science section at its September meeting in Belfast.

The report of the committee of the BAAS, which was well publicized, was based on seven meetings, and the agreed principles were carefully and shrewdly drafted by the chairman Forsyth. (77) The committee boldly rejected the alleged need for uniformity in deductive geometry and argued persuasively for a new era of curricular freedom and variety, based on reformed examination schedules, to give teachers themselves the opportunity to develop school geometry on lines more suited to the twentieth century. The need for practical work and problem solving in geometry was also supported (experimental schemes from Eggar and Perry were appended), and links among the three branches were also encouraged. The recommendations in arithmetic and algebra matched those of the MA, and placed particular emphasis on the use of tables, graphical methods and formulae. The report concluded more prophetically by suggesting that through pruning and simplification the curriculum might be broadened to include introductory elements of trigonometry, co-ordinate geometry and even calculus as part of 'elementary' mathematics. Overall, it was a strong and forward-looking statement of principles with which Perry would have been much in sympathy, though the status of deductive geometry *per se* was not called into question.

EXAMINATION REFORM

Examination reform and the dissemination of new textbooks and teaching aids proceeded in parallel with the various individual and institutional initiatives which have been described. The detailed evidence does not suggest any simple causal chain of events in the implementation of major change in English school mathematics. In the case of examinations the complexity of the system remained undiminished, with no co-ordination of the arrangements in the case of those examinations which were suitable for the developing system of secondary schools. As had been the case with the AIGT in the 1870s and 1880s, political pressure had to be applied in different quarters and large-scale syllabus reform could not be achieved simply.

It was the Civil Service Commission which gave an early lead, in reforming its examinations for army entrance by introducing measurement and drawing into the geometry papers in the 1890s, and, in 1901,

The Teaching

OF

Elementary Mathematics

REPORT OF THE COMMITTEE APPOINTED BY THE

MATHEMATICAL ASSOCIATION, 1902.

LONDON: GEORGE BELL & SONS,

YORK STREET, COVENT GARDEN.

1902

PRICE SIXPENCE NET.

Plate 3.2   First Report on Elementary Mathematics Teaching 1902

the decisive step of dispensing with Euclid's order was taken. (78) The change also applied to the examinations for naval cadetships, for which the heading on the new mathematical papers was short but highly significant: 'In Geometry the demonstrations and sequence of propositions need not be those of Euclid.' (79) These examinations for army and navy entrance directly influenced the public schools and, as Godfrey acknowledged, 'gave a most valuable lead'. (80) He subsequently judged the Commission's influence to be a seminal one for mathematical teaching throughout English public schools. (81) Langley, at the Glasgow meeting of the BAAS in 1901, went so far as to suggest: 'Whatever faults they have had in the past, I know of no papers which have gone so far towards encouraging – I might almost say enforcing – some of Professor Perry's proposed reforms.' (82) Major changes in the universities' examination requirements followed in 1902.

Of the university boards, the Oxford locals moved first, followed by London matriculation, and then the Cambridge locals, before the end of 1902. The changes at Oxford were reported by H.T. Gerrans of Worcester College to the third meeting of the MA's Teaching Committee, at which he was elected a member. The invitation in Oxford's new regulations was unequivocal: 'Any solution which shows an accurate method of geometrical reasoning will be accepted.' (83) But in preparing its geometry report the Teaching Committee felt unable to take advantage of such an early invitation from just one quarter. Forsyth was personally involved with the manoeuvres at Cambridge, which were more difficult and protracted in the case of the Previous (matriculation) examination. In fact Oxford Responsions (matriculation) followed the locals early in 1903, and it was not until May of the same year that major changes were announced for the Previous, which was a particularly important examination for the public schools. Details of the various developments and reactions to them were published in periodicals such as *Nature* and the *School World*, and also technical journals such as *Engineering*.

It is clear that the greatest conservatism was at Cambridge, which eventually responded to the combined weight of many recommendations for change, reforms in other examinations, and a recognition of 'the widespread desire for reform'. (84) Forsyth was elected President of the MA for the two-year period 1903–5, a fitting appointment 'at such an eventful time', given his distinguished position at Cambridge and also 'his acquaintance with the needs and difficulties of mathematical education'. (85) The *School World* judged that the reforms had given the MA in particular 'renewed vigour' and expressed a hope that 'it will deal effectively with important problems in mathematical education which still await solution'. (86)

The new agenda for elementary mathematics teaching was defined by the revised regulations for the Cambridge Previous along the following lines:

(1) In demonstrative geometry, Euclid's Elements shall be optional as a text-book, and the sequence of Euclid shall not be enforced. The examiners will accept any proof of a proposition which they are

satisfied forms part of a systematic treatment of the subject.
(2) Practical geometry is to be introduced, along with deductive geometry, and questions will be set requiring careful draughtsmanship and the use of efficient drawing instruments.
(3) In arithmetic, the use of algebraical symbols and processes will be permitted.
(4) In algebra, graphs and squared paper will be introduced; and a knowledge will be required of fractional indices and the use of four figure tables of logarithms. (87)

The Board of Education closely followed the Cambridge requirements in its own syllabus changes for the entrance and certificate examinations of the two-year training colleges, which were published in the regulations for 1904. Women trainees could still avoid algebra and geometry entirely and this had a narrowing effect on the scope of the mathematical work beyond arithmetic in the elementary schools. But, taken overall, examination reform had been comprehensively secured and in a comparatively short time.

Perry was cautiously optimistic at the height of major examination reform and emphasized the long-term implications:

> because it has occurred in the English way, we know that the reform is real, that it will have a fair chance, that it will go on year after year for many a year to come . . . Freedom has been given to teachers, a freedom much sighed for, a freedom which will create enthusiasm. Those who are most determined to make the reform complete are most anxious to proceed cautiously and to smother intemperate zeal. (88)

A reporter in *Nature*, in referring to the 'movement now in progress throughout the country', added a note of caution: 'we hope to see it carried much farther before crystallisation takes place'. (89) Godfrey's retrospective view of the period pointed to the inevitable conservatism within the system:

> The effect seemed to us at the time to be very great; but I suppose that as a matter of fact a great majority of schools went on teaching in the old way . . . But in those schools which moved with the times the immediate effect was probably rather chaotic. This was quite natural and inevitable; if the former period may be compared to an ice-age, this was the break-up of the ice. (90)

In all this, textbook production and the dissemination of aids and advice of various kinds were major priorities to support teachers in the unprecedented and no doubt somewhat bewildering new climate of freedom for experimentation in the school mathematics curriculum.

Educational suppliers were quick to exploit the expanding market for simple geometrical instruments and squared paper, advertising their products in the educational press. The publication of 'new geometries' – preliminary, practical, theoretical or some combined treatment – was quite extraordinary in the 1900s and particularly over the two-year period 1903–5, during which there appeared around 35 per cent of the total output of first editions over the first quarter of the twentieth century. (91) The majority of these textbooks were reviewed in batches in periodicals such as *Nature*, the *School World* and the *Gazette*; the new market was a highly competitive but potentially very profitable one for the educational publishers. (92)

Although Godfrey could refer to 'the passing of Euclid' by 1906 this certainly did not mean the abandonment of formal deductive geometry as Perry himself had advocated. Rather, the movement opened up the possibilities for practical and experimental work in geometry, and the relationship with deductive geometry in some form now emerged as a major pedagogical issue which continued to engage the mathematics education community for over fifty years.

In the much shorter terms, market-capturing labels such as 'practical', 'experimental', 'heuristic' and 'observational' were exploited by publishers in the titles of new textbooks, particularly in geometry, but also in arithmetic, mensuration and trigonometry. Textbooks which referred to 'practical mathematics' were principally aimed at the technical and military fields, but it is clear that authors and their publishers judged the market to be generally receptive to a 'practical' emphasis, variously interpreted in relation to the branches of school mathematics. Growing attention was also paid to the potential links between mathematics and science teaching, in relation both to syllabus content and pedagogy. (93)

In the case of algebra, the mention of 'graphs' in the new examination syllabuses prompted a swift response, as one teacher pointed out in relation to London matriculation:

> Here *graphs* [author's stress] is the word which has caught the popular eye, witness an advertisement in a morning paper: 'Wanted immediate preparation in mathematics for the London Matric., graphs necessary.' (94)

A number of publications on graphs, the majority containing relatively few pages, suddenly appeared on the market from 1902, as supplements to existing textbooks on algebra. The link between graphs and algebra was strengthened by frequent reference to a new theme, 'graphical algebra'. (95) The growth of practical mathematics for technical students and science teaching had both promoted the dissemination of squared paper but what was new was its widespread adoption in school mathematics. Godfrey enthused, 'GRAPHS have found their way into elementary work, and are now recognised as quite the most valuable instrument in our possession for awakening interest.' (96) The prolific textbook writer H.S. Hall (of Hall and Knight fame) went so far as to refer to a state of 'graphomania' by 1905, which he claimed was particularly affecting younger teachers. (97) But the following assessment is a fitting one: 'The broadcasting of squared paper, though a detail, is a detail of great importance, and representative of the effects of Perry's campaign.' (98)

In the early heady years of reform undoubtedly the greatest general effects were felt in geometry teaching, in both its practical and demonstrative aspects. The following lament in the *Journal of Education* well captures the striking contrast between the 'old geometry', based on Euclid, and the 'new geometry' which drew inspiration from the ideals of the Perry movement:

EUCLID'S ELEMENTS. By AN ANCIENT GEOMETER

FAREWELL! old Euclid: loved of yore, and may be loved again,
When our beatific vision sees thy plane surface, plain;
Unfettered now, we range without thy limited confines;
Thy concept had no breadth at all. *We* must have broader lines.

We shun thy close restrictions, and thy ordered sequence, too:
The ancient Greeks might learn to think; we've other things to do;
Nor can we stimulate again thy sober mental joy –
Euclidian reasoning 'stupefies the normal British boy'.

No more we seek the famous *pons* when standing on the brink –
'Tis but a shallow stream to cross, nor need the tiro shrink;
Bring compasses and callipers and geometric tools,
And waive eternal principle for briefly stated rules.

So we close the battered volume; lay it high upon the shelf,
And adopt more modern methods in our eager chase for pelf:
Thus one more link is severed, and we hail our glad release
From the intellectual thraldom of the glory that was Greece. (99)

As Godfrey pointed out in the opening quotation of this chapter, the early period of freedom to experiment was not one in which the MA might reasonably have been expected to lead from the front in curriculum development. Indeed, following the conservative report on geometry of 1902, the MA did not again report on this branch for over twenty years, by which time a considerable body of practical experience and refinement in pedagogical thinking had built up. The major political battle with examining bodies had been won by the end of 1903. How then did the MA respond to the new opportunity to provide professional support of various kinds for teachers of mathematics who, on a large and growing scale after the 1902 Education Act, became caught up in the reform movement? Like the AIGT, which was a pioneering institution of its type in the nineteenth century, so the MA again found itself in a new and unprecedented set of circumstances in the early years of this century. The detailed evidence indicates that up to about 1908 the MA's scope and influence was rather limited but then it entered a particularly rich period in its development, up to the First World War and after. It remains in this chapter to consider the nature of the MA's response in the very short term

THE ASSOCIATION'S RESPONSE

One obvious performance indicator for an association is the size of its membership. The January total of 242 in 1900 had more than trebled by 1914, but, as the figures show (in Table 3.1) the growth was not uniform over this period. (100)

Table 3.1   Membership Numbers 1900-14

Start of Year	1900	1902	1904	1906	1908	1910	1912	1914
Number of Members	242	295	393	395	433	548	675	744

Given the new circumstances after 1900, 'Teachers feeling the necessity of being in touch with the new movement, joined the Association in considerable numbers.' (101) But this rate of growth was not sustained over the period 1904–8. These were relatively quiet years for the MA, whose Council admitted that for the year 1905 in particular it had 'very little to report', it having been 'very quiet and barren of events'. (102) Greenstreet, the *Gazette's* editor, was prompted to remark: 'We are not sure that this may not be meant for a piece of biting criticism, suggesting that although more remains to be done we have not done it.' (103) Certainly there is no record of any meeting of the Teaching Committee between June of 1904 and April of 1907, in sharp contrast to the efforts of 1902. (104)

The character of the MA's organ, the *Gazette*, also changed in response to the influence of the reform movement. For the purpose of a simple content analysis, articles included in the *Gazette* from 1894 can broadly be classified as concerned either with mathematical exposition or with education and pedagogy. (105) In the former case the *Gazette* essentially provided a service as a minor mathematical serial, in the sense of Archibald's valuable survey published in the two-hundredth number. (106) In the latter case the *Gazette* provided specialist advice and encouragement for teachers who might also turn to general educational periodicals such as the *Educational Times*, *Journal of Education* or *School World* for professional support. The other main features of the *Gazette* from the outset were book reviews, which were always a strong feature, mathematical notes, mathematical problems and solutions, and historical material. Taking educational contributions to include correlation with other subjects, the examination system, teacher supply and education, and educational research, the percentage of the space in the *Gazette* devoted to educational matter as a whole varied very significantly up to the First World War, as Table 3.2 shows. (107) What clearly stands out is an isolated small peak in 1902 and then a significant shift of emphasis in the content of the *Gazette* from 1907, and particularly from 1909 until 1914.

Up to 1900 the *Gazette's* major feature was the regular publication of examination and other problems and their solutions. Here the *Gazette* followed the *Educational Times* and other early English mathematical serials. (108) One Eton master commented in *Nature* on the relevance of this practice at a time of impending major reform: 'It is a large problem which it [the MA] has to face, and it is to be hoped that its publication will not fall too much into the way of merely publishing solutions of interesting

Table 3.2   Educational Content of the *Gazette* 1894-1914

Year	1894	1895	1896	1897	1898	1899	1900
%	1 2		1 6		1 0		3

Year	1901	1902	1903	1904	1905	1906	1907
%	15	32	15	12	11	8	22

Year	1908	1909	1910	1911	1912	1913	1914
%	19	52	40	27	47	40	33

and sometimes recondite conundrums.' (109) In similar vein, Professor Bryan in the *School World* referred to the *Gazette* as a 'hardened sinner' in its partiality for 'pigs in clover' riders, the reference being to a game of marbles which were rolled on a tilted board into recesses or pockets. (110) This feature of the *Gazette* faded rapidly with the growing interest in curriculum reform after 1900 and became virtually extinct after the publication of a special set of solutions to problems in 1907 and 1908.

Unlike *Nature* and the *School World*, the *Gazette* was not used, from the turn of the century, as a major instrument in the build-up to examination reform. Here the new *School World* was particularly responsive and published in March of 1902 a special mathematical number with contributions from Oxbridge dons, including Gerrans of Oxford, Professors Bryan, Minchin and Mathews, and W.C. Fletcher (1865–1959), headmaster of the Liverpool Institute and, from 1904, the chief HMI for secondary schools under the Board of Education. (111) This 'monthly magazine of educational work and progress' continued in its early years to publish a rich range of contributions on aspects of mathematical reform, paying particular attention to the task of defining the various interpretations of 'practical mathematics' in this period. (112) As one contributor put it, there was 'very remarkable agreement in favour of practical methods of teaching', but at the same time 'an equally remarkable disagreement with regard to the meaning and application of such methods'. He claimed that the details were being 'hammered out in hundreds of schools'. (113) To help teachers implement the 'modern method', survey articles were published on the range of available geometrical instruments and simple mathematical tables, and on the varieties and uses of squared paper. In 1906 Greenstreet published a personal 'appeal' in the *Gazette* for a shift in emphasis towards educational and pedagogical matters, and he requested suitable articles and discussions for publication. (114) Furthermore, when Bryan was appointed

President of the MA for the two-year period 1907–9 he vigorously pursued the general question of the range and quality of the MA's professional support for teachers of mathematics.

The MA Presidents prior to Bryan were: Professor Lodge, 1897–9; Sir Robert Ball, 1899–1901; J. Fletcher Moulton FRS, QC, 1901–3; Professor Forsyth, 1903–5; and Professor G.B. Mathews FRS (1861–1922), 1905–7, sometime colleague of Bryan at University College Bangor. (115) Presidential addresses at the annual meeting in January were not a customary feature of this early period, though occasional papers from members did sometimes stimulate a general discussion, which was subsequently reported in the *Gazette*. These discussions pick up in both quantity and quality from the time of Bryan's Presidency. Previously the only discussions of note were initiated by Lodge in 1902 on 'reform', by W.H Wagstaff (a successor to Wormell as headmaster of the Middle Class School, Cowper Street) in 1905 on 'the new geometry', and by Siddons, in the same year, on the question of compulsory Greek in the Cambridge Previous examination! (116) Bryan took a leading role from January 1907 when he sent a paper to be read at the annual meeting on 'The neglected British teacher: a plea for organisation in mathematics'. He followed this up with Presidential addresses in 1908 on 'The uses of mathematics and the training of the mathematical teacher' and in 1909 on the general theme of the relative neglect of mathematics in England. It was Bryan who established a strong precedent for many subsequent twentieth-century Presidential addresses by choosing to focus on general principles and strategies in mathematics education.

Bryan was quick to draw attention to the limited range of the MA's membership at this time:

> the greater proportion of the members are mathematicians who are qualified to benefit our Association by the contribution of papers to our *Gazette*, and by the expression of their opinions on questions connected with the teaching of mathematics; and the large body of mathematical and science masters who would derive benefit from joining our ranks do not appreciate the advantages to be derived from membership. (117)

Bryan shared Greenstreet's concern about the character of the MA's journal and suggested that schoolmasters were being 'frightened off by the somewhat forbidding appearance of certain papers published in the *Gazette*.' (118) In his first year as President he also contributed a bold paper on 'The future of the Mathematical Association'. One member responded to Bryan's criticism concerning the *Gazette*:

> with the exception of the reports and the discussions of the reports of the committee for the reform of Elementary Mathematics, I have rarely found anything of general interest. The whole *Gazette*, it appears to me, is taken up with special solutions of problems of too advanced a type for the ordinary mathematical work of a school. (119)

Bryan urged the MA to promote pedagogical discussions and the dissemination of innovations on a much greater scale than hitherto. In his view, much remained to be done:

I have never been sanguine that the so-called 'reform of mathematical teaching' would leave us much better off than we were before, and the present is an opportune time for discussing such questions. Personally I consider that reform of teaching means something more than mere tinkering with syllabuses, the publishing of school geometries, and the writing off of publishers' losses on the innumerable Euclids that came out just before the change. The teaching of algebra is at present in a hopeless chaos . . . (120)

The subsequent shift of emphasis in the *Gazette* was one response to this call, but the impressive growth in the membership over the period 1907–14 is partly explained by other factors to which Bryan drew attention.

The size of the annual subscription, which was ten shillings (with individual numbers of the *Gazette* priced at 1s. 6d.), probably deterred some potential members. But the financial position of the MA prohibited any reduction here, and, for stability, a sustained growth in the membership was required. (121) More pointedly, Bryan also referred to the MA's general image as another factor to deter a master from joining: 'He has not regarded membership of the Association as suitable for "the likes of him".' Moreover, 'He has never had the Association brought before his notice in such a way as to make him think of joining it.' (122) In 1907 the Council recommended that 'a sum of money not exceeding £50 be applied to the purpose of issuing a circular to mathematical teachers in all grades of schools, including intermediate and elementary schools, calling their attention to the advantages of joining the association'. (123) In this membership drive, Bryan pressed the MA to broaden the composition of the membership as well as to increase its size, since, he argued, 'it is important that the body responsible for framing or adopting recommendations should be representative, and should include all those who are affected by the proposed changes'. (124) To achieve his aims, Bryan also pressed for the establishment of local branches of the MA to promote dissemination, discussion and the representation of a wide range of views. He showed the way forward and became the President of the first such branch, which was formed at Bangor in 1907. The *Gazette* announced:

> there is reason for congratulation in the fact that the [North Wales] Branch has been formed for 'the discussion of matters relating to the teaching of mathematics in schools, etc., *of all grades*'. Here is an important link in the long chain that has yet to be forged before the teaching profession in this country becomes one organic whole. (125)

In his second Presidential address Bryan re-emphasized the need for a network of branches and he provided an illuminating picture of the pioneering work in North Wales:

> The success of this branch is due to our local secretary, Mr T.G. Creak, an old Cambridge wrangler and retired schoolmaster. We have over a dozen members and associates, including teachers in secondary boys' and girls' schools at Beaumaris, Bethesda, Colwyn Bay and elsewhere,

and an elementary teacher from our immediate neighbourhood who has greatly contributed to the value and interest of our discussions by representing a phase of teaching with which it is often extremely difficult to get into proper touch. We have held meetings up to now three times in the year, and on such occasions these hard-worked schoolmasters give up their Saturday half-holiday and come over by train or boat or on foot to the meeting place, generally Bangor. As a rule, one member is asked to open a discussion on some subject, such as teaching of algebra or the extent to which text-books should be used in teaching. Then we sit around a table and talk. (126)

In 1909 regulations were produced and the affiliation of a newly formed Southampton and District Mathematical Society, as a branch, was secured. (127) Before the First World War, branches were also formed in London and Sydney (New South Wales), but it was between the wars that the number and geographical spread of the MA's branches developed sufficiently to constitute a national network. The new regulations for branches created a third category of membership – associate – alongside the existing categories of ordinary and honorary membership. The number of associates was about two hundred between 1910 and 1914, with London's contribution dominating, and branches were permitted to set their own subscription level, one shilling being levied centrally for each associate member. Of course, associate members might subsequently transfer to full membership, but the third option itself proved to be an attractive alternative particularly after the First World War.

In addition to a membership drive and the establishment of local branches, Bryan made a number of other proposals. To improve the *Gazette* he suggested a general 'queries' column, the publication of biographical material and current news, and the inclusion of accessible articles on higher mathematics for teachers. (128) He also recommended paying the editor more for his services! (129) To enhance further the status and professionalism of teachers he proposed the provision of courses and colloquia on the higher branches of mathematics and the publication of lists of suitable books on mathematics, including its history and philosophy. Overall, this was a forward-looking and realistic agenda. But Bryan also hinted at some wider and more speculative possibilities.

He claimed, 'The interests of English mathematicians have been greatly hampered in the past by the absence of any strong influential society comparable with the Deutsche Mathematiker Vereinigung and the American Mathematical Society.' (130) He pointed to the range of services and the quality of the professional support for mathematicians and teachers provided in these countries. In the English context he perhaps surprisingly made no reference to the London Mathematical Society but significantly pointed to the advantages of German and American practice:

We here stand in the greater need of some equally powerful organisation, in view of the prevailing popular prejudice – I might almost describe it as insular prejudice – that exists against matters mathematical. Such a body must make a serious effort to win popularity, and must not merely appeal to the limited class of individuals that are engaged in higher mathematical research. The Mathematical Association is eminently fitted to step in and fill the gap. (131)

This was clearly an ambitious and comprehensive vision for the professional organization of mathematics and mathematics education in England, and, predictably, the MA did not 'step into the stronghold that is awaiting its occupation'. (132) But the issues did resurface some fifty years later and in very different circumstances, as will become clear later in this book. In this chapter the scope and character of the very early work of the Teaching Committee and its subcommittees remains to be considered.

TEACHING COMMITTEE 1902–8

In 1908 the MA reprinted in one volume the complete set of the Teaching Committee's reports to that date, together with the regulations for geometry in the Cambridge Previous examination, which then formed 'the standard for the school teaching of geometry in this country'. It was admitted that the geometry report of 1902 had 'to some extent served its purpose' but for completeness it was included nonetheless. (133) The reports covered the following range of work: geometry teaching (1902); arithmetic and algebra teaching (1902); elementary mechanics teaching (1904); advanced school mathematics (1904); the course of mathematics for entrance scholarships at the universities, i.e. Oxbridge (1907); and mathematics teaching in preparatory schools (1907). This first set of reports already exemplifies a two-pronged strategy in the Teaching Committee's work on mathematics in education, which was broadly to be followed for over fifty years. Reports were focused either on some branch of mathematics – e.g. arithmetic, algebra, geometry and mechanics – or on some institutional context or special-interest group, e.g. mathematics for the advanced student, the scholarship candidate and the preparatory schoolboy. As regards audience and purpose, three aspects of the intended or realized influence of a report are distinguishable.

First, a report might aim to influence examining bodies, both in the construction of syllabuses and in the organization and setting of papers. The Teaching Committee might also pursue this aim further through formal or informal communications with specific examining bodies. Second, a report might directly influence textbook writers, some of whom were members of the Teaching Committee, and through them act upon the teaching force generally. Third, a report might make a significant contribution to the literature in mathematics education and pedagogy, and help to stimulate professional development through reading and discussion among members and non-members of the MA. Certainly many rich and thought-provoking discussions on the MA's reports, from 1908, were subsequently recorded in the *Gazette*. (134) The early reports up to 1908 exemplify all three aspects to a greater or lesser extent.

The reports of 1902 on the three elementary branches were principally concerned with syllabus construction and the removal of undesirable examination requirements. In geometry, examining bodies responded with major changes as part of the general movement for reform but some textbooks only adopted the MA's more modest proposals, the influence being acknowledged in prefaces and advertisements. This close and subsequently long-standing link between the MA's reports and textbook writing featured strongly in the advertisements of George Bell and Sons, the MA's publisher. (135)

A subcommittee for mechanics teaching, including Minchin, Siddons and Tuckey, was set up in 1903 and it reported in the following year. (136) In a tightly packed three-page report there were thirty-eight detailed suggestions, covering preliminary experimental work, the choice of examples and methods – numerical, graphical and geometrical – and various points of exposition in statics and dynamics. (137) The BAAS and Perry also became involved with the teaching of mechanics around this time but there was not the same general sense of urgency for reform as in the case of geometry, which was also taught on a much larger scale in the schools. However, there were some obvious parallels with geometry in relation to the status and functions of experimental work, and the question of correlation with science became prominent in the debates. (138)

The institutional focus of the Teaching Committee's work over the first decade of the twentieth century was limited. It was predominantly a committee of public schoolmasters, with no women representatives until 1908, when three were listed – Miss E.R. Gwatkin of Maria Grey Training College, Miss L. Story of the Royal School, Bath, and Miss M. Storr of Goldsmiths' College, London – out of a total of thirty-nine members. (139) The early composition of the Teaching Committee explains the initial attention paid to the male needs of advanced and scholarship pupils and the work in boys' preparatory schools.

In 1903 the Association of Headmasters of Preparatory Schools discussed the arrangements for instituting a common entrance examination, which were at the time being worked out by the HMC. The scheme included papers in arithmetic, algebra and geometry, and the Association approached the MA for advice concerning the best policy for preparatory school geometry teaching at a time of rapid change in the public schools. Accordingly, the Teaching Committee decided to send a letter to all public schools to determine

> how far they would recognise and insert questions in Practical and Theoretical Geometry in their Entrance Examinations and Scholarship Entrance Examinations, in accordance with the syllabus recommended by the Cambridge Syndicate . . . The object of seeking this information is to afford guidance to Preparatory Schools in the teaching of Geometry. (140)

The letter was signed by the President, Forsyth, and the replies clearly demonstrated 'how very real a reform is being made; every school seems to encourage practical work, and, except in one case, to grant the freedom which the Universities have considered it wise to give'. (141) The preparatory schools also moved swiftly in response to the new opportunities. Godfrey observed: 'So far has the movement gone that out of seventy boys entering a public school [Winchester] in September, 1905, not one admitted that he had learnt "Euclid".' (142)

The Association of Headmasters of Preparatory Schools also pressed the MA for more detailed guidance on the teaching of the three elementary branches. The Teaching Committee, with the assistance of two headmaster representatives and the benefit of responses to a circular sent to over four hundred preparatory schools, reported in 1907. The report ran to ten pages and was unprecedented for the MA in the detailed guidance it provided for teaching various topics, with the needs of the preparatory schoolmaster particularly in mind. The report was also intended to influence the examinations for entrance to public schools. By this time 'a great proportion' of schools used the common entrance examination, instituted in 1904, and the Teaching Committee judged that 'there is reason to hope that the recommendations will be accepted as a guide in future papers'. (143)

The subcommittee on advanced school mathematics reported in 1904 and the brief recommendations focused on the common needs of different classes of boys, including army candidates, science students and engineering students, as well as intending university specialists and scholarship candidates. (144) The mathematical requirements for entrance scholarships at Oxford and Cambridge were the subject of a specific report in 1907. (145) The Council had requested the Teaching Committee to consider this question and 'the changes necessary to meet the requirements of the new Tripos regulations at Cambridge'. (146) This was the briefest of references to a change at Cambridge which was of very great significance for the future of mathematics and mathematics education in England.

MATHEMATICAL TRIPOS REFORM

The characteristics of the nineteenth-century mathematical tripos examination were briefly sketched in chapter two. The examination dominated the study of mathematics at Cambridge, and the mathematical pre-eminence of this university meant that the progress of English mathematics as a whole was fundamentally affected. G.H. Hardy (1877–1947) passed through Cambridge and was fourth wrangler in 1898. (147) He became one of the greatest English mathematicians of the twentieth century and was one of the many strong critics of the mathematical tripos and its cramping effects. As Joan Richards has shown, 'Dissatisfaction with the mathematics which appeared on the Tripos is an almost universal theme in the memoirs of those who were educated late in the nineteenth century.' (148) Hardy remarked, 'It has often been said that Tripos mathematics was a collection of elaborate futilities, and the accusation is broadly true.' (149) According to his historical judgement, 'When, in the years perhaps between 1880 and 1890, the Tripos stood, in difficulty, complexity, and notoriety, at the zenith of its reputation, English mathematics was somewhere near its lowest ebb.' (150) In his final tripos year he judged it to have passed its zenith and by that time there had already been one unsuccessful attempt to abolish the order of merit, which was a key feature of the system. But Forsyth could still complain in 1905:

> I live in a place where examinations seem to be the breath of life, and
> where they are utilised for the purpose of arranging students in an
> artificial order of merit, and in order to see who is the best gymnast
> in over-coming obstacles set by people who had nothing to do with the
> teaching. That is examination run mad. (151).

In relation to school mathematics, the influence of the Cambridge
mathematical tripos was very great. In terms of content and difficulty,
the influence acted directly downwards, through the entrance and scholarship examinations, to affect the advanced work of the leading secondary
schools. But, additionally, many mathematics teachers in the leading
schools were themselves Cambridge graduates and most of the successful
school mathematical textbook writers, certainly up to the 1920s, possessed
a Cambridge degree and were public schoolmasters. (152)

Critically, for both Cambridge and the schools, the mathematical tripos
entered a period of declining popularity from the 1880s. As one Cambridge
don pointed out, mathematics was having to compete with the burgeoning
sciences:

> Between 1882 and 1909 . . . the number of successful candidates in
> Part I., had fallen from 116 to 74; the corresponding numbers in Part
> I of the Natural Sciences Tripos, were 54 and 174, while the class list
> of the Mechanical Sciences Tripos contained 7 names when it began in
> 1894 and 31 in 1909. It seemed clear that mathematicians were drifting
> away to other subjects. (153)

The decline at Cambridge had a major effect on the overall number
of honours graduates in mathematics, a decline which was not arrested
until after the First World War, when growing contributions came from
Oxford, London and the newer civic universities: Birmingham (1900),
Manchester (1903), Liverpool (1903), Leeds (1904), Sheffield (1905) and
Bristol (1909). (154)

The Cambridge decline also provided a practical ground for reforming
the mathematical tripos system. The campaign for reform and arguments
for the defence spread to the columns of *The Times*, and the attack
was supported by a new breed of Cambridge mathematician, including
Forsyth, Hardy and E.W. Hobson (1856–1933), who replaced Forsyth as
Sadleirian professor in 1910. (155) Finally, a new more flexible scheme
in two parts was narrowly approved in 1906, and the controversial order
of merit was abolished in the following year. (156) The mathematical
examinations at Oxford were also reformed before the First World War,
with a shift of emphasis, as at Cambridge, away from an insistence on
specialized techniques and the elaboration of detail, and towards a deeper
understanding of general principles. (157)

The MA Teaching Committee's report on scholarship mathematics
recommended parity in the mathematical demands of the two ancient
universities and provided a schedule of topics in pure geometry, analytical
geometry, algebra, geometrical and analytical trigonometry, differential
and integral calculus, and statics and dynamics. The most important single
recommendation was short and to the point: 'In order to allow of a broader

syllabus the exercises and riders should be simplified.' (158)

Thus, over the first decade of the twentieth century and in parallel with the Perry movement for school mathematical reform, fundamental changes were also taking place in the pursuit and teaching of mathematics at university level. Richards has cogently argued that this was no mere coincidence but was indicative of a major shift in the English vision of mathematics and its educational values:

> the unitary view of truth, which had for so long provided the justificatory framework for geometrical study, crumbled into a more fragmented and specialized view of knowledge and learning. This disintegration allowed mathematicians to develop their subject without integrating it into an essentially scientific unitary view of truth. This, in turn, made it possible to relax the descriptive focus which had so long formed the justification for English mathematical work.
> . . . Reform may have been slow to come, but when it did, it heralded a radical shift in the English view of mathematical study. Nineteenth-century mathematics had been supported and defined within the integrated notion of a liberal education. As that notion was adjusted to meet the demands of a changing world, the English view of what constituted mathematics changed also. (159)

With regard to the ideals of the Perry movement and the development of mathematics in the education of the multitude, much still remained to be done. The demise of Euclid as a school textbook is only one aspect of early-twentieth-century reform, albeit a major one. In helping forward developments on a number of fronts and in the consolidation of good practice the MA came to play a leading role. But there is also evidence of a reaction to some of the effects of the Perry movement in the short term, and with this reaction came a growing need to clarify purposes and to develop the theoretical basis for mathematics education and pedagogy. These and related developments will be considered in the next chapter.

CHAPTER FOUR

REACTIONS AND REFINEMENTS

> . . . the Mathematical Association has been conspicuous as an agent in furthering the democratization of Mathematical Education. It is very certain that no such democratization could be effected without more or less radical changes being made both in the methods of teaching and in the selection of the matter taught. (1)
>
> (E.W. Hobson, Presidential address, 1912)

> At the one extreme there is the school of thought known on the continent as 'Perryismus' which emphasizes the utilitarian motive, and lays stress on concrete illustrations from practical life as the chief mode of presentation; at the other extreme there is the 'high and dry' school, now perhaps suffering temporary eclipse, but always standing for high ideals of scholarship. In drawing up the school mathematical syllabus it will probably be wisest – and certainly safest – to steer a middle course between these two extremes of pedagogic thought. (2)
>
> (Mathematical Association report, 1919)

EDUCATIONAL IDEALS AND PEDAGOGY

Professor Hobson's reference to the 'democratization of mathematical education' importantly captures a major objective in the reform of second-ary school mathematics in the early twentieth century. In his own words 'democratization' was taken to mean 'the concentration of the attention of the Educator, in a much greater degree than formerly, on the work of developing the minds of the average many, and not solely of those of the exceptionally gifted few'. (3) In the context of Hobson's address to the MA it is important to recognize that the 'average many' under consideration was still only a minority of the adolescent population. In 1911 over 80 per cent of the fourteen-to-eighteen age range received no formal schooling and the age of compulsory attendance was not raised to fourteen until the Fisher Education Act of 1918. But one consequence of the Perry movement was that the curricular provision for pupils other than those who were aspiring to mathematical entrance and scholarship examinations at the universities now demanded much more serious consideration on educational grounds. Previously, to use Godfrey's telling description, it was the 'aristocratic theory' which had acted as an excuse for the widespread neglect of individual differences in relation to fundamental questions about content and methods of teaching:

> The aristocratic theory of education has determined the choice of subject-matter in teaching mathematics in schools . . . In the past – the not distant past – the assumption was made tacitly that mathematics could appeal only to the few; that the average boy was essentially stupid and more or less a hopeless problem. This entirely false assumption arose from the aristocratic theory. (4)

Hobson also well characterized the essential features of the mental-and-moral disciplinary argument which had sustained the aristocratic theory for so long but could not survive without serious modification and refinement in response to the rhetoric and campaigning of the reformers:

> the notion of Mathematical teaching was that it should be in the main medicinal and corrective. Its advantages consisted largely in calling forth the use of faculties which are the rarest in the average boy or girl, and were therefore thought to be in special need of development. It was thought to be by no means wholly a disadvantage that these subjects, so treated, were found hard and repulsive by the majority. It was thought that the hard discipline involved in the attempt to assimilate them developed a kind of mental grit, and involved a certain species of moral training, even when the intellectual results were small. (5)

Yet by 1920, the year of Perry's death, the MA's first summary report on mathematics teaching in public and other secondary schools could refer to the school of thought he inspired as one extreme. The other extreme at this time was identified as the 'high and dry' school with its emphasis on high ideals of scholarship, and the historical link with the older aristocratic theory is not made explicit but is clear nonetheless. This polarization was perceived by the German Georg Wolff (1886–1977), who carried out a detailed survey of English reforms and reported in 1915. He contrasted as two pedagogical opposites the traditional *Euklidische Methode* and the newer *praktisch-heuristische Methode*, as advocated by Perry and Armstrong in particular. (6)

These polarizations in thought concerning English mathematics education were partly a consequence of the early extremism of Perry and his associates in advocating major reform and partly also a consequence of a significant reaction to certain aspects of the movement's ideology and some of its consequences in the short term. There is no doubt, however, that the progress of the movement up to the First World War involved a level of curricular activity, both in principle and in practice, which was not to be seen again until the 1950s. Discussion, publication, experimentation and dissemination proceeded on a number of fronts and the MA became centrally involved in the process. Some objectives were relatively swiftly achieved on a large scale whereas the realization of other objectives was more difficult and protracted. Some objectives still formed a focus for development after the Second World War and yet other objectives have remained largely unrealized up to the present time.

Reference to the full range of ideals associated with the Perry movement will help to bring some coherence to the discussion of a rich and complex period in the history of English mathematics education. This agenda, which embraced both intended subject-matter and methods of teaching, will also facilitate some evaluation of the movement's progress and the MA's contribution to it. In relation to the desired scope of mathematics for the multitude, Perry was strikingly optimistic at a very early stage, when he addressed the BAAS at Belfast in 1902:

> It seems probable that at the end of another five years no average boy of fifteen years of age will have been compelled to attempt any abstract reasoning about things of which he knows nothing; he will be versed in experimental mathematics, which he may or may not call mensuration; he will use logarithms, and mere multiplication and division will be a joy to him; he will have a working power with algebra and sines and cosines; he will be able to tackle at once any curious new problems which can be solved by squared paper; and he will have no fear of the symbols of the infinitesimal calculus . . . Five years hence it will be called 'elementary mathematics'. Four years ago it was an unorthodox subject called 'practical mathematics' . . . (7)

The full agenda for reform of content and methods may be summarized as follows:

1. Take account of the pupil's motivation and interests.
2. Base abstract ideas on concrete experience to promote understanding.
3. Employ activities involving the hand and eye, and not just the ear, in conjunction with the brain, and 'graphic(al)' methods in particular.
4. Adopt experimental and heuristic methods: 'Experiment, estimation, approximation, observation, induction, intuition, common-sense are to have honoured places in every mathematical class-room in which the laboratory method has sway.' (8)
5. Postpone logical rigour and any early concern for the foundations, and generally restrict the formal deductive elements, admitting various forms of 'proof'.
6. Simplify, broaden and unify the subject-matter of mathematics, ignoring traditional artificial divisions.
7. Correlate mathematics with science and laboratory work, and generally relate mathematics to life and its applications. (9)

The references to the 'laboratory method' (4) – the American designation for 'Perryismus' – and correlation (7) serve as a reminder of the importance of the links between mathematics and science education in the early stages of the reform of elementary mathematics teaching. In his study of the APSSM, from its foundation in 1900, Layton has drawn attention to the significant contribution of public school science masters to mathematics teaching and also argued that 'by virtue of common membership and from professional contacts in their schools between teachers of mathematics and science, the Association of Public School [Science] Masters benefited considerably from the experience of the Mathematical Association'. (10)

MATHEMATICS AND SCIENCE TEACHING

Eggar of Eton and Siddons of Harrow personified the links between science and mathematics teaching. Following his fifth wranglership in mathematics at Cambridge in 1898, Siddons acknowledged that 'my work for the Natural Sciences Tripos . . . changed my attitude to mathematics'. (11) He subsequently served on the committee of the APSSM as well as taking a leading role in the committee work of the MA from 1902. (12) Both Eggar and Siddons gave addresses to the London Conference of Science Teachers in 1903, when half of the fifth annual conference was devoted to the subject of mathematical reform. This particular conference attracted an unprecedented attendance of over four hundred, which exceeded the total for the membership of the MA at this time. (13)

In 1904 the APSSM discussed a paper on 'the possibility of fusing the mathematical and science teaching in public schools'. Siddons, W.C. Fletcher, appointed in 1904 to the newly created post of chief HMI for grant-aided secondary schools, and C.S. Jackson (1867–1916) of the Royal Military Academy, Woolwich, all contributed on this question of 'fusion' or 'correlation' between mathematics and science teaching. (14) Siddons, Fletcher and Jackson were mathematical reformers principally but their own educational backgrounds and professional circumstances had sensitized them to the importance of cross-curricular links. Jackson gave a paper on the teaching of mathematics and physics at the annual meeting of the MA, in 1904, and it was published in the *Gazette* in the same year. (15) The MA's brief report on elementary mechanics teaching was also published in 1904 and both Siddons and Jackson were on the subcommittee which prepared it. (16) The emphasis in this report on experimental, numerical and graphical methods is striking and 'Slide-Rule Jackson', as he became nicknamed, was accorded the following tribute in his obituary: 'the main work of his life was the breaking down of the barrier that so long existed between Statics and Dynamics, as taught in our schools, and the Applied Mechanics of the engineer'. (17) The particular question of mechanics in relation to mathematics teaching, and the contribution of engineering as well as scientific perspectives, also attracted the attention of the BAAS in the early years of reform.

Having significantly helped forward the movement for major geometrical reform, the BAAS set up a committee in 1903 to investigate the teaching of elementary mechanics. (18) Its membership included Jackson, Siddons and, most significantly, the engineer Perry, who had remarked at the Belfast meeting of the BAAS, in 1902, 'I am sorry to say that the teaching of mathematics and mechanical engineering through experiment is comparatively unknown.' (19) With a view to major reform in mechanics teaching, Perry copied the main lines of his strategy at, and following, the 1901 Glasgow meeting, for the 1905 meeting in Johannesburg. Perry opened a discussion within the mathematics and physics section and Forsyth took the chair. Macmillan subsequently published, in one volume, Perry's address and reply, details of the discussion and a number of subsequently contributed remarks. The MA's report, with which Perry sympathized, was circulated at the meeting and the discussion included contributions from, amongst others, Professors Forsyth and Bryan. The contributors of written remarks included Professors Armstrong and Minchin, as well as Eggar, Jackson, Siddons and Godfrey. (20) Perry's edited volume also included the MA's recommendations and a paper by C.E. Ashford of the Royal Naval College, Dartmouth, on the teaching of mechanics by experiment. In 1905 Godfrey had moved from Winchester to replace Ashford as headmaster of the Royal Naval College, Osborne. (21) The two naval colleges were exceptionally placed with regard to the opportunities provided for wide-ranging mathematics curriculum development, but, outside the fields of naval, military and technical education, progress in mechanics teaching proved to be much more problematic and the resistance to change in this branch as part of mathematics was much greater than in geometry.

Some parallels and contrasts with geometry were well captured by Jackson:

> The habitual omission in geometry of the experimental stage renders in many cases a student's conception of technical terms vague in the extreme. This is now universally conceded and has been remedied.
>
> The omission of the preliminary experimental stage in mechanics has been far more complete than was ever the case in geometry. Had geometry ever been taught as mechanics has been often taught, we should have had editions of Euclid in which the cost of diagrams and the space occupied by them would have been saved. (22)

Jackson was here referring to the teaching of mechanics as part of a specialist mathematics course; such provision developed in the nineteenth century before the subject was taught more widely on experimental and inductive lines as part of physics. In the context of correlation four logical possibilities emerged: mechanics might be taught under either mathematics or science, under both, or under neither. In principle, an appropriate blend of theory, experiment and applications was generally desirable on educational grounds but, in practice, mechanics was taught wholly theoretically as part of mathematics. In the public schools, as Ashford pointed out, the mathematical masters 'naturally treated it as a deductive, not an inductive or experimental, science', and, he added, 'It would have implied something like a slur on the power and accuracy of mathematics to appeal to experiment.' (23). In sharp contrast, Ashford drew attention to the prevailing practices in technical institutions, where 'we see exactly opposite methods': 'mechanics is treated frankly as an experimental science', but, he added, the pupils 'often miss the special training given by the public-school course of mechanics'. Pertinently, he posed the following key question:

> Is it a Utopian ideal that these two lines should converge, and in their junction should admit of the development of a method of teaching mechanics which will provide for the three desiderata, a knowledge of the facts and principles of the science, a strengthening of the reasoning power, and a training in the proper way to study natural phenomena in order to fathom the underlying causes? (24)

In geometry these two lines did converge with dramatic consequences as we have seen. But the merging of these two distinct traditions remained largely a utopian ideal in mechanics. Two major practical barriers to change are identifiable: the requirements of examinations and the capabilities of the mathematics teaching force.

Cambridge strongly influenced both the education of the teaching force and examination syllabuses. As one don, W.H. Besant, confessed to the AIGT in 1883:

> The fact, constantly before us in Cambridge, that Mechanics are being studied with a view to success in examinations tends to make us forget the importance of the practical application to daily life of a knowledge of Mechanics, and the temptation is to luxuriate in the flowery and ornamental problems, which sometimes form the staple of examination questions. (25)

Besant was in no doubt about the pivotal position of Cambridge in relation to the character of the mathematical teaching of mechanics generally:

> the methods of teaching in Cambridge, and the forms of examinations in the Colleges and the University, exercise a very large influence on the teaching of Mechanics throughout the country, very directly on the schools and educational establishments which send young men to the University, and indirectly on many others. (26)

As he went on to point out, the influential examinations of the Civil Service Commission were largely conducted by Cambridge men and Cambridge made a major contribution to the supply of mathematical teachers 'who leave Cambridge imbued with the spirit of the place, habituated to its methods, and probably saturated with its prejudices'. (27) Todhunter, in particular, was quoted as having once remarked that 'no one who required a model or experiment to enable him to grasp a geometrical or mechanical theorem could ever be a mathematician'. (28) Siddons recollected his own school experiences in mechanics: there was no experimentation; graphics in statics and calculus in dynamics were both spurned; and the whole business was made up of problems which were largely springboards for flights of algebraic manipulation. (29) Godfrey summarized the general pattern:

> The British custom is that the physics master treats mechanics experimentally, and the mathematical master works problems of the Cambridge type. This tendency of mathematical mechanics to become lifeless is the inevitable result of the split . . . (30)

The problematic state of mechanics teaching was at least more widely recognized in the early twentieth century but the barriers to major change remained. Somewhat unrealistically, a BAAS report of 1907 recommended: 'Practical and theoretical mechanics ought, if possible, to be taught by the same person; mechanics and mathematics ought not to be treated as distinct from each other.' (31) By this time, correlation of school subjects, including mechanics, was attracting more attention, and some public schoolmasters were beginning to experiment with practical work of a relatively ambitious kind conducted in specially equipped *mathematical* laboratories

As part of the general development of science teaching, an introductory course in physics – elementary physical measurements – was well established in the early years of the twentieth century. The course might or might not have been correlated with the mathematical work, particularly in the areas of arithmetic and mensuration, but, as the example of Harrow illustrates, in some cases the practical work was actually taken over by the mathematics staff:

> at a time [1902–3] when great changes were being made in the teaching of Mathematics, some drawing and measuring was begun in the ordinary mathematical lessons, but this was quite independent of the work . . . which was still being done in the science schools. About 1906, the course of measurements and weighing previously done in the science schools by the science masters was begun in the mathematical laboratories under the supervision of the mathematical masters. (32)

In the public schools it was not only the interest of individual teachers in pursuing the principle of correlation which serves to explain the rather surprising birth of school mathematical laboratories. A major stimulus was provided by new examination requirements for army entrance which were announced in 1904. For elementary mathematics in the leaving certificate examinations, practical measurement of length, area, volume, weight and angle was prescribed, as well as the principle of Archimedes, and further practical work in mechanics and hydrostatics was required in the competitive examinations for entry to Woolwich and Sandhurst. (33) As Siddons admitted:

> About 1904, owing to changes in the Army entrance examination, it became necessary to teach practical mechanics to boys in the Army Class. It was then that the mathematical laboratories were equipped and some mechanics was first taught from the experimental point of view. (34)

At Harrow two such laboratories were established, one for measurements and the other for mechanics.

At Winchester, Godfrey and his department developed a parallel course to the one at Harrow and a mathematical laboratory was also established. The course was published as Godfrey and Bell's *Note-Book of Experimental Mathematics* (1905) and it included 124 experiments with the requirements for army entrance particularly in mind. (35) A reviewer of textbooks on 'practical (or experimental) mathematics' in the *Gazette* acknowledged Perry's inspiration and the importance of changes in the army examinations. He added, 'The new requirements have already produced a crop of text books.' (36) Godfrey referred to the course in elementary physical measurements as 'experimental arithmetic' and much of this work was also commonly referred to around this time as 'practical arithmetic'. As he pointed out, 'A good deal of the work can be done in an ordinary class-room. But water and a balance cannot be treated respectfully outside a room fitted more or less specially for the purpose.' (37) He also made some revealing remarks about the new questions of organization and classroom atmosphere raised for mathematics teachers by laboratory work:

> A bottle-washer (5s. a week) will be needed, unless the boys are allowed to help themselves to apparatus from the cupboards. But, to begin with, it is hardly safe to allow this. Difficulties of discipline do not occur; the interest is too great.
>
> The master will have to decide whether the class is to be kept together, or whether each boy is to go at his own pace. The latter plan will get more work out of the class . . . On the 'Go as you please' system, each boy must be provided with very definite printed instructions; otherwise the master's task will be an impossibility. However, there is no lack of books which cater for this demand.
>
> Boys can work in pairs, and talking may be allowed safely (it must be confined to the matter in hand). At the outset there will doubtless be cases of petty looting (especially of mercury). A suitable 'example' will generally put a stop to this; temporary banishment from the measurement room is a severe punishment. (38)

These developments at Winchester and Harrow and similar developments at Clifton College and Oundle School were described in the Board of Education's *Special Reports*, all under the heading of 'practical mathematics' and with the needs of intending army entrants or engineers particularly in mind. (39) The whole field of correlation, including the provision for practical measurements and mechanics, attracted the attention of both the MA and the APSSM from 1908.

The secretary of the APSSM first approached the MA early in 1908 suggesting a joint meeting, which it was eventually agreed should take place in 1910 at Westminster School. In preparation, a special committee was set up to investigate and report upon a wide range of aspects of correlation between the two subjects: the provision for practical work in geometry, measurements, physics and chemistry; correlation in the elementary practical work through joint syllabus construction, the use of common definitions, and the choice of mutually supportive problems and examples; the use of simple tables of logarithms and slide rules; and the teaching of mechanics. (40) The committee comprised six members of the MA, six from the APSSM and two representatives of the Association of Head Masters of Preparatory Schools. Godfrey, who chaired the committee, Siddons, Jackson and D.B. Mair (1868–1942) of the Civil Service Commission were included from the MA. (41) W.G. Borchardt of Cheltenham, a leading writer of mathematics textbooks, was appointed by the APSSM along with A. Vassall, a founder member of the APSSM and a colleague of Siddons at Harrow.

In the meantime the MA had also been approached by P. Abbott of the Polytechnic School, Regent Street, in his capacity as secretary of the Federated Associations of London Non-Primary Teachers. A joint meeting on the subject of 'practical mathematics' was arranged to take place before the end of 1908 at the Polytechnic. (42) Perry opened the meeting with an address on the correlation of the teaching of mathematics and science and Bryan took the chair. The scale of the meeting, which was attended by over 150 people, was unprecedented for the MA. (43) By comparison, the annual meeting of the MA in 1905, which included the first annual dinner, attracted about sixty members, a third of whom attended the dinner at the Criterion Restaurant. (44) The joint venture with the Federated Associations apparently led to some friction between the MA and the APSSM, whose secretary objected to its timing as 'forestalling the action of the Joint Committee'. (45) But this did not stop the MA from devoting a whole number of the *Gazette*, in January 1909, to a full report of the proceedings, to which representatives of other educational journals had also been invited. (46) The joint committee of the MA and the APSSM reported later in the same year.

The joint committee had distributed a circular to around 1300 boys' schools listed in the *Schoolmasters' Year Book* but only 279 questionnaires were returned, a number which rather limits the value of the statistical results. The returns comprised: 55 out of 100 public schools, 175 out of 800 grammar schools and 49 out of 400 preparatory schools. The different proportions of returns clearly reflect different levels of interest in the joint committee's concerns, which, it must be admitted, best fitted the circumstances in the public schools. The report of sixteen pages does, however, shed much light on principles and practices in relation to the committee's terms of reference. (47)

In practical measurements the committee found that the work was still normally done in a laboratory under a science master, though measurements not involving the use of a balance or water were taught by the mathematics staff in 11 per cent of the public schools and 15 per cent of the grammar schools which replied. (48) Clearly, laboratory work as part of mathematics was only a minority interest, partly stimulated by the army requirements, and the committee's recommendation that mathematics teachers might profitably take on much of this work, along the lines of the committee's own proposed syllabus, was and continued to be a long way from the reality in most schools. However, Siddons and Vassall followed the syllabus closely at Harrow and also produced a textbook to match it. (49)

In mechanics it is not surprising to find the following conclusion: 'In no subject is the want of co-operation between the Mathematical and the Science Masters so apparent as in mechanics.' (50) Apart from the army requirements, a strong bifurcation still existed in the provision for this branch: a theoretical examination course for the minority of mathematical specialists and, on a larger scale, a short but 'necessarily inadequate' course of statics for younger pupils, taught in a practical way by science staff, but unrelated to the mathematics curriculum. The recommendation that the work in practical statics should be transferred to the mathematics staff was a bold one but unrealistic given the relative lack of competence and confidence of the majority of teachers. (51)

Despite the reform of the Cambridge mathematical tripos, H.H. Turner, Savilian professor of astronomy at Oxford and President of the MA, 1909–11, referred in his Presidential address to the Cambridge influence as a continuing one:

although much physical learning is now included in the schedule for the mathematical tripos, it is treated in a symbolic manner, without observation or experiment. The fence between mathematics and science is still there. And not only is it in these high places, but it is a well-known boundary in school teaching. (52)

Turner subsequently commended the innovatory work being developed in 'practical mathematics', involving laboratory work at some public schools. (53) But Godfrey, one of the leading innovators, was forced to admit, 'the influence of the Cambridge school of applied mathematics in its decadence is still dominant' and he could point to only limited progress from the worst extremes of artificiality. (54)

For one year only, the annual January meeting of the MA was moved in 1910 from King's College to Westminster School, with a morning for MA business and an afternoon devoted to the joint meeting with the APSSM to consider the report on correlation. On the suggestion of the APSSM it was also agreed to hold a joint annual dinner on the same day. (55) Forsyth presided over a large gathering at the joint meeting and the proceedings were reported in the *Gazette* and other periodicals such as the *School World*. (56) Not surprisingly, the meeting produced little by way of new thinking and strategies for progress. (57) But the social links between the two associations were maintained for a number of years, through joint annual dinners and collaboration in the choice of dates for the annual meetings in January. From 1911 the MA's annual meeting regularly took place at the London Day Training College and, from 1933, at the London Institute of Education, until the Second World War.

T.P. Nunn (1870–1944) was vice-principal of the London Day Training College from 1905 and held a London University chair in education from 1913; he joined the MA in 1909. (58) He contributed to the discussion at the joint meeting in 1910 and went so far as to suggest that the report's recommendations on correlation were only moderate in character. Before moving into teacher training, Nunn had taught both mathematics and science in a variety of schools and technical institutions. He became second master of the William Ellis Endowed School, whose innovatory correlated syllabus for upper school mathematics and science was published by the Educational Supply Association in 1903. (59) He also contributed an unusual article to the *Educational Times*, in 1908, on the teaching of science in correlation with both mathematics and geography. (60) He was elected President of the MA, 1917–18, an exceptional honour for a non-Cambridge man, and at the beginning of his term of office the MA's annual meeting was extended to a day and a half, including a morning devoted to an exceptional joint meeting with the Geographical Association. Not surprisingly it was Nunn who contributed the major paper, on the subject of map-projections. (61)

Nunn was also an innovator in mechanics teaching, which again became the focus for an MA subcommittee, during the war years, and a report was published in the *Gazette* in 1918. In 1916 this subcommittee, which included, amongst others, Nunn, Siddons, Jackson and Mair, circularized all boys' and girls' secondary schools in England, Wales and Scotland 'in which it might be presumed that mechanics was taught'. (62) Out of just under two hundred schools replying, 85 per cent taught some mechanics.

One quarter taught the subject under mathematics only, one third under science only, and the remainder under both. The bulk of the report was devoted to appendices of specimen schemes, including contributions from Nunn and Siddons. But, by this time, there is evidence that interest in the general issue of correlation had waned and that progress towards the ideals of the reformers had been frustrated.

In 1912 a survey paper from Eggar on elementary mechanics teaching was published in the Board of Education's *Special Reports*. In spite of the efforts of the BAAS, MA, APSSM and a small number of innovators, Eggar had to admit that little general progress had been made towards the blending of theoretical and experimental mechanics to produce accessible courses of defensible educational worth as part of the 'democratization' of mathematics education. He added; 'In the case of the ordinary public or secondary school . . . Mechanics does not form part of the general education of all boys.' (63) Grant-aided secondary schools for boys and girls, Fletcher reported, taught virtually no mechanics beyond simple statics. (64) Fletcher himself had undertaken pioneering work in mechanics teaching, including the invention of 'Fletcher's trolley', before he moved to HMI in 1904. (65) In his capacity as chief HMI he dwelt at some length and with evident frustration on the problematic relationship between mathematics and physics in schools, drawing unfavourable comparisons with Germany, where centralized curriculum control included the imperative: 'Pure Mathematics and Physics must always be taken together.' (66) A similar position to that of Germany also existed in France and, in relation to English conditions, Wolff pertinently asked; *'Was ist die Physik ohne Mathematik, was der mathematische Unterricht ohne den physikalishen Einschlag?'* (67)

The joint report of the MA and the APSSM was reprinted in 1917, by which time a Prime Minister's committee was undertaking a wide-ranging enquiry into the whole position of science in British education. Under the chairmanship of Professor J.J. Thomson, in 1918 it produced a report which painted a gloomy picture on the subject of correlation:

> it is easier to get a science master who is able to teach elementary mathematics than a mathematical master with a corresponding knowledge of Science; but few schools can spare a science master for any part of the mathematical work . . . effective correlation between the two subjects is rare and is not increasing . . . (68).

Merely to recommend close correlation was by now an overworked tactic and the Thomson Report pointed to teachers as 'the key to the educational situation'. Turning the focus to teacher education, the committee suggested that the best way forward was to produce teachers capable of combining a mathematical and scientific outlook and for schools to make suitable appointments of joint-specialists. (69) But this would have involved breaking the existing patterns of specialization and career advancement, which were firmly established. The backgrounds of individual innovators such as Eggar, Siddons, Jackson, Fletcher and Nunn were very much the exception rather than the rule. Research and teaching in the universities had become increasingly specialized in the domains of mathematics and science, and the earlier nineteenth-century correlated tradition of mathematical physics no longer held sway. (70) There had also been a shift of research interest from applied to pure mathematics. It does seem that there was little chance of new applied mathematics courses or effective correlation developing at either university or school level in England.

Perry had once jokingly remarked: 'the marriage of mathematics and science seems to me like that of December and May – the marriage of a man of seventy with old bachelor habits to a bright young virgin of seventeen'. (71) To borrow Perry's metaphor, it is clear that there was some sort of engagement but that this particular marriage never took place. However, the level of interest in this area was high during the reform movement's early years. By the end of the 1900s there is also evidence of growing concern about the quality of implemented change resulting from the Perry movement. As with correlation, problems over the supply and calibre of teachers affected the realized curriculum in the schools.

TEACHERS OF MATHEMATICS

At the joint meeting of the MA and the Federated Associations in 1908, Perry expressed clear frustration with the character of some of the major changes in the curriculum:

> It astonishes me to see how little comprehension there seems to be of the proposals made by the British Association committees. We recommended experimental geometry with common-sense reasoning, and everybody seems to think that we asked for a babyish use of rulers and compasses following a series of propositions. We asked for interesting work in weighing and measuring and care it taken that all such work shall be made as uninteresting as possible. We recommended some work with graphs on squared paper, and some teachers do nothing but graphs, and there are dozens of books to help on the craze. (72)

In a carefully drafted survey paper for the International Congress of Mathematicians, which met in Rome in 1908, Godfrey confirmed this general pattern. On geometry he commented:

> As was to be expected, many of the new developments were extravagant and had no permanent effect. In particular, there was temporarily a tendency to over-emphasize the practical and experimental side of the work . . . there is some reason to think that boys have lost something of their power of expressing geometrical reasoning in words . . . At one stage of the movement there seemed to be a danger that experimental verifications would be taken for proofs . . . (73)

The movement in algebra was against the 'too great stress on manipulative skill, at the expense of intelligent study of the why and wherefore'. Teachers had sought to 'lighten the "toil" by introducing graphs, logarithms, tables and other interesting matters at a comparatively early stage'. Godfrey added:

> Following the usual law, the reform went too far. Some teachers and textbooks were not content to touch lightly on graphs . . . There was a tendency to abandon analytical in favour of geometrical and graphical methods. The laborious working of algebra exercises was cut down more and more, until there was a danger that boys would become helpless in dealing with the most straightforward algebraic expressions. (74)

The joint meetings of the MA – with the Federated Associations and with the APSSM two years later – generated lively discussion during which some of the problems associated with the teaching force were clearly exposed. Perry expressed some surprise that 'many teachers seem to have no individuality, no originality, nor even the power to think for themselves at all'. (75) Godfrey felt that the recommendations of the committee would have little effect unless 'some steps . . . can be taken to give a new point of view to the mathematical master'. (76) Armstrong drew attention to the need for professional training of mathematics teachers, particularly in relation to the subject's applications. Perry's view was more simplistic: 'it almost seems that at present we must impose some system of teaching so complete in every detail that any teacher can follow it exactly'. (77) But, more pertinently, he did also draw attention to a major problem of teacher supply:

> Until salaries are doubled and forms halved in their number of boys there will be things very open to criticism . . . It is our duty to . . . see that [teachers] are better paid, for that is the only way in which a greater proportion of able men are to be induced to become teachers. (78)

The declining supply of honours mathematics graduates in England, and particularly from Cambridge, was not arrested until after the First World War. The period of reform in school mathematics also coincided with the early stages of expansion of the system of grant-aided secondary schools for both boys and girls under the new Board of Education and LEAs. The steadily increasing demand for academically competent teachers of mathematics was a long way from being met. The study of science was growing in popularity, partly at the expense of mathematics, and graduates were being attracted to jobs outside teaching and in such areas as the Civil Service, engineering and manufacturing. HMI Fletcher was in no doubt about the scale of the problem in around 650 grant-aided secondary schools. Out of around 2500 staff teaching some mathematics beyond arithmetic he judged it to be a matter for 'grave concern' that about half 'have had no instruction in mathematics beyond what they have had at school'. (79) He stressed that poor qualifications resulted in conservatism, over-reliance on textbooks, which might themselves be of poor quality, and a tendency to misinterpret the spirit of reforms, however communicated. Many of the new ideals concerned teaching methods rather than new subject-matter and effective implementation required pedagogical sensitivity and balanced judgement. The need for some form of professional initial training, to supplement academic qualifications, was a long way from being generally accepted and the provision for in-service training was only in its infancy. Here the MA came to play a major part through the work of its committees and their published reports, which influenced teachers directly and also indirectly through the refinement of examination syllabuses and guidance in textbook production. But Fletcher's general conclusion was a sobering one: 'When all difficulties of tradition and organisation are allowed for, the chief difficulty remains – the poverty of much of the teaching.' (80)

Thus progress towards the ideals of the Perry movement was partly inhibited by problems of teacher supply and inadequate teacher education, both academic and professional. The character of curriculum development on a large scale was also affected by a growing reaction to the movement's values and the consequences for the place and purposes of mathematics in a liberal education. Here it is possible to disentangle three distinct interpretations of 'practical mathematics' in the debates: a syllabus in mathematics for technical students along the lines of Perry; laboratory-based work as part of the mathematics curriculum; and a way of teaching the subject in the spirit of the Perry movement's guiding pedagogical principles. Reaction came in two principal forms. One questioned the values of practical mathematics as mathematics; the other questioned the values of a more practical pedagogy *per se*, whether pursued in a mathematical laboratory or an ordinary classroom.

REACTIONS TO REFORM

In relation to pedagogy, as HMI Strachan noted, 'At various times the reform movement has been brought into temporary disrepute by an excessive devotion to so-called practical work or by alliance with the extreme heuristic school.' (81) The work stimulated by the revised requirements for army entrance attracted some of the earliest criticism. The *Gazette* published a strong reaction from one master of St Paul's School:

> The policy of 'overturn, overturn' has been pushed too far: if numerical calculations, graphical representations, and geometrical drawing are not merely to be an aid, but a substitute for a systematic knowledge of the theory of Elementary Mathematics, the value of the subject as an educational instrument will be but small. (82)

The author felt that the new demands required of candidates only 'a few knoblets of knowledge which will enable them to solve questions of a strictly practical and "useful" kind'. Laboratory work was being 'dignified by the title of "Practical Mathematics"', and was 'somewhat out of place' as part of mathematics. (83) The *School World* published a more general critique from the senior mathematical master of Bradford Grammar School. In geometry he felt that 'exercises which merely test a pupil's skill in draughtsman's work are surely for the art room'. He dismissed activities involving drawing, measuring, folding and cutting as no substitute for the serious business of deductive proof, adding that 'geometry is not an experimental science', and, in algebra, purposeless 'graphomania' was also deprecated. (84) By 1910 some of the leading reformers were themselves expressing concern over the exaggerated practical tendencies. Godfrey commented on the practical excesses in geometry:

> But it was soon realized that this would make the subject invertebrate, that there must be a certain element of severity in every school study, and that for purposes of general education geometry must still stand or fall by the logical training it gives. (85)

He judged that 'the transitional period is still on us' and that 'perhaps it is still too soon to give a final opinion'. In relation to algebra he added:

> The pendulum is now swinging in the opposite direction. If its oscillations can be damped in time, we may hope to settle down to a system which shall give reasonable skill in quite straightforward manipulation, and at the same time set graphical work in the true position it should occupy in elementary teaching. (86)

In addresses to the BAAS in 1910 and the MA in 1912, Professor Hobson well summarized the principal challenges now facing those at the centre of mathematics curriculum development in England. In geometry and mechanics the pressing need was to work out the best mix of the practical and experimental elements with the theoretical and deductive elements, bearing in mind the differentiated needs of the pupils according to age and intellectual attainment. (87) He cautioned:

> Purely numerical work, calculation with graphs, problems in which the data are taken from practical life – all these are excellent, up to a certain point, and they form the right avenue of introduction to scientific conceptions. But if this kind of work is unduly prolonged, and too exclusively practised, it tends to develop a one-sided mechanical view of the capabilities of Mathematical methods, and the study ceases to be in any real sense educational . . . the most important educational aspect of the subject is as an instrument for training boys and girls to think accurately and independently; and with this in view, the more general and theoretical parts of the subject should not be entirely sacrificed either to the exigency of providing useful tools for application in after life, or to the supposed need of sustaining interest in the subject by a too anxious adherence to its concrete and practical side. (88)

There is also some evidence of a further hardening of attitude in some quarters. The *Gazette* published in 1914 a strong plea that

> the authorities of the Mathematical Association will keep in the future, as they have done in the past, a firm faith that the primary value of mathematical study is not to be found in such results as skill with the penny ruler, the scissors and the scales, but in the culture that all genuine mathematical study has been held to give from the days of Plato to those of Russell and Whitehead. (89)

After the War, C.H.P. Mayo, who was Siddons's head of department at Harrow, looked back on some of his own experiences of reform with a sense of relief. He confessed that he had never had much sympathy with the extreme swing towards 'materialism' in the form of practical and laboratory work: 'the elementary and pottering experimentation gave no mental grip, and their value was almost negligible'; it was 'pandering to the spirit of mere utility in education'. He welcomed the reaffirmation of a more disciplinary view in mathematics aligned with 'a strong return to the Classics' as part of 'the revolt from the materialism to which circumstances forced us some twenty or more years ago'. He added, 'the mathematical laboratories at Harrow, hailed almost as the saviour of the study, are no longer used'. (90)

Reactions to practical mathematics as a course of study *per se* can be traced back to the beginnings of the Perry movement at the turn of the century. An early response in *Nature* was typical:

> the syllabus . . . is admirably adapted for a *technical* training. In practical mathematics, where mental training is of minor importance, exigencies of time will compel the teacher to omit explanations, or only give them roughly, for his chief object is to enable his pupils to apply mathematical results, as distinct from reasoning, to problems in engineering, science, or kindred subjects. (91)

The gulf separating the Cambridge school of mathematicians, led by Forsyth, and the technical institutions, working on Perry's lines, was a major one to which the German commentator Wolff drew attention in a section of his survey report of 1915, significantly entitled '*Die Reformbewegung in England. (Perry und Forsyth)*'. (92) From a pure mathematical standpoint the major bone of contention was that Perry's scheme involved rapid progress through an ambitious range of useful mathematical content, which necessitated a lack of attention both to general principles and to a systematic theoretical development of the subject. In short, it was broad but necessarily shallow mathematically. On these grounds it continued to be sniped at by mathematicians. Addressing the MA, Professor Hobson remarked, 'I gather that, in some of the current teaching of practical Mathematics, a kind of perverse ingenuity is exhibited in evading all discussion of fundamental ideas, and in the elimination of all reference to general principles.' (93) When asked to clarify whether he had in mind Perry's syllabus or laboratory work, he added, 'I think I had both in my mind. I used the word "practical" to distinguish from the mathematics which deals with principles.' (94)

In an essay-review of a textbook by Perry, published in *Nature* in 1913, Professor Bryan acknowledged that the 'revolution' in mathematics education over the previous decade 'owes its success largely to the indefatigable exertions of Professor John Perry'. But the following example serves well to exemplify the mathematical objections to Perry's own scheme:

> Prof. Perry . . . says that 'in many important calculations we need to use Napierian logarithms, whose base is 2.71828'. 'Why 2.71828?' asks the intelligent student. No answer is given; and this is what Prof. Perry calls 'practical mathematics'. We should call it cram. But the author

> continues to drag in this apparently useless and meaningless symbol e throughout the book . . . (95)

Furthermore, by the time of the First World War, Perry's approach to mathematics in the specific case of the higher education of engineers was also discredited and he was forcibly retired from Imperial College in 1913. He was replaced by, of all people, Forsyth, who would have shared the views expressed by Hobson, Bryan and other Cambridge mathematicians. The preponderance of opinion now favoured the handing over of the higher work in mathematics for engineers to mathematical specialists and the older tradition of practical mathematics for engineers was rejected. (96) In the case of evening technical education, however, Perry's legacy was still much in evidence after his death in 1920.

MATHEMATICS IN TECHNICAL EDUCATION

The provision and character of mathematics for technical students was understandably not an early priority for the MA and its Teaching Committee. In 1909 a paper was read at the annual meeting, on the mathematical training of technical students, and some discussion resulted, but, in the following year, an exceptional contribution to the *Gazette* on elementary mathematics in evening schools included the observation: 'the *Gazette* contains little of special interest to those concerned in the work of the evening classes, which are so important and special a feature of our British system of education'. (97) Up to 1924, another contributor to the *Gazette* could still report: 'No effective steps have been taken to consider the mathematical needs of technical students and the most satisfactory way of dealing with them.' The hope was expressed that the MA 'may feel able, in the future, to extend its activities to the realm of Technical Education'. (98) Action was forthcoming in the same year.

Professor H.T.H. Piaggio of University College, Nottingham, took a leading role in the extension of the MA's work to the field of evening technical education. He drafted a position paper on the subject which was circulated to 'selected persons', together with a covering letter inviting co-operation, and to stimulate discussion Piaggio's paper was also published in the *Gazette*. (99) The Association of Teachers in Technical Institutions (ATTI) also turned its attention to mathematics at this time and devoted space to the subject in its *Technical Journal*. The level of interest generated was sufficient to justify the appointment of a special subcommittee of the Teaching Committee to consider this hitherto unexplored field. Piaggio acted as chairman of the subcommittee, which included two representatives of the technological branch of the Board of Education, co-opted representatives of the ATTI and the Association of Principals in Technical Institutions, and also Tuckey, chairman of the Teaching Committee and the only member not specifically involved in the technical field. A report was published in 1926 and its substance in summary form was discussed at the January meeting of the MA, before the full report was published. (100)

Eton College,
WINDSOR.

Dear Sir,

The General Teaching Committee of the Mathematical Association is considering whether it would be desirable to issue a report on Practical Mathematics as taught in evening continuation schools and technical colleges.

It has been suggested that such a report would be useful and that the various problems connected with the teaching of this subject need to be discussed.

The Committee have decided, as a preliminary, to stimulate discussion on the subject, in order to discover whether the need for such a report is widely felt, and to obtain clearer ideas of the particular teaching problems to be solved. Professor Piaggio has written an article for the Mathematical Gazette with this object in view, and an advance proof of this is sent to you herewith. It is hoped that, as one who is interested in and informed upon this subject, you will be able to give the Committee your views.

If the Teaching Committee take up the matter, a sub-committee would be formed to which it would be important that the best available men should be co-opted —— it might be desirable to obtain the help of some who are not members of the Association ——. This sub-committee would consider the details in the first instance, and the suggestion of names of persons who should be asked to assist might prove of great value.

A considerable proportion of the members of the Mathematical Association are not directly concerned in the teaching of Practical Mathematics but the subject is of general interest to all teachers of Mathematics as well of direct interest to some of them and it is felt that this particular problem should not be divorced from other problems of Mathematical teaching.

Yours truly,

Hon. Sec.

General Teaching Committee,
Mathematical Association.

Plate 4.1   Letter of Inquiry into Practical Mathematics 1924

The general tenor of the report followed that expressed in earlier reactions to practical mathematics as a course of study whilst at the same time acknowledging Perry's seminal influence on the reform movement:

> His methods have been adopted very widely. When they were first introduced they aroused great enthusiasm, and it was hoped that henceforth no difficulty would be experienced in imparting a good working knowledge of mathematics to every student of average capacity. Subsequent experience has proved that these hopes were too sanguine. Some very good work has been done, both by teachers and students, and yet, in the opinion of many, the results obtained are somewhat disappointing. (101)

The main recommendations in the report clearly reflected Piaggio's summary judgement that

> *Practical Mathematics* is regarded very unfavourably by many mathematicians, and . . . may be summed up as Calculus . . . with as much as possible of the academic mathematics required to lead up to this and with constant reference to engineering applications. (102)

Piaggio also went so far as to claim that 'an evil tradition has grown up that lack of logic makes an argument particularly convincing to practical men'. (103) The MA's report deprecated the over-emphasis on unconnected rules and the inattention to fundamental principles. The need for a more unified treatment of the subject was advocated, with more attention to various technical applications, and all this required that 'the teacher should possess a sufficiently liberal knowledge to enable him to present the subject in this manner'. (104) The report more tentatively suggested a little deductive geometry for junior (14–16) technical students, to restore the educational balance overall. Greater future involvement from technical teachers in the MA's activities was also invited but, as with correlation, the early thrust was not sustained between the two world wars. This initial involvement of the MA in the technical field was, however, an isolated initiative. Undoubtedly the mainstream work of the Teaching Committee from around 1910 was concentrated on the development of the various branches of mathematics as part of a liberal education in public and other secondary schools, including the extension of this work to accommodate the specific needs and circumstances in girls' schools.

TEACHING COMMITTEE'S FIRST TWENTY YEARS

Siddons acted as secretary of the Teaching Committee from 1902 until 1912, under a succession of Presidents who took the chair. He became chairman in 1912 and held this position continuously until 1919, with Abbott as concurrent secretary. Looking back, at some remove, on the first twenty years' work of the Teaching Committee, Siddons made the following generalization concerning its published output:

> Of all the reports published before 1918 it might be said that they consisted of short general statements of the aims of teaching, followed

by brief statements of what should be included and what should be cut out of our teaching and examination syllabuses. I feel that this was the best plan while our first aim was to get examination papers altered . . . From 1918 onwards our reports have been of a different character: they have become admirable essays on the teaching of different subjects and, in general, addressed to the teacher rather than to the examiner. (105)

It should also be added that textbook writers acted as an important intermediary between the Teaching Committee and the teaching force. Such writers might either have been directly involved in the Teaching Committee's work or indirectly influenced by its reports.

Siddons's generalization is broadly sound but the character of the reports did begin to change in 1907 when the first detailed report on preparatory school mathematics was published. Furthermore, the 1909 joint report with the APSSM was distinctive in character and based on evidence from a wide-ranging survey, as was the report of 1907. In spite of the disruption caused by wartime conditions, the MA's published output up to around 1920 was impressive in terms both of its range and of its attention to principles in the choice of content and methods of teaching mathematics as part of a general secondary education. To use Hobson's term, educational 'democratization' – at least for boys but still only for the minority – was the overriding consideration in all this work. What is also striking about this period is the closeness of the link between the MA and particular secondary examining bodies whose mathematical examinations became directly influenced in various ways.

A contributor to the *Gazette* in 1925 judged that the MA 'has probably achieved more important results by bringing influence to bear upon examining bodies than it has by direct action upon teachers'. (106) There is certainly evidence to support this conclusion, and the case of geometry after the breakthrough of 1902–3 exemplifies some of the tactics employed. The 'new geometry' was first discussed at the annual meeting of the MA in 1905. After the abandonment of the insistence on Euclid's order of propositions, concern was being expressed about the difficulty of examining in deductive geometry. However, the weight of opinion expressed at this meeting was against the imposition of a new standard sequence and Forsyth was in no doubt on this point:

He trusted that neither this Association nor any body of teachers would ever attempt to re-instate and re-establish one definite order in Geometry to be mechanically imposed on all. Teachers now have their freedom; let them value their freedom, even if it brought a little chaos. (107)

In the following year Godfrey expressed optimism on this important sequence issue:

chaos tarries; examiners find no difficulty, and the result of freedom has been an effective agreement among writers of text-books as to order and content. So long as freedom is permitted, so long will progress be possible. (108)

A minute of Council in January of 1907 records: 'A letter was read in which the Association was asked to fix an order of propositions in Geometry. It was decided that the proposal should not be entertained.' (109) On this issue the Council's ruling fixed the MA's policy, from which it subsequently never wavered, in spite of renewed pressures for uniformity in the 1920s (which will be discussed in chapter five).

The Teaching Committee continued to keep an eye on the geometry papers set by various examining bodies and took direct action in 1911. Concern had been expressed over some lack of clarity in certain types of question. Accordingly a simple but pointed circular was sent out, under Hobson's signature, to over fifty examining bodies and various educational journals. (110) The number of bodies approached is at first striking and in the same year the Consultative Committee of the Board of Education published a massive report on the whole question of examinations in secondary schools, following two years of investigation. (111) The complex and unco-ordinated provision for secondary school examinations, which had multiplied the AIGT's difficulties as a pressure group, still existed, and the harmful effects on an expanding system of secondary schooling had also multiplied. A national system of school certificates and higher school certificates was not finalized until the end of the First World War. In the meantime the MA's Teaching Committee worked towards building close relationships with individual boards with which its own members were associated in one way or another.

In 1911 a revised syllabus for the army entrance examinations was submitted to the Teaching Committee for criticism and 'most of the changes suggested were adopted by the War Office subcommittee'. (112) In the following year the Teaching Committee also began to work closely with the Oxford and Cambridge Joint Board, which was an examining body closely associated with the public schools. In addition to direct action through circulars and correspondence with individual boards, the MA also included a new feature in the *Gazette* from 1910: a 'Pillory' for notorious examination questions. (113) This was another, albeit minor, tactic designed to 'get at' individual boards. But the use of published reports became a much more important lever in relation to the development of examination syllabuses in elementary mathematics.

In geometry it is the non-appearance of a major report of the MA until 1923 which is perhaps surprising. In 1920 Godfrey expressed the opinion that the time had still not yet come for the MA 'to support with its authority any particular method of teaching Geometry'. (114) It was the Board of Education that took a major lead here by issuing in 1909 an important circular, numbered 711 and entitled *Teaching of Geometry and Graphic Algebra in Schools*. (115) Fletcher was the anonymous author of this circular, which took a distinctly progressive line concerning the role of intuition and experiment and powerfully argued for a broader axiomatic basis in deductive geometry for schools. Major examination reform had only slightly relaxed the burden of learning geometrical proofs, and fifty or more might still be required for an examination, including formal proofs of some of the fundamental propositions in Euclid Book I. To exploit intuition in demonstrations at this stage in a course meant broadening the basis of assumption, which also further complicated the sequence issue. As Godfrey pointed out, 'This endless controversy as to the best sequence in Book I arises from the impossibility of compromising satisfactorily between the claims of pedagogy and mathematical rigour.' He added: 'The Board of Education Circular simply cuts the knot, by treating these fundamental theorems as postulates.' (116)

For the first time three developmental stages in geometry teaching were proposed. In brief, the first was introductory, bringing in the fundamental notions and the use of instruments; the second intuitive and experimental, leading up to the fundamental propositions; and only the third deductive, but using a wide base of assumption developed in the first two stages. The position adopted in the circular was generally in advance of examination requirements, textbook design and, consequently, many teachers' practices. But it prompted many and varied reactions and boldly provided a clear sense of direction in its developmental blend of the practical and Euclidean traditions in geometry. The first meeting of the London branch of the MA, in 1909, was principally devoted to a discussion of the circular's recommendations in geometry. There was a very large attendance of about 220 at the Polytechnic, Regent Street – a much larger gathering than for an annual meeting of the MA at this time – and the wide-ranging discussion, which was fully reported in the *Gazette*, was opened by Siddons. (117)

Given the undeveloped state of professional training for mathematics teachers, the publication and widespread distribution of the Board's circular was timely, and particularly so at a formative stage in the development of the grant-aided system of secondary schools. A contributor to *Nature* in 1914 pointed to the circular's 'marked and unquestionably beneficial influence on elementary [i.e. secondary] education', and added, 'We do not know of any geometrical textbook, published since that date [1909], which has not taken account of it.' (118) Much later, in a 1959 obituary tribute to Fletcher, Siddons judged that the tangible effect of the circular was 'very far-reaching and led up to the reforms that have since been made in the teaching of geometry'. (119)

Given the lead of the Board of Education in geometry, it is perhaps surprising that the MA's Teaching Committee chose to establish a new subcommittee on geometry as early as 1913. (120) In the circumstances, what is less surprising is that a report was not published until ten years later, by which time the composition of the subcommittee had changed. There was, however, a pressing need for a substantial appraisal of the teaching of algebra, including its potential for metamorphosis through the emergence of 'graphic algebra' as one product of the Perry movement. A start on this appraisal had been made in the Board's circular 711, which pressed for the acceptance of graphs as a powerful pedagogical tool, to be woven into the fabric of algebra teaching, and not merely grafted on as an additional topic, albeit a novel one, as had been common in the early years of reform. It was Godfrey who saw a clear opportunity to tackle algebra teaching as a whole, including its potential for broadening to incorporate introductory elements of trigonometry as part of a general education.

At the annual meeting of the MA in 1910 Godfrey gave a stimulating paper in which the central aim was to disentangle the 'educational' from the 'technical' aspects of algebra. (121) In Godfrey's sense the educational aspect emphasized the central ideas of this branch, which justified its inclusion as part of a liberal education. The technical aspect referred to the techniques of algebra, required by the future user of this branch, either in applications or as part of a course for mathematical specialists. For all pupils the central ideas which captured the spirit of algebra were identified as: generalization and the uses of formulae; functions and graphical representation; and problem solving involving equations. As Godfrey stressed, ideas could not be developed without techniques, but his paper provided a rationale for what would now be referred to as differentiation in the curriculum according to ability. He remarked: 'I do not know that any representative body has recommended this discrimination between different classes of pupils in algebra teaching.' (122) Godfrey persuaded the MA's Teaching Committee to take the initiative and a small subcommittee, including Siddons, Tuckey and Nunn, worked in detail on a major report which was finalized for publication in 1911. Nunn's thinking and influence in algebra teaching were also seminal at this time. (123)

Emphasis on the need for curricular differentiation and the attention to educational principles were important features of the final report, which was also clearly designed to influence the requirements of examinations. A strong case was argued for systematically cutting and simplifying the early stages of algebra to allow its broadening to include elements of what was then called 'numerical trigonometry'. This reference to trigonometry was also made explicit in the title of the report, and the qualification 'numerical' was included to denote a treatment suitable for the non-specialist, which was an innovation at this time. As the report made plain in its introduction:

> Many teachers wish for opportunity to develop with their pupils mathematical ideas that they feel to be of greater educative value – ideas drawn from mechanics, mensuration, solid geometry, infinitesimal calculus, and, more especially, from numerical trigonometry. Custom, represented by public examinations, has at present the effect of withholding this opportunity. On that account need has been felt for an inquiry into custom, and the present report is the outcome of such an inquiry. (124)

The report hoped for 'the hearty co-operation of examiners, upon whose policy so much depends', (125) and growing links with particular examining bodies are evident from around this time.

In 1911 the Oxbridge Joint Board held a meeting with representatives of the HMC, including Godfrey, and the Headmasters' Association, to consider the MA's proposals on algebra and trigonometry. (126) At this time also, the MA entered into detailed communications with the Joint Board, particularly in connection with the introduction of experimental questions in trigonometry. (127) In 1912 Godfrey was appointed as one of two examiners in mathematics for the Joint Board's school certificate and this, no doubt, helped further to develop a close working relationship with the MA. Early success encouraged the Teaching Committee to approach other examining bodies, including London University on the question of

MATHEMATICAL ASSOCIATION
Teaching Committee

DRAFT LETTER TO REGISTRARS OF UNIVERSITIES, SECRETARIES
OF EXAMINING BOARDS, ETC.

Dear Sir,

The Teaching Committee of the Mathematical Association,
in continuation of the work of the Association for the
Improvement of Geometrical Teaching, has from time to time
issued reports on the teaching of various branches of elementary Mathematics. These reports, besides exercising an
influence upon the teaching of Mathematics in schools, have
received the attention of Examining Bodies, who, in more
than one important instance, have referred proposals for
changes in their regulations and syllabuses to the Committee
for consideration and advice. The Committee, encouraged
by these instances to believe that their co-operation is
recognised as helpful, have directed me to bring the existence of the Committee to the notice of bodies who conduct
the examination of schools in Mathematics.

The Mathematical Association has about 700 members who
represent all grades of schools and the teaching bodies of
most British Universities. The Teaching Committee has
recently been reconstituted on a wider basis so as to produce a representative body competent to deal with questions
connected with the teaching of Mathematics in secondary
schools. I enclose a list of the members of the Committee
who are assisted by Special Committees immediately representative of the Public Schools, other Secondary Schools and Girls'
Secondary Schools respectively.

I beg that you will kindly submit this letter in the
proper quarter.

I am,

Yours faithfully,

T. PERCY NUNN
Hon. Secretary

Plate 4.2   Letter to Examining Bodies 1912

the use of tables of logarithms in their school examinations. (128) Close links were soon established with the Oxford Delegacy and the Cambridge Syndicate in particular, and in 1912 the Teaching Committee was prompted to send out a general circular letter to advertise its potential role in examination syllabus reconstruction. In 1912 also, the following important resolution from Godfrey was passed:

> That in making recommendations concerning examination syllabuses and papers the committee should have regard to the published reports of the committee except in cases in which the reports have been classed by the committee as obsolete. (129)

At the same meeting the first geometry report of 1902 was classed as obsolete.

Co-operation with examining bodies continued throughout the First World War and a new link was established, with the Northern Universities Joint Matriculation Board (NUJMB). This board was established in 1903, to act jointly for the newly chartered Universities of Manchester, Liverpool and Leeds. It became, along with the London Board, one of the two largest university examining bodies, and it developed strong links with the developing system of grant-aided secondary schools in the north of England. Fruitful co-operation between the MA and the examining boards of Oxford and Cambridge, the NUJMB and the Civil Service Commission did not, however, extend to the London Board in the same period.

The Teaching Committee pressed for a number of changes in London's requirements: the exclusion of outdated 'contracted methods' of approximate calculation and the introduction of tables of logarithms; the broadening of arithmetic to include simple mensuration; simplifications in algebra, with some alternative questions in numerical trigonometry; and the introduction of some calculus in the optional more advanced syllabus. (130) Up to 1914, however, there was no progress and Siddons was prompted to make some remarks on the MA's tactics in its relations with examining bodies:

> The direct method of attack is not always the most suitable, as I think the Committee has found to some extent. It is always necessary to enquire privately of somebody who knows what is the best way to do it . . . I am afraid at London University we were not successful. We took a lot of trouble to find out what was the proper method of attack, and nobody seemed to know, and the method we were ultimately advised to take has not proved successful. (131)

A subcommittee continued to work on the problem of London's requirements through the war years, and in 1918 a further subcommittee was appointed 'to report periodically on the current examination papers of public examining bodies, so far as mathematical subjects are concerned'. (132) By this time, and following the algebra report, a number of reports on other aspects of mathematical education had also been published.

Ten years after the establishment of the MA's first Teaching Committee in 1902, its composition and range of interests had developed sufficiently to justify its re-constitution on a broadly representative basis. The new

MATHEMATICAL ASSOCIATION

General Committee

Miss L. Ashcroft - University College, Reading (57, Kendrick Road, Reading)
S. Barnard - Rugby School - 1 Whitehall Road, Rugby
Miss A.E.Bennett - North London Collegiate School - 82, Manor Park Road, Harlesden, N.W.
J.V.H.Coates - Alleyn's School, Dulwich, S.E.
Miss A.B.Collier - Newnham College, Cambridge
W.J.Dobbs - 24, Fairfax Road, S. Hampstead, N.W.
C.V.Durell - Winchester College
C. Godfrey - Royal Naval College, Osborn, I.W.
Miss E.R.Gwatkin - 84, Anfield Road, Liverpool
Miss H.P.Hudson - Newnham College, Cambridge
A. Lodge - The Croft, Peperharow Road, Godalming
J.W.Mercer - Royal Naval College, Dartmouth
W.E.Paterson - 7 Donovan Avenue, Muswell Hill, N.
Miss H.M.Sheldon - High School, West Hill, Sydenham, S.E.
A.W.Siddons - Garlands, Harrow-on-the-Hill
C.J.L.Wagstaff - 68, Westbere Road, Cricklewood, N.W.
C.S.Jackson - 85, Nightingale Place, Woolwich, S.E.
P. Abbott - 5, West View, Highgate Hill, N.
Rev. E.W.Barnes, D.Sc., Trinity College, Cambridge
H.T.Gerrans - 20, St. John Street, Oxford
Professor F.R. Barrell - 1, The Paragon, Clifton, Bristol
Dr. Nunn London Day Training College, Southampton Row WC
J.S.Norman - The New Beacon, Sevenoaks, Kent
E. Kitchener - The Golden Parsonage, Hemel Hempstead, Herts.
Miss Punnett London Day Training College, Southampton Row, WC
H.D.Ellis - 12 Gloucester Terrace, Hyde Park, W.
C. Pendlebury 39 Brandenburgh Rd [illegible]
Professor E.W.Hobson, D.Sc., The Gables, Mount Pleasant, Cambridge
W.J.Greenstreet - The Woodlands, Burghfield Common, Mortimer, Berks.
D.B. Mair - The Moorings, Banstead, Surrey
G. St. L. Carson - For Tonbridge School - Tonbridge Kent
G. H. Hardy - Trinity College, Cambridge.
[illegible]

Plate 4.3   General Teaching Committee 1912

regulations provided for a General Teaching Committee, including representation from three Special Committees: for public schools, i.e. schools listed in the *Public Schools Year Book*; for 'other secondary schools for boys', i.e. secondary schools not listed in the *Year Book*; and for girls' schools. The composition was specified to cover a range of sectional interests; predictably, schools within the elementary system were not formally represented at this time. The first list of members of the new General Committee contains many familiar names associated with the reform movement, and the formal recognition of the interests of girls' and 'other secondary' schools did stimulate some distinctive work. Activity was not suspended during the war years but the membership of the committees was largely frozen from 1914 – when a second election under the new constitution took place – until 1920. (133)

In the case of the public schools, the Special Committee continued to develop the earlier work of the MA's Teaching Committee with particular reference to the needs of non-specialists. Here it was also supported by the work of the Curriculum Committee of the HMC, which in 1909 had produced an influential syllabus for the nine-to-sixteen age range. (134) The syllabus deliberately spanned the preparatory and public school age ranges, and its main recommendations were reaffirmed in the first report of the Public Schools Special Committee, which was published in 1913. (135) The MA's report went on to suggest various alternative courses for non-specialists, post-sixteen, including work in further algebra, trigonometry and pure geometry, analytical geometry, calculus and mechanics. Godfrey played a leading part in preparing the HMC's and the MA's recommendations for non-specialists, building on his pioneering work at Winchester. Siddons later remarked that Godfrey 'had the ear of the Headmasters' Conference which of course had great weight with examining bodies'. (136)

C.V. Durell (1882–1968) acted as first secretary of the Public Schools Special Committee. He started teaching at Winchester in 1905, when Godfrey moved to Osborne, and he became the senior mathematical master in 1910. His first textbook was published in 1906 and he joined the MA's Teaching Committee in 1910. He became a prolific textbook writer for the MA's publisher, G. Bell and Sons, for over half a century, working both alone and in partnership with a number of other leading public schoolmasters: Tuckey, Siddons, R.C. Fawdry (Clifton), G.W. Palmer (Christ's Hospital) and R.M. Wright (Eton), who were all also actively involved in the first twenty years' work of the Teaching Committee. (137)

Following Godfrey's work in algebra, Durell gave his first paper to the MA on the teaching of arithmetic and it was published in the *Gazette* in 1911, together with a summary of the resulting discussion. (138) Durell made a strong case for various omissions and simplifications in the interests of broadening the mathematical syllabus. The Public Schools Special Committee and the Teaching Committee were prompted to take the debate further, into the war years. Efforts initiated by Siddons to secure greater uniformity in arithmetical algorithms led to the publication of a report in the *Gazette* in 1915, and in the following year a general report on arithmetic teaching in public schools was also published in the *Gazette*, but not separately, given the need to economize on paper. (139) This report took up many of Durell's earlier proposals and was particularly aimed at examining bodies, though questions of principle and method also received due attention. As a whole the report presented a convincing case for many desired and overdue reforms in arithmetic teaching.

By comparison with the Public Schools Special Committee the work of the 'Other Secondary Schools' Special Committee was more modest in its extent but surprisingly progressive in outlook. The principle of broadening the mathematics curriculum in a general secondary education strongly underpinned a brief two-page report which was published in 1914. (140) W.J. Dobbs acted as secretary of the Special Committee and was an outstanding radical of this period. From 1910 until 1919 he taught at Holloway County Secondary School. As Howson has suggested, some of his ideas in geometry teaching were many decades ahead of their time and particularly concerning the potential of motion geometry. His extraordinary geometry textbook – including aspects of trigonometry, mensuration and co-ordinate geometry – was published in 1913 but, predictably, was a commercial failure. (141) The principle of correlation as applied to the various branches of mathematics – unification or fusion as it became known – also underpins the Special Committee's report and Dobbs's thinking, both of which were strong on idealism and vision but a long way from the practicalities of implementing curriculum change in secondary schools on a large scale. But the evidence of progressive tendencies in at least some non-HMC schools for boys is striking nonetheless.

MATHEMATICS FOR GIRLS

The establishment of a Girls' Schools Special Committee in 1912 was in itself a significant event in the history of the development of mathematics education for girls. W. Hope-Jones (1884–1965) of Eton, a leading personality and wit who joined the MA in 1917, recalled his Cambridge days and 'the alarm felt at the beginning of this century . . . at the growing success of the women'. 'H-J' couldn't resist quoting the following lines:

> I've spent all my cash on a crammer;
> I shall only get beta or gamma;
> But the girl over there,
> With the flaming red hair,
> Will get alpha quite easily, damn her! (142)

From the 1880s women had begun to sit the degree examinations at Cambridge, Oxford and London, and resulting qualifications provided a high-status and direct route into secondary teaching. The changing pattern up to 1912 was well summarized by Louisa Story in the Board of Education's *Special Reports*:

> at first the difficulties were great owing to the fact that the supply of well-qualified teachers was wholly inadequate . . . the equipment of those teaching before [1881] was in the main meagre: a smattering

of arithmetic and algebra, with little knowledge of principles, and perhaps two books of Euclid learnt more or less by rote. In the twenty years following the opening of the Tripos Examination to women, 250 students took honours in Mathematics at Cambridge alone, and it was with the entrance into the teaching profession of this band of highly qualified women that the organisation of mathematical teaching may be said to have begun. (143)

Story's survey of 180 schools linked with the Association of Head Mistresses found that approximately one third of senior mathematical mistresses had taken the mathematical tripos and a similar number a London pass degree but, following the pattern for men, very few had undertaken any professional training. Story spelt out the predictable consequences for the curriculum in mathematics at girls' as well as boys' schools: it had become 'a preparation for the future mathematical student at the Universities, rather than an education for the average pupil'. (144) To use Godfrey's terminology, the 'aristocratic theory' could be applied to girls as well as boys, and the principle of 'democratization', in Hobson's sense, now required the attention of mathematical mistresses as well as masters.

Understandably, with the aim to gain parity of esteem, the main lines of development in mathematics education for girls generally followed those already being developed for boys but a number of factors continued to contribute to inequality of opportunity between the two sexes in mathematics. There were traditionally lower expectations for girls in elementary schools and for women entering and undergoing training in the colleges. Such expectations were carried over to the developing system of secondary schools for girls. Less time was devoted to mathematics in girls' secondary schools, given a shorter school day and a tendency for girls to leave school at an earlier age. Overall, women teachers were less well-qualified mathematically, and there was greater variability in the curricular opportunities provided in girls' schools. (145) Furthermore, in the context of the Perry movement, as Sara Burstall, headmistress of Manchester High School, pointed out, instability had resulted from 'a revolt, led by the engineers', with the main thrust being

> against the actual methods and material of mathematical teaching in the schools which have been found too academic for the needs of life, that is, the needs of boys . . . Practical Mathematics of various kinds is introduced, and school Mathematics is more definitely directed towards the demands of careers which do not concern girls . . . It is closely related to the characteristic industries and activities of *men* . . . (146)

Clearly there was much work to be done by the leading mathematical mistresses in shaping a suitable twentieth-century mathematical curriculum adapted to the needs of girls and the existing conditions in girls' schools. By 1910 the MA had started to accommodate the specific interests of girls and women, and significant progress was made in this aspect of its work over the next ten years.

In 1908 the rules of the MA for the first time included the clause:

'One of the secretaries shall be elected from the lady members of the Association.' (147) This guaranteed at least one woman on the Council, and the position was first occupied by Miss E. Greene. She did not, however, become involved with the work of either the Teaching Committee or the Girls' Schools Special Committee. The key personality at this early stage appears to have been Miss Gwatkin, who replaced Miss Greene as a secretary in 1910. (148) Miss Gwatkin taught at Roedean and Maria Grey Training College before moving to a headship at Queen Mary's High School, Liverpool. She was the first woman to attend a full meeting of the Teaching Committee, in 1910, and she also joined the important subcommittee on algebra teaching. The final report included a paragraph in which the existence of girls was first officially recognized by the Teaching Committee:

> The Committee have in view the requirements of girls as well as those of boys, and the word 'boy' being used for convenience of expression, what is here predicated of boys is to be extended to girls, except where the context renders such an extension of meaning obviously unsuitable. (149)

In the same year a significant resolution was passed 'That no report on the later stages in mathematics in Secondary Schools for boys shall be published without the statement of any modifications which may be considered desirable for girls' schools.' (150) Under the new constitution of 1912, seven women were listed as members of the General Committee, including Margaret Punnett (1867–1946), a colleague of Nunn and vice-principal at the London Day Training College.

Miss Punnett replaced Miss Gwatkin as a secretary of the MA in 1912, though the latter continued to represent women's interests on the Council, along with Miss Greene. Miss Punnett continued to give loyal secretarial support to the MA until 1939 when she was replaced by Elizabeth Williams. (151) For much of her period of office she worked in partnership with Charles Pendlebury (1854–1941) – 'the "Todhunter" in arithmetic' – who became a secretary of the AIGT in 1886 and held this office continuously for a remarkable fifty years. (152) Miss Punnett was also elected as first secretary of the Girls' Schools Special Committee' in 1912, under the chairmanship of Miss Gwatkin. (153)

The proportion of women members of the MA increased from 7 per cent at the turn of the century to over 20 per cent by 1914. It should also be added that women were becoming increasingly involved as associate members within the branches, and principally in the London area up to 1914, when out of 115 listed associates over 70 per cent were women. (154) Following the London branch's major discussion of circular 711 at its first meeting in 1910, a number of other discussions were arranged annually, with attendance figures typically exceeding a hundred. In 1912 one such discussion was opened by Miss Burstall on mathematics education for girls, and full details were published in the *Gazette*. (155) By this time other contributions from women to the now more pedagogically oriented *Gazette* had started to appear, and women were also beginning to play some part in the sometimes lively discussions at the MA's annual meetings. (156) As Miss Punnett remarked during a discussion on arithmetic, 'It seems a pity to leave unanswered the Chairman's invitation – or challenge – to someone to speak on behalf of the girls.' (157)

Miss Punnett herself was quick to make a contribution to a discussion on the algebra report, which had boldly placed the expectations for girls on a par with those for boys:

> Many opinions have been expressed for and against the theory that boys and girls are equal in this matter – it is evident, in fact, that the time is not ripe for a definite and unanimous conclusion on this point. It is very difficult to say to what extent the present comparative inferiority of the mathematics in girls' schools is merely due to an ancient tradition to that effect. The best way of solving the problem would seem to be to put the mathematics for boys and girls, for the present, on the same footing and to be guided by experience in making the necessary modifications in the work of the girls. (158)

Plenty of contrasting views were certainly being expressed around this time and the Board of Education's *Special Reports* included wide-ranging contributions from Misses Story, Burstall and Gwatkin, as well as Mrs Henry Sidgwick of Newnham College, Cambridge. (159) Not all women shared Miss Punnett's optimism and one school of thought, exemplified by Miss Burstall, drew attention to the manner in which mathematics had forced its attentions upon girls' schools through the male-dominated examination system. As part of the general movement to develop the educational opportunities for girls and women, access to existing examinations had gradually been achieved, and the incentive to gain examination success, which was a widely accepted measure of educational advance, was a powerful one. In such circumstances, educational arguments based on mental and moral discipline were again simply articulated for girls, as for boys. For example: 'It was said . . . that women could not reason; they were to be taught how by studying Euclid.' (160) Given that circumstances in girls' schools differed from those in boys' schools, a case was made in the debates for reducing the amount of mathematics and science for girls. Miss Burstall was not a member of the MA and her view was unlikely to have found any favour within the Special Committee, which started its work in 1912. Miss Punnett's optimism provided the driving force: 'those who wished to give mathematics a quite subordinate position . . . should at least wait until the experiment had been fairly tried of teaching it on lines really adjusted to the interests and activities of girls'. (161)

In spite of its associations with utility for men, the Perry movement had stimulated widespread experimentation in both girls' and boys' schools. Miss Story in the *Special Reports* drew attention both to circular 711 and to the publications of the MA which had 'done much to stimulate interest in graphic methods which are now largely used in girls' schools'. (162) Practical work, variously interpreted, in arithmetic, mensuration and geometry had also generally gained favour. The Girls' Schools Special Committee started work in its first year on the preparation of a detailed report on mathematics for girls in the eight-to-sixteen age range, including a preliminary questionnaire survey. It is interesting to note that, in 1912 also, at a time when science teaching in girls' schools was also 'passing through a critical period', science mistresses formed the Association of Science Teachers, which was quite separate from the APSSM. (163)

The Special Committee's work continued into the war years and its final report was published in 1916. (164) It ran to twenty-six pages, making it the largest report produced by a committee of the MA up to that time, and seventeen women were listed as contributors, including two Cambridge dons: Miss A.B. Collier of Newnham College and Miss H.M. Sheldon of Girton College. Not surprisingly, curricular differentiation on the basis of gender was broadly opposed in principle, and the 'need of unity' between the branches was also stressed, following the recommendations of the 'Other Secondary Schools' Special Committee. Two aspects in geometry were distinguished under the headings 'investigational' and 'formal', with the former providing a foundation and then the two proceeding in parallel in the proposed syllabus from around the age of thirteen. The MA's earlier recommendations in algebra and numerical trigonometry were reinforced, and a start on the latter at the age of fourteen was favoured. The report was principally devoted to an elaboration of a teaching scheme on a year-by-year basis, to provide a solid framework for mistresses teaching mathematics, including attention to details of presentation, particularly in arithmetic. An innovatory syllabus for 'arithmetic of citizenship' was also proposed as a suitable alternative for some older girls, and a list of references was provided. This syllabus and a scheme of 'household arithmetic' had been developed by Nunn and Miss Punnett in conjunction with the demonstration schools of the London Day Training College. Overall, the report fittingly exemplified the pedagogical sensitivity and industry of the leading women teachers of school mathematics in this period.

LOCAL AND INTERNATIONAL LINKS

The major involvement of teachers and particularly women as associates of the MA through its large London branch was an early form of in-service provision but the geographical scope of the branches as a whole was very limited up to 1920: London, Southampton and District, North Wales and an Australian branch at Sydney. In 1914, members and associates of both the Southampton and North Wales branches numbered less than twenty in each case; the Sydney branch attracted nearly fifty associates but only one woman. (165) In these circumstances it is perhaps surprising that an Association of Teachers of Mathematics for the South-Eastern Part of England was formed in 1911 and it had no formal links with the MA. (166) It was the brain-child of G.E.St L. Carson (1873–1934), who had been appointed in 1908 as head mathematical master at Tonbridge School, a public school in Kent. This new Association was intended to embrace all types of school in the south-east and it produced its own *Journal* from the outset. The comprehensive ideal for the membership was spelt out by Carson in his first editorial:

> In so far as any type of school or teacher is unrepresented among its members, in so far will it fail in its object of asserting the unity

> of purpose which should animate all those who teach the subject
> . . . England is almost alone in preserving an unnatural separation
> between the professed mathematician and the teacher of Elementary
> Mathematics. (167)

Carson had taken some part in the work of the MA's Teaching Committee
from 1907 but his move from Battersea Polytechnic down to Kent clearly
provided an opportunity to develop a local organization outside the London
area. The Association attracted forty-six members in its first year including
eight from Tonbridge School itself; but women were still in the majority
overall. A.N. Whitehead (1861–1947) gave the first Presidential address,
at Tonbridge School, on the place of elementary mathematics in a liberal
education. Whitehead was a distinguished mathematician and a general
educationist. His addresses and publications in mathematics education were
broadly concentrated on the philosophical aspects, including contributions
as President not only of the South-Eastern Association but also of the
London branch of the MA, in 1913, and of the MA itself, for the two-year
period, 1915–17. (168)

Three numbers of the slim *Journal* were planned for issue annually
but, in the event, only eight issues were published. Carson's personal
contribution of papers for the *Journal* was impressive. His aim was to
achieve a membership of at least a hundred with the *Journal* acting as
a principal means of communication among teachers in the region. In
1913, however, Carson left the area to take up a post in mathematics and
education at the University of Liverpool and he severed his connections
with the Association in the following year. The Association does not appear
to have survived the combined effects of Carson's departure and the onset
of war. But it had made a short-lived and distinctive contribution to the
development of professionalism in English school mathematics teaching.
International activity in this same period provides further evidence of the
development of professionalism in mathematics education as a field of
investigation, communication and publication.

The first International Commission on Mathematical Instruction (ICMI)
was formed in 1908 at the fourth International Congress of Mathematicians
(ICM) in Rome, on the suggestion of the American mathematics educator
D.E. Smith. Both Smith and Godfrey contributed papers at Rome to
the section of the ICM devoted to the history, philosophy and didactics
of mathematics. (169) Initial discussion was stimulated on developments
in mathematics education in a number of countries: Germany, France,
England, America, Austria, Hungary, Italy, Switzerland and Greece. The
ICMI developed the initial interest demonstrated in 1908 by requiring the
various countries to appoint subcommissions and to prepare reports on
the state of mathematics education, for presentation to the fifth ICM at
Cambridge in 1912. Within ten years the ICMI stimulated a very rich and
wide-ranging published output, which provides one measure of the world-
wide concern for mathematics education in this remarkable period. Eighteen countries published 178 reports, amounting to over twelve thousand
pages. Germany's output was by far the most prolific – 5393 pages – with
the American contribution about one fifth of Germany's and the United
Kingdom's about one sixth. (170)

The Board of Education was approached and agreed to appoint an advisory committee to act also as the British subcommission. The British reports were published in 1912 as two impressive volumes in the Board of Education's series of *Special Reports*. (171) Fellows of the Royal Society were well represented on the advisory committee: Sir George Greenhill, Sir Joseph Larmor, Professors Love and Hobson, and G.H. Hardy. Jackson acted as secretary and Godfrey's involvement provided an important schoolteacher perspective. In the build-up to the ICM at Cambridge various meetings and international exchanges took place which revealed that pedagogy was in a more developed state on the continent in comparison with England. Following the widespread influence of the Perry movement, the balance between intuition and rigour was chosen as a first major area for international comparisons, and Godfrey became energetically involved with the British efforts. (172) The first President of the ICMI was Professor Felix Klein, whom Godfrey judged to be 'perhaps the most prominent among the leading mathematicians of our day who have devoted themselves to the improvement of mathematical education'. (173) His early contributions on pedagogy and teacher training are well represented in an international bibliography produced by Smith and Goldziher for the ICMI. This bibliography contains over eighteen hundred items on mathematical education published between 1900 and 1912. The size of the German contribution is impressive and the range of topics covered gives a good indication of the international agenda for mathematics education in this period. In addition to the teaching of the individual branches of mathematics, sections are devoted to descriptive geometry and geometrical drawing, graphs, logarithms and the slide rule, the function concept, the correlation and applications of mathematics, the history of mathematics in teaching and teacher training. (174)

In the planning for the ICM at Cambridge, Hobson requested the co-operation of the MA, which formed a small subcommittee comprising Jackson, Greenstreet and Abbott. The principal task was the preparation of an exhibition of books, models and school work, including contributions from educational publishers and suppliers and the London County Council. The *Gazette* issued to coincide with the period of the Congress included portraits of the principal officers at Cambridge and a photograph of a statue of Sir Isaac Newton as a frontispiece. (175) Reports from the various countries amounting to around nine thousand pages were presented at Cambridge, and Jackson commented on the value of the ICMI's work in the following terms:

> The problem of combining a coherent and logical scheme of mathematical education with due attention to the average boy and to the value of topics arising from familiar daily life in developing interest and an appreciation of accuracy, is a difficult one, but is in process of solution. The labours of the Commission – in particular of the German and American contributors – have forwarded the process of solution in many details. (176)

The twentieth-century emphasis on 'intuition and experiment' formed part of the 'solution' world-wide, and Smith summarized the interpretations and trends in Austria, France, Germany, Switzerland, America and England, drawing on the quantitative data in various papers, including one from Godfrey concerning English conditions. (177) Godfrey's summary will serve as a reminder of some of the principal gains from the Perry movement:

> The use of graphical methods in elementary algebra teaching is universal and entirely a 20th-century development. Other aspects of the same movement are the adoption of descriptive geometry by the mathematicians, and the use of handy 4-figure tables, and of graphical methods in statics, and, though, in these cases, the victory is less complete than that of the 'graph', it is remarkable and equally modern. (178)

The proceedings at Cambridge also included contributions from Nunn on calculus in schools, Carson on mechanics teaching and Whitehead on general aims in elementary mathematics teaching. The two volumes of *Special Reports*, comprising thirty-nine papers and running to over nine hundred pages, provided a wealth of illuminating detail concerning English developments, but a lack of co-ordination and synthesis of the contributions limited the value of the material for purposes of international comparison. To serve the ICMI's purposes, a young German teacher, Georg Wolff, was given the task of providing a general overview of English secondary school mathematics. He came to this country in 1913 and his findings were published two years later as a lengthy report, written in German, and including much historical detail and penetrating analysis of English reform. (179)

The work of the ICMI continued into the war years with some financial support from the MA, which also established a small subcommittee, whose membership included Godfrey, to continue the investigations after the Board of Education had withdrawn its support in 1914. (180) Two foci were chosen for consideration at a meeting in Paris in 1914: calculus in schools and mathematics in higher technical education. The interest in elementary calculus teaching was one aspect of the movement to broaden the scope of school mathematics. Godfrey again undertook the necessary investigations within a framework prepared by the ICMI, and nearly one hundred public schools co-operated in a survey. (181) At the meeting in Paris it was decided to take the work of comparison into the field of teacher training but only two reports were published during the War, from Germany and Belgium, and the sixth ICM at Stockholm was cancelled. All the early momentum had effectively been lost and the ICMI did not resume its work until 1928. But the activity and output over the period 1908–14 is an early feature of the international history of mathematics education.

A prefatory note to the *Special Reports* judged that 'the immediate cause which led to the formation of the International Commission was a divergence between mathematical and pedagogical requirements in the schools and Universities'. (182) The diminution of this divergence was a principal objective in the 'democratization' of mathematics education on an international scale. As we have seen, the MA played a leading role in English developments through the wide-ranging work of its various committees, its published reports, its annual and branch meetings, its growing membership, and the circulation of its organ, the *Mathematical Gazette*. The shift in the balance of the *Gazette*'s content from mathematical exposition to education and pedagogy was marked by 1914. Looking back on Greenstreet's period of editorship, Broadbent judged that the period 1900–14 was 'perhaps the golden age of the *Gazette*' in comparison with the period 1918–30 when its content was 'less bright and vigorous'. (183) The meticulous and very detailed index of the first fifteen volumes of the *Gazette*, 1894–1931, clearly substantiates Broadbent's conclusion. (184)

In addition to the published addresses, articles, reports and syllabuses, and summaries of some of the major discussions at the annual meeting and the London branch, the *Gazette*'s reviews and notices of books were always wide-ranging and informative, and covered both elementary textbooks and more advanced works. The mathematical reviews, articles, notes and answers to queries continued to ensure that the *Gazette* also maintained its reputation as a minor mathematical serial, and Broadbent went so far as to judge that Hardy's contributions were 'its outstanding features' and particularly his book reviews. (185) The list of books reviewed includes a very small number of pioneering contributions to the literature in mathematics education, including Benchara Branford's *A Study of Mathematical Education* (1908) and Carson's *Essays on Mathematical Education* (1913). Such publications are a further small indicator of the gradually growing status of mathematics education as a field of enquiry in England, although the work of the ICMI demonstrates that both Germany and, to a lesser extent, America provided the lead in the early twentieth century. (186)

The growing attention paid to principles and pedagogy in mathematics education in England is bound up with the gradual involvement of universities in the general study of education and teacher training and the growth of professionalism within teaching as a whole. Branford gave extension lectures at what became Leeds University, before he moved to become an inspector of London schools. Nunn was a leading spirit at the London Day Training College and Carson became a reader in mathematics and lecturer in education at Liverpool University before he joined HMI. (187)

In January 1918 the MA's Teaching Committee set up a subcommittee to prepare a general report on the teaching of mathematics in public and secondary schools, with particular reference to the following aspects:

1. The educational value of Mathematics as a school subject.
2. The position of Mathematics in the school curriculum.
3. The co-ordination of Mathematics with other subjects in the school curriculum.
4. Mathematics as a subject for Examinations. (188)

The subcommittee was well chosen to tackle this challenging task and included, among others, Professors Whitehead and Nunn, Miss Punnett, Miss Gwatkin, Godfrey and Mair. (189) Their report was published in 1919 and was very different in character to all its predecessors:

They have been concerned mainly with questions of detail. Discussions of root-principles have been avoided, possibly on account of the

REPORT OF THE MATHEMATICAL ASSOCIATION COMMITTEE ON THE TEACHING OF MATHEMATICS IN PUBLIC AND SECONDARY SCHOOLS.*

SUMMARY OF RECOMMENDATIONS.

1. That a boy's educational course at school should fit him for citizenship in the broadest sense of the word; that, to this end, the moral, literary, scientific (including mathematical), physical and aesthetic sides of his nature must be developed. That in so far as mathematics are concerned, his education should enable him not only to apply his mathematics to practical affairs, but also to have some appreciation of those greater problems of the world, the solution of which depends on mathematics and science.

2. That the utilitarian aspect and application of Mathematics should receive a due share of attention in the earlier stages of the mathematical course.

3. That the mathematical course in the earlier stages should not be concerned exclusively with Arithmetic, Algebra, and Geometry; that such subjects as Trigonometry, Mechanics, and the Calculus, should be begun sooner than is now customary and developed through the greater part of the boy's school career, so as to give him time to assimilate them thoroughly, and enable him to cover more rapidly, at a later stage, the higher parts of Arithmetic, Algebra and Geometry.

4. That no boy should leave school entirely ignorant of Applied Mathematics (e.g. Mathematics relating to the Stability of Structures, Motion of Bodies, Electrical Plant, Astronomy, etc.).

5. That, while the average boy should receive careful and adequate instruction, the boy of high talent should receive special attention, as the value to the race of carefully trained superior talents is incalculable. A well-equipped secondary school should be so staffed as to be able to educate *pro viribus* both the average boy and the boy of genius.

6. That a boy who takes Mathematics as his main study in the later part of his school life should also, in general, study Science, as well as carry on some form of literary study; and that the general educational purpose underlying the choice of these various subjects should be made manifest to the boy.

7. That the time devoted to Mathematics in the Secondary Schools before the period of specialisation should be at least six periods per week (excluding time for preparation at home).

* Throughout this Report the word *boy* is to be taken as referring to pupils of either sex.

8. That the teaching and organisation of Mathematics and Physics should be in the closest possible co-ordination.

9. That every teacher of Mathematics should go through (1) a course of *mathematical training* at the University to be followed by (2) a course of *professional training* in the Theory and Practice of Teaching with special reference to Mathematics, at a Training College, the two courses not to run concurrently.

10. That the mathematical teacher should also receive training of a less intensive kind in some subject in which his Mathematics can be definitely applied, e.g. Geography, Physics, Chemistry, Engineering, Manual Training, Astronomy, etc.

11. That teachers of insufficient ability or knowledge should not be promoted to be Heads of Departments simply on the ground of long and faithful service. Long and faithful service deserves recognition, but in some other way. The Head of a Mathematical Department has to teach the advanced work—which requires knowledge—and to draw up the general school syllabus—which requires outlook.

12. That Heads of Mathematical Departments and Specialist Teachers of the higher branches of Mathematics in the Advanced Departments of the Secondary Schools should have tolerably short routines in order that they may be able to read more widely in their subject and to study its modern development (cf. 15). Only thus can the knowledge imparted to the boys be kept up to date.

13. That an External Examination Syllabus should be frequently revised by a joint body consisting of representatives of the teachers themselves and of the external examining body. Otherwise the syllabus, being stereotyped, tends to become obsolete, and teachers have to teach what they have ceased to value.

14. That it is more important to TEACH boys than to EXAMINE them; that the number of examinations at present conducted in the majority of schools should be reduced, inasmuch as the setting of examination papers consumes the master's time and energy, thereby lowering his teaching capacity, while the continuous pressure of working at examination papers for days on end is an unproductive strain on the boys.

15. That every Secondary School should be provided with a Mathematical Library, containing books of a more general character than the ordinary text-books, in order that the pupils and masters may be enabled to widen their horizon and catch a glimpse of the regions beyond.

16. That portraits of the great mathematicians should be hung in the mathematical class-rooms, and that reference to their lives and investigations should frequently be made by the teacher in his lessons, some explanation being given of the effect of mathematical discoveries on the progress of civilisation.

Plate 4.4   Recommendations on Secondary Mathematics 1919

difficulty in coming to an agreement. The present report is of a more general character. It is hoped that such a report will prove useful not only to the mathematical teacher and examiner but also to the general public, and in particular to the non-mathematical element among those directly or indirectly concerned in the organisation of education. (190)

The report included a list of sixteen recommendations which admirably demonstrate the range of the subcommittee's deliberations. In many ways the report symbolizes a culmination of a period of unprecedented activity in English mathematics education. There was still much work to be done between the wars in the consolidation and dissemination of good practice, but the main lines of advance were now well established, at least in principle, and the period of major upheaval and innovation had passed. The ways in which the MA furthered its contribution to curriculum and professional development during a lengthy period of relative stability, at least as regards mathematics in education, will be the principal subject of the next chapter.

CHAPTER FIVE

CONSOLIDATION AND DISSEMINATION

> The work of our Association and its Teaching Committee over the
> last 35 years has revolutionised the approach to every branch of
> school mathematics . . . Within the Association's reports . . . will
> be found the collected experience and resource of generations of the
> best teachers of school mathematics. (1)
>
> (W.J. Langford, Presidential address, 1958)

> The road from unadulterated Euclid has been long and arduous. It
> must be hoped that, in future, changes will be made steadily, so that
> there will be no more long periods of stagnation in the teaching of the
> subject each followed by a great upheaval. (2)
>
> (Ministry of Education report, 1958)

The historical judgement and plea in the Ministry of Education's report
on the teaching of mathematics in secondary schools are by Arthur
Rollett (1902–68), the then staff inspector for mathematics. (3) He
was an active member of the MA and was elected as only the third
former-HMI President, for the year 1967–8. (4) His sentiments suggest
a clear line of continuity in English school mathematics spanning half a
century, from the early years of the Perry movement in the 1900s, until
the 1950s. There is also some similarity of outlook to be found in another
report on secondary mathematics teaching, produced by a committee of
the Incorporated Association of Assistant Masters in Secondary Schools
(IAAM), whose membership included some MA representation. (5) The
chairman of this committee was Cyril Daltry (1902–81), a teacher educator
from the London Institute of Education and a leading disciple of Nunn. (6)
The report was published in 1957 with an introduction which underlined its
historical context:

> The teaching of mathematics is still in a state of uneasy transition
> from the traditional forms which prevailed up to the beginning of the
> present century. Changes since then have affected aims, methods and
> syllabuses. The final outcome of these changes is still undecided . . .
> (7)

The IAAM report on mathematics teaching was the seventh in a post-war
series covering the principal subjects of the secondary school curriculum:

science, modern languages, history, English, geography, classics and, last but not least, mathematics. The report looked back to the year 1919 as the last time that a general survey of secondary mathematics teaching had been published, on this occasion following the work of the special MA subcommittee of which Nunn and Godfrey were members. This earlier report was reprinted with minor revisions in 1928. The fact that it was not superseded for nearly forty years is indicative not only of the original report's forward-looking character but also of a subsequent state of relative stability in both school mathematics and the educational system. (8)

MATHEMATICS IN SECONDARY EDUCATION

It is important to recognize that, between the wars, 'secondary' education was the preserve of a minority. In this period the proportion of pupils gaining access to grant-aided secondary schools from public elementary schools was only of the order of 10 to 15 per cent. In addition, many pupils in grant-aided secondary schools left at sixteen, often on grounds of economic hardship. In the cases of both public and other secondary schools for boys and girls – co-education was exceptional – the main parameters affecting the whole school curriculum were established by around 1920 and were not to be modified in any fundamental way until after the Second World War. All the professional organizations with a specific concern for the place and shape of specific academic subjects in the secondary curriculum were well established by the First World War: mathematics (1871), modern languages (1892), geography (1893), science (for men 1901 and for women 1912), classics (1903), history (1906) and English (1907). In addition to the work of the MA and ICMI in mathematics, over the period 1915–19 four major committees on education were appointed by the government: to investigate the positions of science, modern languages, classics and English in the educational system. Two major reports – the Thomson Report on science and the Leathes Report on modern languages – were published in 1918, and two further reports – the Crewe Report on classics and the Newbolt Report on English – were published in 1921. (9)

The publication of the MA's first general survey report on mathematics in secondary education (1919) was part of a more general concern for curriculum design and development. This concern included questions of breadth and balance in the curriculum and particularly in relation to the competing claims of scientific and technical subjects on the one hand and literary and humanistic subjects on the other. The prospect of some form of educational reconstruction after the war years prompted the five subject associations representing literary and humanistic subjects to take the unprecedented step of collaboration in the preparation and circulation of a set of general resolutions. (10) The MA was approached and lent its general support to the main thrust:

> The Teaching Committee of the Mathematical Association concurs with the Councils of the Classical, English, Geographical, Historical

and Modern Language Associations in the view that any reorganisation of our educational system should make adequate provision for both humanistic and scientific studies; that premature specialisation should be avoided; and that technical preparation for a particular profession should be conceived in such a spirit that it misses none of the essentials of a liberal education. (11)

In relation to the specific claims of mathematics, a statement was prepared by Godfrey and Nunn, and signed on behalf of the MA by Whitehead as President and Siddons as chairman of the Teaching Committee:

> from a school course of mathematics the pupil should acquire: (1) an elementary knowledge of the properties of number and space; (2) a certain command of the methods by which such knowledge is reached and established, together with facility in applying mathematical knowledge to the problems of the laboratory and the workshop; (3) valuable habits of precise thought and expression; (4) some understanding of the part played by mathematics in industry and the practical arts, as an instrument of discovery in the sciences and as a means of social organisation and progress; (5) some appreciation of organised abstract thought as one of the highest and most fruitful forms of intellectual activity. (12)

In the event, the provisions of the Fisher Education Act of 1918 were focused on questions of educational opportunity, including access to grant-aided secondary education, particularly through the development of a system of free places, and not on the shape and content of the secondary curriculum. However, problems of congestion in the curriculum – referred to as 'the squeeze of subjects' – did prompt the Board of Education to issue a circular in 1922. (13) More importantly for educational advance as a whole, 1922 also brought economic crisis and the consequent Geddes Axe which nullified many of the Fisher Act's provisions and cut teachers' pay. But at least the raising of the minimum elementary school leaving age to fourteen remained secure.

SCHOOL CERTIFICATE EXAMINATIONS

The arrangements for a national system of school certificate examinations in secondary education, which were eventually implemented in 1917, were of enormous consequence for the subsequent state of the curriculum as a whole and in its constituent parts. As one prophetic letter to *The Times Educational Supplement* in 1913 put it:

> The British public slumbers while a bombshell is being manufactured. The Consultative Committee of the Board of Education is hatching a scheme . . . to substitute one examination as the door to all the professions, and this examination is to be open only to those who come from a 'recognized secondary school'. (14)

The Consultative Committee had started work as early as 1902 on the complex question of examinations in relation to secondary education. The fact that it took fifteen years to hammer out some kind of settlement is a reflection of the sensitivity associated with any kind of state involvement in the affairs of the powerful and independent university examining bodies in England. It was not necessary to look at continental developments to find possible models of centralized control. Across the border in Scotland the Education Department was responsible for both examinations and inspection, leading to the award of secondary school certificates. But the detailed investigations of the Consultative Committee clearly exposed a number of administrative difficulties in England: the multiplicity of examinations and the various bodies' independence; the complexity and incompleteness of comparability between examinations; competitive excesses reinforced by advertisement; the impotence of the Board of Education; and the separation of inspection, involving HMI, and examination. The Committee also pointed to: the restricting influence of syllabuses on content, methods and experimentation; the disintegration of classes preparing for different examinations; the teachers' limited role as examiners; and the absence of uniform standards. (15)

Consultations with the universities, teachers' associations and LEAs eventually yielded a mutually acceptable scheme which was laid out in a series of circulars issued between 1914 and 1918. Two examinations were to be provided, one to test a general secondary education around the age of sixteen (the first examination or school certificate) and the other (the second examination or higher school certificate) to test two further years of more specialist work. The school certificate followed the existing lines for the examinations of the university boards at this level. Schools were invited to opt for just one board and candidates were to be assessed in at least five subjects chosen from three compulsory groups: science and mathematics, 'English subjects' and foreign languages. Two levels of pass were specified in each subject: a pass and a pass with credit. The latter corresponded to university matriculation standard in the school certificate and also satisfied the general entrance requirements of the various professional bodies. In addition, science and mathematics formed one of the groups of subjects for the higher school certificate.

In the case of grant-aided secondary schools under the Board of Education, regulations limited the examining of a general secondary education to the school certificate examination, conducted annually. The Board acted as a co-ordinating authority, assisted by a Secondary School Examinations Council (SSEC), which represented the interests of the universities, the LEAs and the teachers. Some provision was also made at this time for the use of schools' own special syllabuses and teachers' estimates of attainment. The seven approved bodies in 1918 were the Cambridge Syndicate, the Oxford Delegacy, the Oxbridge Joint Board, the NUJMB, and the Boards of London, Durham and Bristol Universities. The Central Welsh Board was also added two years later. As Roach has fairly concluded, the scheme was subsequently 'to dominate the secondary schools during the inter-war period'. (16)

The progress of the school certificate examination system between the

115

wars was considered by the Consultative Committee in a major report on secondary education published in 1938 and prepared under the chairmanship of Will Spens. The system had reduced the problem of early specialization and helped to raise the general level of attainment but it had also given rise to some unintended consequences. A cardinal principle laid down in 1918 – that this examination should follow and not determine the curriculum – became reversed in practice. Excessive demands were being made upon pupils and these were exacerbated by the growing status accorded to the certificate by employers and parents. Furthermore, a pass with credit became a prized end in itself, given its link with matriculation and superior status. Here the purposes of certification for a general secondary education and qualification for the universities or the professions were fundamentally in conflict, with a consequent harmful backlash effect on the curriculum. (17)

The Spens Report drew attention to the striking uniformity in the general secondary curriculum, dominated as it was by the seven academic subjects. The traditional pattern in the public and older grammar schools was largely followed by the newer county and municipal secondary schools, after 1902, and was reinforced by the school certificate examinations. In 1926, in decreasing order of popularity as measured by the number of examination entries, the following subjects head the list: English, French, mathematics, history, geography, art, Latin and chemistry. In 1937 the only difference in this order was the interchange of art and Latin. (18) Technical and vocational subjects other than art had essentially become marginalized in secondary schools. In the view of the Spens Committee the examination system had the effect of 'stereotyping and narrowing the curriculum' along conventional academic lines'. (19)

With mathematics and science as one of the three groups of subjects for a school certificate, the place of mathematics in the secondary curriculum remained strong and secure. By 1930 around 95 per cent of candidates were taking mathematics, which was usually compulsory for a matriculation certificate. A report of the SSEC in 1932 noted that 'almost all' the boys and 'a large proportion' of the girls took this subject. (20) Additional mathematics was also taken by around 5 per cent of the candidates. The total number of annual entries for mathematics increased from around fifty to seventy thousand between 1926 and 1937. (21) As regards syllabuses in mathematics, the SSEC reported that these varied 'but slightly', although London was out of step with the other seven approved examining bodies.

Although the principal function of the SSEC was to maintain parity of standard between the boards, it was only an advisory body for the Board of Education; the SSEC might make suggestions to particular boards but it had no power to implement change. The SSEC acted as a forum for discussion and it promoted the dissemination of information and advice through its regular reports and occasional more detailed 'investigations'. Results of such investigations, in 1918, 1924 and 1931, were communicated confidentially to the boards, and this evidence led to a first full report which was published in 1932. But, as one commentator from the Cambridge Syndicate remarked: 'its faith in the outworn practice of publishing official reports and hoping that reforms will follow has not been justified'. (22)

Between the wars it was the MA that took direct action to change London's examination requirements in mathematics.

INTER-WAR SYLLABUS REFORM

At the MA's annual meeting in 1920 a mistress opened a discussion on the teaching of logarithms. She referred to the support for their use from the examining boards of Oxford, Cambridge and the NUJMB but drew attention to London's intransigence. (23) Nunn referred to its policy as 'a serious and mischievous thing' apparently justified on the ground that logarithms should not be introduced because the full theoretical basis of indices was not appropriate in the syllabus. (24) Pressure from the MA was supplemented by the efforts of a group of nine schools which used the special syllabus provision for the school certificate, thus circumventing London's restriction. (25) London's response was recorded in the annual report of the MA's Council for the year 1921. New syllabuses were prepared which incorporated 'many of the suggestions of the Association' including the use of logarithms, no insistence on contracted methods of calculation, and the introduction of some mensuration into the arithmetic syllabus. Some calculus was also included in the alternative, more advanced, syllabus. (26) However, London continued to be out of step with other boards in both geometry and numerical trigonometry.

London's syllabus in geometry was limited to the substance of Euclid Books 1–4, thus omitting similarity (Book 6). Only geometrical proofs were permitted; there was no detail of required theorems provided; and no place for trigonometry. School certificate mathematics was the subject of a major discussion at the London branch of the MA in 1930. One frustrated schoolmaster remarked: 'Which was best from the educational point of view: to force a pupil to learn up 60 theorems which he would soon forget, or to teach him such subjects as trigonometry?' (27) Both the London branch and the Teaching Committee made direct representations to the London board at this time. The SSEC also referred in critical terms to London's syllabus, though the board was not named. Pressure proved effective: in 1931 the London branch was notified that from 1933 some alternative questions in trigonometry would be set in the school certificate examination of the London board. (28)

Carson, who joined HMI and became staff inspector for mathematics between the wars, judged that it was 'the act of the schools themselves' which had prompted examining bodies, with varying degrees of sympathy, to alter their requirements and to accommodate generally desired changes in mathematics teaching, particularly the introduction of logarithms, the provision for numerical trigonometry and, in additional mathematics, the earlier treatment of calculus. (29) It should be added that the MA played a crucial role in this process of examination syllabus renewal over a period of some twenty years, from 1910. What is particularly striking is the length of the time it took to implement general change in response to proposals whose roots go back to the early years of the Perry movement. However, it is important not to exaggerate the extent to which the examination system slowed down the process of curriculum development. As Godfrey fairly remarked: 'English education is dominated by examinations', but he added: 'The most serious opposition to a general movement . . . will come from teachers; examiners generally cede to a fairly universal demand.' (30) The MA was ideally placed to press such demands, particularly through its reports and representations.

In 1932 the Council of the MA took steps to standardize the procedure for making representations to examining or other bodies, such pressure having hitherto sprung from the initiatives of the full Teaching Committee, a subcommittee or special committee, or a branch of the MA. For the future a clear policy was spelt out:

> Any Committee or Branch of the Association desiring to make a representation to an examining or other body or authority shall either state in making the representation that they are speaking for that Committee or Branch only, or, if they wish for the support of the whole Association, shall refer the matter to the General Teaching Committee . . . The representation, if agreed upon, shall be forwarded by the Chairman of the General Teaching Committee to the proper body or authority. (31)

By this time, however, the principal objectives in relation to the requirements of examining bodies had largely been achieved. Combridge first became involved with the work of the MA in 1927 and according to his recollections:

> I cannot remember anything like pressure group activity during the following twenty years . . . we were chiefly concerned with improved ways of teaching recognised portions of the curriculum and with keeping an eye on Boards of Examiners in case any of their questions proved objectionable from a pedagogic point of view . . . aggression was confined to the discussions at the annual conference, the correspondence in the *Gazette* (seldom very lengthy) and the occasional letter of protest from one of the Hon. Secretaries to an offending Board. (32)

The subject of examinations certainly stimulated some lively inter-war discussions, which were reported in the *Gazette*. The topics covered included: the examination arrangements of the Oxbridge Joint Board (1928); the grouping system for the school certificate (1929); syllabuses for mathematics in the school certificate (London branch, 1930); and the variations in additional mathematics syllabuses, particularly in the cases of calculus and co-ordinate geometry (1932). The discussion on the grouping system was opened by Miss Gwatkin, who spoke on the provocative question: 'Should a candidate for the school certificate be allowed to take, in place of the mathematics and science group, a group containing drawing and music and possibly other subjects?' (33) Questions associated with differentiation in the mathematics curriculum on the basis of gender continued to engage the attentions of the Girls' Schools Committee of the MA between the wars.

MATHEMATICS FOR GIRLS

In 1921 the Girls' Schools Committee turned its attention, perhaps surprisingly, to the teaching of mechanics. A general report on this branch had been published in the *Gazette* in 1918 but only one women had contributed. The state of mechanics teaching in girls' schools, however, was attracting general criticism from teachers, university lecturers and examiners. Thus the Girls' Schools Committee chose to investigate the matter and circulated a questionnaire to 418 schools, 172 of which replied. A brief report of the findings together with some suggestions for work both pre- and post-matriculation was published in 1923. (34) Of the schools surveyed, over a quarter taught no mechanics at all though nearly a half taught some experimental mechanics to younger girls as part of physics. Provision for more advanced mechanics was made in 60 per cent of the schools, commonly including some experimental work, but often only one or two girls were involved. The consensus of opinion in the schools was against teaching mechanics to all girls, given the prevailing circumstances: the inexperience of many mathematical mistresses in both physics and experimental work, the inadequacy of the facilities, and the limited supply of adequately trained women teachers of physics. Nevertheless, the Committee argued a case for an introductory course of practical mechanics for all girls, as part of mathematics or science, and provided a suggested syllabus. The possibilities for correlation were raised, and a syllabus for a post-matriculation course, with experiments, was also provided.

In 1923 the Consultative Committee of the Board of Education reported at length on all aspects of differentiation of the curriculum for boys and girls in secondary schools. (35) For nearly twenty years the Board of Education's regulations for secondary schools had made some allowances for the traditional differences in the scope of and provision for mathematics in boys' and girls' schools. From 1909 the Board granted the specific concession that housecraft might be substituted for science or mathematics, apart from arithmetic, for girls over fifteen years of age. (36) HMI Fletcher explained that the Board had adopted a 'waiting observant attitude' concerning differentiation, and, although the general policy was not to differentiate, greater flexibility regarding the scope of mathematics in girls' schools was occasionally granted. (37) The Board's aim and the general trend in practice was to provide at least two years of geometry and algebra for all girls, and often more, up to the minimum for boys: 'Algebra to progressions or the binomial theorem, and the equivalent of Euclid I-IV and VI.' (38) However, the concession concerning housecraft continued to be offered to some schools, and, in certain circumstances, girls were allowed to drop mathematics or science. But the Consultative Committee found that 'such applications are not so frequently made at the present time as they were in former years'. (39) The grouping system and the syllabuses of the school certificate examinations from 1918 did not differentiate on the basis of gender, although the Consultative Committee's report in 1923 still suggested that 'there might well be some differentiation between boys and girls both in subject-matter and methods of teaching'. This view, it was claimed, was 'widely held by competent authorities'. (40)

Certainly the evidence pointed to girls' inferior mathematical attainments as measured by examination results and corroborated by the findings of teachers and HMI. Furthermore, advanced courses in mathematics and science were being provided in many more boys' than girls' schools: out of 230 such courses recognized by the Board in 1921–2 only 41 were in girls' schools. The Consultative Committee drew attention to a number of persistent causal factors affecting girls' performance in mathematics: inferior provision and teaching in both elementary and secondary schools; parental attitudes; girls' lower motivation for the subject; and the fewer opportunities for exploiting utility and correlation with physics in particular. (41) The conclusion was a pessimistic one:

> These differences – aptitude, teaching and interest – are cumulative. As far as girls are concerned, though they may be partly due to girls' greater susceptibility to mental fatigue, it is doubtful whether this amounts to a difference in educable capacity of the sexes. But some differentiation in this subject seems called for. It should take the form of allowing girls to drop the subject at an earlier stage; and perhaps, also, of teaching them the subject with greater reference to practical applications. (42)

Predictably, the tenor of the Consultative Committee's report drew the attention of the Girls' Schools Committee of the MA.

The Girls' Schools Committee undertook its own fact-finding and analysis leading to the preparation of a memorandum which was published in *The Times Educational Supplement* as well as the *Gazette*. (43) Girls' lower attainments could not be denied but the use of the term 'inferiority' was deprecated, given the evidence of inequality of opportunity. For example, the Committee found that generally girls took roughly one period a week less mathematics than boys. Furthermore:

> Where boys and girls are given equal opportunities, as in some mixed schools, the consensus of opinion is that very little difference in capacity between boys and girls is shewn in work up to Matriculation standard, but that boys have much more natural interest in Mathematics than girls. (44)

Problems concerning both teacher supply and qualifications persisted. In a representative sample of girls' schools only one third of the mathematics teachers had an honours degree in the subject and only a half had any kind of professional qualification, these being chiefly the less qualified mathematically. The Committee concluded:

> the present standard of attainment in girls' mathematical work can be improved without making demand for more time than is now given. The first need is to increase the supply of well-qualified teachers of the subject. Girls who show mathematical ability should be encouraged to do post-matriculation work, which should include both Pure and Applied Mathematics and Physics . . . The second need is to use the time already allotted to better advantage. (45)

In relation to the 'second need', the timetabling of separate branches of mathematics, possibly involving different teachers, was discouraged, and the use of double periods was encouraged; also, an early start on mathematics beyond arithmetic in the secondary school was recommended to improve girls' motivation and to reduce later pressures. The MA's Committee took a generally more optimistic line than the Consultative Committee:

> While it is probable that girls will in general not achieve as much in Mathematics as boys, it should be possible both to remove the strain experienced by far too many girls in efforts to reach the 'credit' standard of the School Certificate examination, and to disprove the well-worn but unsound statement that 'Girls can't do Mathematics.' (46)

Concerns over the strain on girls caused by the school certificate examinations, particularly the effects of the credit system, were also accompanied by persistent efforts to modify the system of subject groups to obtain a closer match with the whole curriculum for girls, including its traditional provision for aesthetic and practical studies: art, music, handicrafts and domestic subjects. This fourth group of subjects was optional for the school certificate in the 1920s, and the discussion opened by Miss Gwatkin at the annual meeting of the MA in 1929 was focused on the possibility that girls might substitute this group for the mathematics and science group. (47) No such fundamental change resulted in the short term, but in 1938 the group system for the school certificate was virtually abolished. A pass in the mathematics and science group or the languages group was now required along with a pass in at least one other group from the four now offered to candidates. (48) By this time the place of mathematics as a school certificate subject for boys was very firmly established, but for girls, as the Norwood Committee noted in 1943, the position was much more variable:

> With girls the situation is different; in girls' schools the place assigned to Mathematics varies far more than in boys' schools according to the attitude of the Head Mistress and the strength of the mathematical staff. Thus in some schools very few girls drop the subject; in others a third or even more omit it from the School Certificate Examination. (49)

In summary, the nineteenth-century pattern of inequality of access to mathematics between boys and girls continued into the post-war period.

In 1929 the Girls' Schools Committee produced a follow-up report to the one published in 1916. The earlier report had provided a clear sense of direction and detailed advice on the preparation of schemes for elementary mathematics in girls' schools, and the new report leant heavily on its predecessor. (50) A recommended reading list of books, reports and articles was appended, but the report as a whole was consolidatory regarding aims, content and methods. The other work of the Girls' Schools Committee between the wars was much concerned with the area of assessment and examinations, and spanned a wide range of age and attainment in girls' education. At one extreme, there are frequent references in the minute to the requirements of university entrance scholarship examinations a Cambridge (Newnham and Girton Colleges) and London (principall Royal Holloway and Westfield Colleges), as well as occasional reference to the higher school certificate. At the other extreme, interest was alse shown in the LEAs' entrance and scholarship tests for secondary schools including the work of psychologists on intelligence testing. Efforts were also made to extend the assessment of mathematical ability and attainmen upwards to cover the first four years of secondary schooling. (51) But the remarks of Miss Punnett at an MA Council meeting in 1936 suggest that in contrast with the committee work of the men, the women's contribution between the wars lacked a general sense of mission:

> she felt that the position of the Girls' Schools Committee was unsatisfactory. It had no direct share in preparing many of the reports which applied quite as much to Girls' Schools as to Boys' and was even often at a loss to find useful work without overlapping with that of the Boys' Schools Committee. (52)

In the period from 1923 to 1938 it was the men involved in the Boys Schools and General Teaching Committees who were largely responsible for implementing a major programme of report production covering the various branches of school mathematics.

INTER-WAR COMMITTEES

In 1920 the scheme for the election of three Special Committees and the General Teaching Committee was revived. The membership of committee had been frozen for six years, but Pendlebury reported to the Council tha the interest shown in the new elections had been 'very disappointing'. (53 This prompted a review of the constitution and a simplified scheme wa eventually approved at the annual meeting in January 1923. The interest of public schools and 'other secondary' schools were now merged in a single Boys' Schools Committee. The Teaching Committee now comprised si members elected by the Council together with equal representation – si elected members each – for the Boys' and Girls' Schools Committees; the President and two honorary secretaries acted *ex officio*. (54) The new committees served until 1923 when the period of office was extended from three to four years. The simplified scheme for the election of the MA' committees remained in force until 1937, when a new set of regulations wa introduced. (55) The inter-war period of major report production coincided with a period of constitutional stability for the MA.

The work of the Boys' Schools Committee in the 1920s was concentrated principally on the concerns of public and preparatory schools, and the representation of 'other secondary school' interests was only marginal. The committee of twelve members in 1926 included eight public schoolmasters from Charterhouse (two), Winchester (two), Marlborough, Rugby, Christ' Hospital and Dulwich. Two members came from non-public secondar schools, one from the LCC inspectorate and one from Woolwich Royal Military Academy. (56)

Despite the Teaching Committee's early work on preparatory school mathematics, the problem of public schools' differing scholarship requirements again loomed large in the 1920s. The Public Schools Special Committee had reported on this matter in 1922 and drawn attention to the fact that the motive of competition had encouraged some public schools to go significantly beyond the scope of the nine-to-sixteen syllabus for non-specialists, which had been reissued by the HMC and the Association of Preparatory Schools in 1916. (57) The MA lent its support to the principle that this syllabus should be generally accepted as a reasonable maximum, but some schools remained unmoved. Headmasters again pressed the MA to take action, and the Boys' Schools Committee reported on the situation in 1926. (58)

The earlier general principle was reaffirmed, and the syllabus was reprinted to provide a basis for 'a more certain test of mathematical ability than a wide schedule of book-work' in order to 'defeat the crammer'. (59) Thirty public schools had lent their direct support to this principle, and the Committee expressed the hope that, in the interests of both preparatory and public school mathematics, the syllabus would become a universal standard for the purposes of both teaching and examining. In connection with teaching methods, the Committee also referred to the close match between the syllabus and the substance of a general report on preparatory school mathematics published in 1924. (60)

On the admission of the Boys' Schools Committee, the MA's report of 1924 was 'evolutionary rather than revolutionary':

> Its main purpose is to bring to notice again the conclusions of the 1907 Report, with such amendments as later experience has shown to be necessary; also, in Geometry, to embody some of the suggestions made in the important Circular 711 issued by the Board of Education in 1909, and such parts of the recent Mathematical Association Report as closely affect the teaching at the preparatory school stage.
>
> Owing to the war there have been great changes in teaching personnel, and it is thought desirable to call the attention of those now teaching in preparatory schools to these conclusions. (61)

The report acknowledged that circular 711 was 'the first authoritative pronouncement' on stages in the teaching of geometry. (62) A more detailed circular – 851 – was issued in 1914. It followed broadly similar lines to circular 711 and was again written by HMI Fletcher. (63) However, the history of geometry teaching in England was also affected in a major way by the MA's first authoritative pronouncement on this branch since 1902: a 74-page report which was first published in 1923. (64)

GEOMETRY IN SCHOOLS

From around 1920 there was renewed interest in the question of a sequence for deductive geometry. In 1921 the IAAM received representations from schoolmasters claiming that much time was being wasted in the early stages of geometry teaching and that there was a need for uniformity in examination requirements. A survey of all boys' schools in England and Wales indicated that 90 per cent of masters favoured a new uniform sequence of theorems, to guide ordinary teachers after twenty years of freedom. However, the figures for girls' schools indicated that under a half of the mistresses desired such a return to uniformity. A committee of the IAAM, which included Durell and Fletcher, produced a memorandum on geometry teaching. It was published in 1923 as the first of a series of memoranda to be produced over the next ten years on various secondary school subjects. (65) The memorandum included only a suggested schedule of numbered theorems since the committee felt that it was neither desirable nor possible to stereotype a sequence at this time. The committee judged that there was 'still room for considerable diversity' in deductive geometry. (66) On the question of lightening the deductive burden, and increasing the elements of intuition, the committee classified a number of formal proofs as not suitable for examination purposes and others as not even appropriate for the classroom. Here the line of continuity with the Board's circulars and the influence of Fletcher are both clearly evident. Examining bodies were also gradually responding to the movement away from the foundations in school geometry by not requiring proofs of certain propositions, particularly the fundamental propositions in Euclid Book 1. (67) In 1922 the sequence question also attracted the attention of the MA.

At a meeting of the General Teaching Committee in April of 1922, with Godfrey in the chair and twelve members in attendance, the sequence question was discussed at length and 'nearly every member' contributed. The following motion was carried unanimously: 'it is most undesirable that examining bodies should reduce the freedom of the teacher by imposing an obligatory sequence of propositions in Geometry'. (68) A copy of this resolution was sent to the secretary of the IAAM's committee, and, what is more, it was decided not to entertain any invitation to co-operate in a conference on this matter. In the event, the MA and IAAM were not at odds on the sequence issue. But the MA's report on geometry teaching was on much more wide-ranging and ambitious lines than that of the IAAM.

The MA subcommittee on geometry was appointed in 1922 and pursued its task for eighteen months under the chairmanship of Professor Neville of University College, Reading, with Miss Punnett acting as secretary. Godfrey and Tuckey joined the subcommittee at the outset, and Nunn, who had taught Neville at William Ellis School, was also subsequently drawn in. Around this time both Godfrey and Nunn contributed papers on geometry teaching to the *Gazette*. (69) Neville was a high-flying mathematician who had distinguished himself at Cambridge before moving to Reading in 1919. He made early scholarly contributions to the fields of analytical and differential geometry. (70) On the face of it the subcommittee was well qualified to pronounce on both the mathematical and the pedagogical aspects of geometry for schools.

A reviewer in *Nature* welcomed the MA's report on geometry 'for its freshness and the authoritative character of the source from which it comes'. The main thrust of the report's recommendations was plainly summarized:

> by the time a boy is through his Fifth Form, or School Certificate work, he should not merely know the more interesting theorems of Euclid I.-IV. and VI., but should also have systematised or organised his knowledge at least back to the fundamental propositions, i.e. Euclid I. 4,8,26,27–29. Special emphasis is laid on this systematising; and this is unquestionably the point which needs the attention of teachers at the present time . . . (71)

The report itself underlined in no uncertain terms the importance of Euclidean-style rigour as the culmination of geometry in a general secondary education:

> we believe that the average boy should be submitted to Euclidean rigour at the right time and not before. In most cases the right time is at the age of 15 or thereabouts . . . The Euclidean discipline was ineffective in the old days because it was given too soon; perhaps the danger at the present day is that it may not be given at all. (72)

However, the general tenor of the MA's report was to some extent out of step with the developmental pedagogy embodied in the Board of Education's circulars. The MA committee's position was simply summarized: 'The Board of Education, in a Circular issued in 1909, recognised three stages in elementary geometry. The Committee would amalgamate the first two of these, but would subdivide the third.' (73) The implications of this split were worked out in great detail in the body of the report.

The decision to combine the Board's first two stages in a newly designated experimental stage A was uncontroversial. Following this, the deductive stage B was broadly in the spirit of the Board's final stage, the principal aim being to give pupils a wide-ranging experience of deducing geometrical knowledge, in the form of theorems and riders, with a broad basis of assumption and still some recourse to intuitive and inductive methods. But the report went on to advocate a more rigorous, systematizing stage C:

> A course ending with Stage B might be stimulating, but would certainly be ragged and unfinished. With dull boys probably nothing more can be accomplished . . . On the other hand, able boys will feel the need of rounding off and consolidating their study. This is the purpose of Stage C. (74)

It was envisaged that stage B would last from about twelve and a half to fifteen years of age and stage C from fifteen to sixteen or seventeen years of age. Thus the intention was to introduce stage C work before the school certificate examination. The committee recognized some fundamental difficulties in relation to the implementation of these proposals:

> There is little experience to guide one in making recommendations as to this stage. Teachers who have adopted new methods in teaching geometry have often omitted it altogether; on the other wing there

are those for whom school geometry comprises nothing but this stage [C], with an imperfectly blended addition of drawing and measurement. (75)

Given the importance attached to work at stage C, the committee had little alternative but to work out the mathematical possibilities in some considerable detail, and to deal, in particular, with a number of 'disputed points' concerning such aspects as: congruence and superposition, use of motion and symmetry, the treatments of parallelism and similarity, use of limits, and the problem of incommensurables. Such mathematical concerns did to some extent undermine the pedagogical and pragmatic strength of the report as a whole. Durell, writing in the *Gazette* in 1925, was unequivocal on this point:

There is little doubt that many teachers are seriously bewildered by this Report. It is not an easy document to read and frequently it is difficult to ascertain the precise nature and application of its recommendations. (76)

He added that the speculative nature of the geometry report was uncharacteristic of MA reports: 'they have not hitherto been used to provoke discussion, but to urge particular methods which have been tested by experience'. He concluded: 'There is a real danger that geometrical teaching may be injured by a misunderstanding and mis-application of the views expressed.' (77) Furthermore, Durell's was not an isolated voice.

A second edition of the report was published in 1925. The changes to the text were very minor ones but a significant note was added to the introduction:

Occasion may be taken to emphasise the distinction, which a certain amount of the criticism to which the Report has been subjected appears to ignore, between what a teacher should know and what he should teach. A great deal of school geometry is a compromise, and the teacher's problem is to present the subject as a coherent whole. He will succeed best if he knows something of the extremes of logic and empiricism which his course is laid to avoid, but the arguments which are relevant to a discussion of the contrasted merits of different courses form no part of the instruction which he has to impart. (78)

Neville himself was convinced about the fundamental importance of recent developments in the foundations of geometry for a complete view of the scope and limits of school geometry:

I will suggest that it has only lately become possible for any mathematician to see truly the difference between proving that the angles at the base of an isosceles triangle are equal, and proving that the angle in a semicircle is a right-angle; the explicit recognition of the distinction between deduction and organisation is a recent achievement, and we need feel no surprise that it must exercise over school teaching a profound influence. (79)

Tuckey, a member of the geometry subcommittee, acknowledged that Neville and Nunn were principally responsible for the final report, for which Neville also acted as editor. (80) In an obituary tribute to Neville, Broadbent commented: 'It requires no great skill in textual criticism to recognise Neville's influence and, in many places, his own subtle but precise turns of phrase.' (81) In Broadbent's view the report was 'revolutionary', particularly in relation to the systematizing stage C. Here Nunn had a particular hand in developing the proposal that the parallel postulate might be replaced by a principle of similarity. (82) A reviewer in *Nature* judged that the adoption of such a principle would mean 'a revolution in existing practice' and, predictably, no such revolution in fact took place. (83) As Broadbent has pointed out, the other members of the subcommittee, including Godfrey, were not 'weaklings', but the dominance of Neville and Nunn – former pupil and teacher – in the shaping of the report is perhaps surprising. (84) Durell went so far as to remark:

> The dimensions of the Report make it possible to doubt (a) whether the Report represents the *considered judgement* of all members of the sub-committee and (b) whether the approval given by the Teaching Committee was much more than a mere matter of form . . . (85)

Certainly the minutes of the Teaching Committee make only passing reference to the progress of work on the geometry report and there appears to have been little general discussion of its substance. (86) What is surprising is that both Godfrey and Nunn had expressed serious reservations about the suitability of stage C work before the school certificate examination.

Godfrey had proposed a model in four stages with the third and fourth stages corresponding broadly to stages B and C of the MA's report. (87) Nunn pointed to 'very close congruence' between his own developmental thinking and Godfrey's: 'Stage 4 should be postponed until after the age of 16 . . . and . . . it should be made more rigorous and philosophical than would be suitable for the non-specialist'. (88) However, Nunn appears to have thrown his energies principally into working with Neville on the difficulties at the final stage of deductive geometry, and Godfrey's reservations concerning the treatment of deductive geometry for the 'non-specialist' were neglected in the final report. The fact that examining bodies were still lagging behind by requiring stage C proofs of some theorems may have inhibited a more progressive line from the subcommittee. But Howson's conclusion concerning the history of this report is a fitting one:

> By nature it was a milestone, marking the conclusion of one set of reforms and initiating a period of consolidation. Unfortunately, because it was allowed to stand unchallenged, it became, through its many reprintings and several editions, a millstone, a restraining influence on the development of geometry. (89)

The geometry report ran to a third edition in 1929 and a fourth edition appeared in 1944, with only a footnote added since the second edition of 1925. By comparison with the other reports of the MA it became a 'best-seller' and the report's three-stage model provided an unambiguous and generally accepted basis at least for communication amongst teachers, examiners and textbook writers, from the 1920s until the 1950s. However, the implemented curriculum in schools over this same period was a different matter, and the IAAM's report of 1957 drew attention to an important historical trend: 'the drift from Euclid'. (90) Here the pure mathematical idealism of Neville was at odds with the pedagogical realism of HMI, led by Fletcher, and major textbook writers such as Durell. Both HMI and successful school textbook writers were attuned to the needs and capabilities of both teachers and pupils in the growing system of grant-aided secondary schools. As early as 1918, HMI Strachan was prompted to remark: 'Probably we shall never be happy until we get right away from the Euclidean tradition.' (91) Some ten years later, Carson, now an HMI, detected the start of a tendency to go beyond Euclid 1–4 and 6, to study curves other than the circle, solid geometry and also some descriptive (projective) geometry. He guessed that 'teachers may be deciding unconsciously that further study of the axioms, is, for the present, the flogging of a dead horse'. (92)

As the importance for schools of the systematizing stage in school geometry gradually declined so also the significance of the sequence question for geometrical theorems faded. Here the detailed proposals in the 1923 report of the IAAM did have a strong influence on some major writers of school geometry textbooks, including Durell. (93) But by 1951 Tuckey could dismiss the sequence question as 'out of date' and he drew attention to a continuous movement:

> away from the formal setting-out of a series of propositions in logical sequence as in Euclid's *Elements* and towards the somewhat haphazard discussion of various geometrical properties arrived at by methods which permit the use of algebra, trigonometry and perhaps accurate drawing . . . at the start of the century a pupil was expected to learn proofs of 100 theorems; about 1925 teachers were content to exact proofs of about 50 theorems, while in 1951 they consider themselves fortunate if their pupils master a dozen. (94)

Furthermore, as the importance of theorem memorization ('bookwork') for examination purposes gradually declined, so the importance of deductive problems ('riders'), constructions and calculations involving the use and application of geometrical knowledge increased. The question of the proper balance between riders and theorems was one concern among many for a subcommittee of the Boys' Schools Committee of the MA, which reported on geometry teaching in 1938.

Tuckey referred to the MA's 1938 report on geometry as 'a much more detailed and some would say a much more humdrum document'. (95) By contrast with the 1923 report, the preparation of the follow-up report took five years and involved around a dozen writers working under the chairmanship of Tuckey. The final report ran to 135 pages plus a 55-page appendix covering fourteen specific topics. (96) The style of this report and the manner of its production followed the by-this-time well-established pattern for the Boys' Schools Committee, which had already reported in detail on arithmetic (1932) and algebra (1934). The publication of the 1938 geometry report completed the Boys' Schools Committee's comprehensive overview of the three elementary branches of school mathematics.

The second geometry report was deliberately evolutionary as opposed to revolutionary in character and it provided a wealth of detailed suggestions for practical and deductive work in both plane and solid geometry at stages A and B. The work at stage C was now subdivided into two stages – the organization of derived propositions and the organization of primitive propositions – and it was discussed in two chapters running to under a fifth of the first 135 pages. By this time it was clearly recognized that work at the foundations of geometry involving the organization of primitive propositions was inappropriate for the vast majority of secondary school pupils. As Fletcher, an influential member of the subcommittee, pointed out: 'It was all very well to talk of revolution as long as one was not responsible. Those responsible for drawing up a report had to have some remembrance of the existing state of things and what was practical.' (97) As a former staff inspector for mathematics, Fletcher strongly emphasized the need to recognize and cater for the limitations of the general teaching force in secondary mathematics. He went on:

In so far as the First Report attempted to be revolutionary, it was a failure. The First Report was extremely interesting but the most interesting part was useless for its purpose. That was one of the root difficulties which had to be dealt with in writing the Second Report. It was not possible to be revolutionary. (98)

The minutes of the Boys' Schools Committee clearly demonstrate that the second report was very much a team effort extending over a lengthy period and involving the accumulation and refinement of scripts from Fletcher, Tuckey (Charterhouse) and a number of other leading public schoolmasters, including Hope-Jones (Eton), Daltry (The Roan School), Snell (Harrow), Robson (Marlborough) and Parsons (Merchant Taylors'). Exceptionally, one master – Riley – was from a central school. (99) A large measure of consensus concerning overall strategy existed within the subcommittee with one major exception: the question of the relative importance of bookwork and riders in a school course.

A minority, led by Fletcher, argued in the final section of the appendix that the report 'goes too far in its insistence on learning proofs of standard theorems and on a particular style of writing out these proofs'. (100) In this context, examination requirements were an important consideration for the majority of the subcommittee, who supported the *status quo*. But the minority's emphasis on problem solving, including the use of algebraic and trigonometric methods, proved to be prophetic, as Tuckey subsequently acknowledged:

the ideas set out in Appendix 14 on the 'Relative Importance of Propositions and Riders' proved the most influential in the whole Report, and led directly to the geometrical part of the modern 'alternative syllabus' crystallised later in the *Jeffery Report.* (101)

When the MA discussed the second geometry report at its annual meeting in 1939 there was certainly some overt support for the minority view. One mistress 'rejoiced to see the old tradition of the outstanding importance of propositions challenged' (102), and another member regretted 'the failure to make any reference to the correlation between trigonometry and geometry'. (103) Yet another complained: 'Most schools spent the last year out of the four- or five-year course almost entirely in learning up theorems. That was really a gross waste of time.' (104) One member went so far as to opine:

> It would be a great pity if school mathematics in course of time got into a deep ditch, made all the more deep by the most efficient work of committees drawing up fine reports for the guidance of those who were already in a very deep rut. (105)

Such responses partly reflected a developing concern in the 1930s about the shape of mathematics for the multitude, which, in particular, raised fundamental questions about the place of formal deductive geometry in a general secondary education. The majority view embodied in the second geometry report was underlined in Snell's contribution to the discussion:

> He personally felt that deductive geometry had an important part to play in the liberal education of any pupil who would take a secondary education. Two thousand years ago the Greeks discovered the art of deductive geometry. It would be rash hastily to agree with those who thought that education was purely practical and would, for that reason, discard it. He advocated that there should be careful thought as to the value of the deductive element in geometry as an essential part in a liberal education. (106)

The debate continued to occupy a central place in the build-up to the Jeffery Report of 1944, which itself had a profound influence on the development of secondary school mathematics in the post-war era, as we shall see. But the major reports of the MA between the wars were concentrated on the separate branches of school mathematics and did little to foreshadow post-war developments in the mathematics curriculum as a whole.

REPORTS ON SCHOOL MATHEMATICS

Following the publication of the first geometry report in 1923, a small subcommittee was appointed in 1927 to consider the teaching of mechanics, and its report was published three years later. (107) The subcommittee was chaired by Tuckey, and Robson acted as secretary; Fletcher and Dobbs, two early innovators in mechanics teaching, were also members. However, there was little to be said which had not already been said either in the mechanics report of 1918, which was inspired by Nunn, or the report from the Girls' Schools Committee in 1923. Fletcher openly admitted some lack of motivation for the task:

> it was one thing when full of a subject and anxious to write about it to produce something; it was quite another when, not particularly interested, one was commanded by superior authority to produce something. (108)

The subcommittee regarded its task as 'a much humbler one': 'The best they could do was to try and say what few commonplace things they could which they thought would be of use to ordinary teachers.'(109)

Before the second geometry report was published, the Boys' Schools Committee had already worked at length and in great detail on both arithmetic and algebra, and major reports were published in 1932 and 1934. The arithmetic report was organized on a topic basis and roughly in a developmental sequence, beginning with the four rules and ending, perhaps surprisingly, with a short section on statistics. Here it was admitted:

> It is one of the outstanding defects of our mathematical education that in the great majority of courses it fails to include even the most elementary knowledge as to the handling and interpretation of statistics. (110)

Hope-Jones, a member of the arithmetic subcommittee, had made a very early and isolated plea in the *Gazette* of 1924 for some teaching of probability in schools, and, in 1933, a discussion on the study of statistics in a school course was reported in the *Gazette*. (111) But statistics was not a feature of the alternative Jeffery syllabus of 1944, and the 'defect' of its general neglect in school mathematics persisted until the 1950s. The arithmetic report of 1932 included sections on mensuration and graphs as well as some more tentative proposals for optional work on 'arithmetic of citizenship' and business arithmetic and accounts. The bulk of the report was, however, devoted to the detailed exposition of well-tried practices covering, by this time, a well-established range of content.

The algebra report of 1934 also covered a well-established range of topics, treated in alphabetical order after a brief introduction. (112) The range comprised: beginning algebra, dimensions and degree, equations, factors, fractions, graphs, logarithms, mechanical operations, negative numbers, oral work, problems, simple series, symmetry, transformation of formulae and variation. The general philosophy for algebra in a general education largely followed the inspiration of Godfrey and Nunn which had helped to shape the important earlier report of 1911 on elementary algebra and numerical trigonometry. By the 1930s, however, the case for including some trigonometry in a general secondary education no longer needed to be pressed. Starting with the topic of similarity, it had become gradually accepted as a valuable extension of work in arithmetic or geometry. It was no longer necessary to argue a case for some trigonometry to provide an outlet for work in algebra, and trigonometry does not feature in the algebra report of 1934. The SSEC reported in 1932 that it was 'now the common practice in schools to teach . . . the use of numerical trigonometry in pre-certificate Forms' and this practice was encouraged by the provision of alternative questions on trigonometry in the school certificate examinations. (113)

In some ways trigonometry may be regarded as a catalyst in the very slow twentieth-century movement towards the breaking down of the traditional barriers separating the various branches of school mathematics: the unification or fusion of mathematical content. The MA's report of 1934 argued:

> There is not, or ought not to be, any such isolated subject as elementary algebra in the curriculum. There is a subject, elementary mathematics, and it is inevitable that algebra should be part of it. This fusion of elementary mathematics is one of the fundamental changes that has taken place in mathematical teaching during the present century. (114)

Between the wars, however, the treatment of school mathematics in separate branches was pervasive: examination requirements, textbook production, school timetables and teachers' perceptions all acted against the tendency towards fusion. Inevitably in this period, the MA's policy and means of production for its major reports did not serve to break the mould. On the contrary, its reports – on arithmetic, algebra, geometry and mechanics – did much to distil and disseminate good practice. These reports, the *Gazette* and the branches provided forms of in-service training at a time when the general provision was meagre. The MA's reports were regarded as authoritative and rightly so given the meticulous care put into their production by leading teachers of mathematics, combined with the close scrutiny of university mathematicians when drafts were considered by the full Teaching Committee. As J.B. Morgan, President of the MA for the year 1963–4, has fairly concluded: 'The 1930s were a vintage period for the Association . . . These Reports were best-sellers, and became fine recruiting agents.' (115)

The Teaching Committee responded to the significant gap in its coverage of elementary mathematics by appointing a subcommittee in 1938 to report on the teaching of trigonometry. War interrupted the progress of this work, which was not resumed until 1945. Eventually, in 1950, a full report on trigonometry was published as the first of a new series of reports concerned specifically with work beyond the school certificate stage. (116) Trigonometry in both the school certificate and more advanced work was covered in this one report, but the policy of publishing separate reports on the branches of school certificate mathematics was beginning to show some signs of strain. The report referred to trigonometry as 'a unifying factor' and added:

> The presentation by the Mathematical Association at this juncture of a separate report on the teaching of trigonometry does not imply that it should be treated in isolation from other branches of mathematics. On the contrary, the report . . . regards trigonometry as an important agent in the fusion of arithmetic, algebra, geometry and even mechanics into a single subject. (117)

One critic in the *Gazette* of 1954 commented on the MA's policy for report production in relation to unification:

> The practice of the Mathematical Association has not been very consistent in this respect: it misses no opportunity to give a verbal blessing to unifying the presentation of mathematics, but it continues apparently content with preparation of reports on the separate subjects – convenience is scarcely a sufficient explanation. (118)

Progress towards unification was bound up with the development and gradual adoption of alternative syllabuses based on the Jeffery Report of 1944. But, up to 1950, the MA's trigonometry report could still claim:

> The trend of development in the teaching of mathematics is towards unification of its separate branches, but this development is still in its early stages, and for the present it is not out of place to speak of 'bringing trigonometrical ideas into geometry'. (119)

Such a statement clearly suggests the continuing pre-eminence of geometry as a branch of elementary mathematics for public and grammar schools in the immediate post-war period. Between the wars, the MA's major reports on the branches of school mathematics all catered largely for the needs of public and grammar schools. During this period of consolidation the MA also expanded its professional support through a growing membership, the annual meeting, the development of branches, the circulation of its reports and the *Gazette*, and the growth of the library.

MEMBERSHIP, BRANCHES AND MEETINGS

In January 1918 the total membership of the MA was quoted as 653, a figure that including 8 honorary members. By January 1940 this figure had increased to 1784; it included 9 honorary members and also 84 junior members. (120) In his Presidential year, 1934–5, Professor Neville had appealed for a larger and broader membership base, and junior membership, which was introduced in 1936, was one valuable extension of the MA's range of influence. (121) New advertising was targeted on lecturers and tutors in universities and colleges, and, in addition, the possibility of affiliation of student mathematical societies was also raised. The Cambridge University Archimedeans Mathematical Society provided a test case and this society was provisionally approved as a junior branch in 1938, with a membership of 220. (122) New rules for junior branches were approved, and, in 1939, the Oxford University Invariant Society and King's College Mathematical Society were also recognized as junior branches. (123)

The growth of the MA's membership between the wars is shown in Figure 5.1. There was a steady increase and then an improved rate of growth from the mid-1930s, which was abruptly arrested by the outbreak of the Second World War. In addition to Neville's membership appeal and the introduction of junior membership, the dissemination of the MA's reports

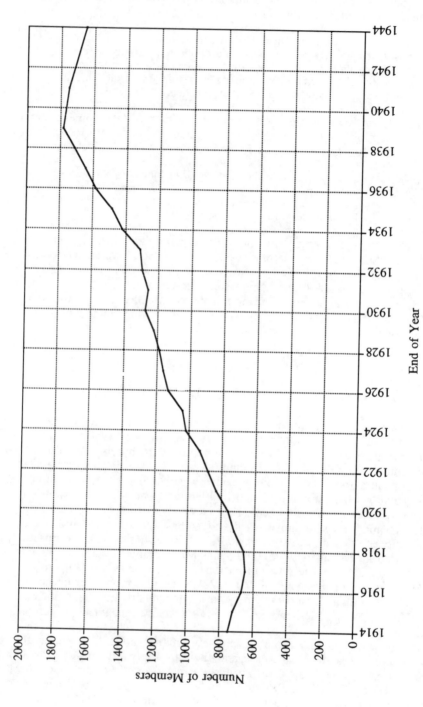

Figure 5.1 Graph of the Membership 1914-44

helped in recruitment, particularly in the 1930s, and the growing number of branches also brought the possibility of full membership of the MA to the attention of a growing number of 'associates'. In January 1918 the number of associates, principally from the London and Sydney branches, was about 170. The Southampton and District branch had lapsed in 1914 and was not restarted until 1931, and the North Wales branch was the only other branch formed before 1920. (124) By 1936 the number of branches had increased to eleven in England and Wales, one in Northern Ireland (1935), three in Australia and one in New Zealand (Auckland, 1935). By this time there were around 650 associates plus 473 MA members also associated with branch activity. (125)

In England, three branches – Yorkshire, Bristol and Manchester – were formed in 1920, to be followed by branches in the Midlands (1926), the North-East (1928) and Liverpool (1929), and three more branches – Sheffield, Plymouth and Nottingham – in 1939. In Wales, the Cardiff branch was formed in 1923 and the South-West Wales branch ten years later. In Australia, Sydney, New South Wales, was joined by Queensland (1922) and Victoria (1924). (126)

The scale and variety of the activity of the Yorkshire branch, from 1920, helped to extend the MA's influence outside the London area. This branch was formed at a meeting in Leeds University, which was attended by nearly a hundred men and women teachers from secondary schools, technical colleges and the universities. The first chairman was Professor W.P. Milne, who had recently moved from Clifton College, Bristol, to a chair in mathematics at Leeds University. In its first year this branch took on the responsibility of organizing an exceptional second general meeting of the MA, extending over two days – Whit Monday and Tuesday – in Leeds. Hitherto, general meetings had been confined to London, once a year in January. The *Gazette* enthused: 'a Yorkshire greeting will be extended to its parent by the infant branch, already a lusty bantling'. (127)

The Leeds programme was a rich and varied one, both professionally and socially. The proceedings were fully reported at very short notice in the July 1920 number of the *Gazette*, which included unusual contributions on thread and cloth construction, the mathematical theory of the 'sateen arrangement' in weaving, and the teaching of mathematics to textile students. (128) A number of eminent mathematicians attended the meeting: Professor Whittaker, the MA President, from Edinburgh, Professor Gray, Lord Kelvin's successor, from Glasgow, Professors Leahy of Sheffield, Heawood of Durham and Neville of Reading, and Sir George Greenhill. Fawdry summarized the general impact of the meeting in the following terms:

> the experiment of holding a meeting of the Association outside London was highly successful, and . . . a high standard has been set for any future efforts of a similar kind.
> Many teachers inclined to find their daily task dull and monotonous must have felt inspired afresh, not only by contact with men of vigorous personality and wide outlook, but also by the evidence of the importance of their work in its bearings upon many branches of modern industrial operations. (129)

Isaac Newton
1642–1727

A Memorial Volume
edited for the Mathematical Association
by W. J. Greenstreet

A VOLUME of Essays on various subjects connected with Newton's life and work.
The Contributors are :—

Prof. H. E. ARMSTRONG, F.R.S. ; Prof. A. E. BURTT, Ph.D. ;
J. M. CHILD, M.A. ; J. L. E. DREYER, D.Sc. ; Prof. A. S.
EDDINGTON, F.R.S. ; Prof. A. R. FORSYTH, F.R.S. ; D. C.
FRASER, M.A. ; Prof. A. E. HEATH, Ph.D. : Prof. H.
HILTON, D.Sc. ; J. A. HOLDEN, M.A. ; the Rev. J. J.
MILNE, M.A. ; Prof. J. PROUDMAN, F.R.S. ; Prof. L. J.
RUSSELL, M.A. ; Prof. D. E. SMITH, LL.D. ; Prof. G. N.
WATSON, F.R.S. ; Prof. E. T. WHITTAKER, F.R.S. ; H.
ZEITLINGER.

Some unpublished documents and letters of
Newton's are included, and there are 14
illustrations, apart from numerous diagrams.

G. BELL AND SONS LTD · PORTUGAL STREET · LONDON · W.C. 2

Plate 5.1   Newton Memorial Volume, 1927

In addition to the general focus on mathematics in relation to Yorkshire industry, the Leeds programme included an exceptional session on initial teacher training in mathematics, opened by Professor Milne, whose paper addressed an aspect of mathematics education in England which was 'still in the experimental stage'. (130) Nunn had produced earlier papers on the subject, in the Board of Education's *Special Reports* of 1912 and the appendices of the MA's general report of 1919. (131) But Milne's very early contribution also deserves recognition. In 1920 he not only took a leading part in the establishment of the Yorkshire branch and the organization of the Leeds meeting, but he was also responsible for one of the Board of Education's very early in-service courses for mathematics teachers, held at Durham University, also in the summer of 1920. The topics considered at Durham included a number of key items from the Perry movement's agenda: the teaching of trigonometry, logarithms, early calculus, mathematical laboratories, and correlation with other subjects, including geography. (132)

One other early initiative in teacher education, spearheaded by Milne, deserves recognition. In 1918 an article by Milne on the uses and functions of a school mathematical library was published in the *Gazette*. (133) A teachers' and scholars' library subcommittee of the MA was formed, with Milne as secretary, and a first list of books for teachers was circulated with the *Gazette* during 1918. (134) This was the first step in the occasional publication of lists of books suitable for school libraries. A first revised and extended list was published in 1926. (135)

Following the success of the Leeds meeting, the MA's Council considered a proposed follow-up at Edinburgh in 1921. The possibility of co-operation with the Edinburgh Mathematical Society was raised but no meeting in fact took place. (136) From 1921 until 1939 the MA held just one meeting annually, in London in January. It was not until 1949 that the MA again held a general meeting outside London, in Birmingham in April.

Yorkshire branch activity continued to flourish in the 1920s and 1930s, with a membership exceeding a hundred, and meetings held termly, not only in Leeds but also at other locations, including Sheffield and Hull. The papers presented at these meetings were collected together each year and published in the impressive annual reports of the branch. It was also under the auspices of the Yorkshire branch that a special weekend meeting was held at Grantham in 1927, to celebrate the two-hundredth anniversary of the death of Sir Isaac Newton. (137) The programme of addresses, visits and a commemorative church service attracted around two hundred visitors. The event was strongly supported by leading members of the mathematical and scientific establishment including Sir J.J. Thomson, (Master of Trinity), Sir F. Dyson (Astronomer Royal), J.H. Jeans (Secretary of the Royal Society), and Professors G.H. Hardy, H.H. Turner and E.T. Whittaker. (138) Newton's bicentenary was also commemorated by the publication of a special memorial volume which was edited for the MA by Greenstreet. (139) Originally it was planned to issue a special number of the *Gazette*, but Greenstreet's appeal for contributions had yielded a generous and varied response, which justified the separate publication of this contribution to Newtonian literature.

Year Book
& learned
& Scientific
Societies

List of Papers read before the Association and its Branches durin⟨
Session 1928–1929. *Those marked " P " have been published.*

Discussion on the Choice of Groups by Candidates for School Certificates. Jan. 8. *P.*

Barbier, *Prof. P.*, M.A.—Notes on the History of Mathematical Terms in

the Vulgar Tongues of Wester⟨ Europe (French and English May 11.

Blacklock, *J. H.*, M.A. — The Plan⟨ tarium at Berlin. May 11. *P.*

Brodetzky, *Prof. S.*, M.A., Ph.D. — Gravitation. Dec. 4.

Burchnall, *J. L.*, M.C., M.A. — The Common-Sense Inequalities. Nov. 28.

Buxton, *A.*, M.A. — Some General Theorems in Geometrical Optics. Oct. 22.

Chignell, *H. J.*, M.A.—The Use and Abuse of Formulæ. Jan. 8. *P.*

Curtis, *Prof. W. E.*, D.Sc. — Modern Scientific Research. Mar. 16.

Daltry, *C. T.*, B.Sc.—What we should Teach in Graphs. Nov. 10.

Dennis, *T.*—That we can be too Thorough. Oct. 30.

Dodd, *Dr F. H.*—Mathematics and the Difficult Child. Oct. 6.

Fawdry, *R. C.*, M.A.—The Teaching of Elementary Mechanics. Nov. 20.

Fletcher, *W. C.*, M.A.—Mercator's Projection. Dec. 7.

Forder, *H. G.*, B.A.—The Axioms of Geometry. Jan. 7. *P.*

Gimson, *B. L.*, B.Sc.—Experiments in Interesting the non-Mathematical Child. Feb. 9.

Hayden, *H. A.*, M.Sc.—Vectors and Tensors. Jan. 14.

Heawood, *Prof. P. J.*, M.A.—Magnitude and Minuteness—a Crux in Calculation involving the Use of the Binomial Theorem arising out of a Problem of Probability. May 4.

Levy, *Prof. H.*, D.Sc., F.R.S.E. — Modern Mathematical Problems in Aerodynamics. Jan. 7. *P.*

Lodge, *Prof. A.*, M.A. — Dimensions and Identity of Vector Direction. Feb. 2. *P.*

M'Carthy, *J. P.*, M.A. — Orthogonal Projections in Elementary Mathematics. Aug. 3.

Massy, *—.*—The New Quantum Theory of Ideal Gases. Sept. 25.

Milne, *Prof. W. P.*, M.A., D.Sc.—The Genus of a Curve. Oct. 20.

—— The History of the Equation. Oct. 26.

Priestley, *Prof. H. J.*, M.A.—The Early History of the Theory of Limits. Mar. 22.

Proudman, *Prof. J.*, D.Sc., F.R.S.— The Effects of Capes, Bays, and Islands on Local Tides. Feb. 9.

Purchon, *W. S.*, M.A.—Number in Design. Feb. 11.

Robinson, *Prof. H. R.*, D.Sc. — The Diffraction of Electrons. Mar. 18.

Sheppard, *W. F.*, D.Sc., LL.M. — Variety of Method in the Teaching of Arithmetic. Jan. 8. *P.*

Simonds, *E. F.*, M.A., Ph.D.—Some Features of American Mathematical Teaching. May.

Smith, *Miss D. R.*, M.A.—The Report on the Teaching of Mathematics in Girls' Schools. Oct. 19.

Steggall, *Prof. J. E. A.*, M.A., F.R.S.E. — Methods of Voting in Theory and Practice. Jan. 8. *P.*

van der Heyden, *A. F.*, M.A.—Fads and Fancies in the Teaching of Elementary Mathematics. Oct. 20 and May 4.

Watson, *Prof. G. N.*, Sc.D., F.R.S.— S. Ramanujan, the Indian Mathematician, 1887–1920. Feb. 20 and Mar. 8.

Plate 5.2   List of Papers 1928–9

The early work of the Yorkshire branch was ambitious in both conception and scale. Less ambitious, but more typical of branch activity outside London, was the North-Eastern branch, which was formed in 1928. Strachan, a member of HMI, was involved in the branch's formation and he also delivered the first Presidential address on the subject of 'recent progress in mathematical teaching'. (140) At this meeting fifty-five members were enrolled and nine others applied for associate membership. The membership was drawn from a wide range of educational institutions – universities, colleges and schools for boys and girls – in the Newcastle, Northumberland and Durham areas. At the second general meeting of the North-Eastern branch, also in 1928, Professor Milne of Leeds University was invited to speak on 'the history of the equation'. An attendance of sixty-five included students from the education departments of Armstrong College and the Durham Colleges, and Milne had chosen his subject to exemplify the relevance of the history of mathematics for both teachers and learners. (141) His paper is included in a published list of papers presented to the MA and its branches during 1928–9. (142) This list gives a good indication of the level and variety of topics covered in mathematics, history of mathematics, and mathematics education, during the inter-war period.

In 1929 the Council of the MA took up the general question of the relation between the branches and the parent Association. Branches were invited to send in suggestions and a subcommittee was set up to report to the Council at its next meeting in January, 1930. In order to have new rules in place as soon as possible, it was also decided that a special general meeting should be held in February, 1930, to finalize the recommendations of the annual general meeting, held in the previous month. (143) The changes to the rules, which brought formal branch representation on the Council, were passed unanimously.

A proposal to reduce the annual subscription – set at 15s in 1920 – was rejected in 1930. The argument against a reduction was clearly spelt out by the subcommittee of Council:

> a reduction of the subscription would not lead to a large increase in the number of members of the Association, and . . . could be met only by a reduction either in the number of the issues of the *Gazette* and other publications, or in the size of each issue, or in both. The Council do not consider that this reduction would be desirable, especially in view of the suggestion that the *Gazette* should include more material than heretofore from the Branches. Moreover it must be borne in mind that more than three-quarters of the members of the Association do not belong to any Branch, and that the *Gazette* and the reports issued by the Association form almost the only link between these members and the Association. (144)

To increase the appeal of the *Gazette*, particularly to schoolteachers, branches were asked to send to the editor reports of interesting meetings and manuscripts of interesting papers; and some financial support – in the form of discretionary grants – was made available for this purpose.

The relation between the branches and the General Teaching Committee was also considered at this time, and the recommendations of the subcommittee of Council were largely adopted. Formal representation for the branches was rejected: this 'would not only introduce a new principle into the appointment of that committee, but would also seriously hamper its work by making it unwieldy in size'. (145) However, closer co-operation was advocated through inviting recommendations for membership of the Boys' and Girls' Schools Committees, using co-option where appropriate, and encouraging two-way communication: keeping the branches informed about the Committees' agendas and inviting opinions from the branches. The aim to develop the sense of common purpose and community among the branches also underpinned the establishment of a Branches Committee from 1932:

> consisting of the representatives of the Branches on the Council, together with the secretaries of those Branches not represented on the Council . . . it should appoint its own chairman and secretary. Its duties shall be to further the exchange of information among the Branches, to report to the Council any matters of which that body should be cognisant, and in general to encourage and further the activities of the Branches. It shall also consider proposals for the formation of new Branches and report on them to the Council. (146)

The progress of the membership of the nine branches in England, which were active through the 1930s, is shown in Table 5.1. Between 1931 and 1939 (excluding Southampton and District) the number of MA members in England, linked with the branches, increased from 405 to 468 (plus 4 junior members), but the number of associates dropped from 443 to 355. (147) Thus the total numbers involved in these eight branches did not show an

Table 5.1 Branch Membership in the 1930s

| | Bristol | | Cardiff | | Liverpool | | London | | Manchester | |
	M	A	M	A	M	A	M	A	M	A
1931	16	27	22	17	15	38	180	110	29	88
1938	20	23	47	40*	21	45	213	65*	36	69

	Midland		North-Eastern		So'ton and District		Yorkshire		Key M
1931	33	36	64	11	-	-	46	116	Members A Associates
1938	39	35*	44	14	10	33	48	68*	* includes 1 junior member

The Mathematical Association.

President:

Professor G. H. HARDY, D.Sc., F.R.S.

THE ANNUAL MEETING of the Mathematical Association will be held at The London Day Training College, Southampton Row, London, W.C.1, on MONDAY, 4TH JANUARY, 1926, at 5.30 p.m., and TUESDAY, 5TH JANUARY, 1926, at 10 a.m. and 2.30 p.m.

MONDAY EVENING, 5.30 o'clock.

1. "Some Problems of Atomic Structure", by Professor E. N. DA C. ANDRADÉ, D.Sc., Ph.D.

TUESDAY MORNING, 10 o'clock.

BUSINESS.

2. The Report of the Council for the year 1925.

3. The Treasurer's Report for the year 1925.

4. The Election of Officers and Members of the Council for the year 1926.

There are two vacant places on the Council in consequence of the retirement (in their turn) of Professor S. BRODETSKY and Dr. W. F. SHEPPARD.

5. The Council will propose that Rule VII be altered as follows: that the words in brackets below be omitted, and the words in italics be added:—

Any Member of the Association may nominate Members for election to the Council [either by writing to one of the Secretaries, or by proposing them at the Annual General Meeting]. *Such nominations must reach one of the Secretaries not later than the 25th day of October preceding the Annual General Meeting.*

6. 10.30 a.m. "Measurement of Intelligence", by Professor C. SPEARMAN, Ph.D., F.R.S.

Prevalent claim to measure intelligence by mental tests. Unexpected difficulties that have arisen; equivocality of the word; historical explanation. Proposed definitions: adaptability to new situations; capacity to learn; nergenetic "anarchic" power. The three doctrines: "monarchic", "oligarchic" and "anarchic". Theory that tests average or sample ability. Theory of Two Factors; a discovery in tables of correlations; deduction of g and s; nature of s.

7. 11.30 a.m. Discussion on "The Proper Function of the Mathematical Gazette", to be opened by E. R. BROWN, B.A.

8. 12 noon. "Modern Theories of Integration", by E. CAREY FRANCIS, M.A. (Fellow and Lecturer of St. Peter's College, Cambridge).

The integral defined as the inverse of a differential co-efficient; failure of this definition. Another method of approach; the Riemann integral; integration of a continuous function. Extension; measure; the Lebesgue integral; integration of a bounded function. Further extensions.

NOTE.—There will be a Publishers' Exhibition of books during the day. It has not proved possible to arrange the proposed Exhibition of Work in Girls' Schools.

TUESDAY AFTERNOON, 2.30 o'clock.

9. 2.30 p.m. The President's Address: "The case against the Mathematical Tripos".

10. 3.30 p.m. Discussion on the "Report on the Teaching of Mathematics to Evening Technical Students".

NOTE.—The times stated are approximate.

Honorary Secretaries
{ C. PENDLEBURY, M.A.
39 Burlington Road, Chiswick, W.4.

MARGARET PUNNETT, B.A.
The London Day Training College, Southampton Row, W.C.1.

Plate 5.3 Annual Meeting 1926

increase over this period. This is perhaps surprising, given the initiatives taken in the early 1930s to raise the profile of the branches and the fact that the membership nationally did show a significant increase over the same period. On the positive side, three new branches were formed in England during 1939, before the war disrupted MA activity.

The number of local meetings of a branch normally varied between three and six in a year with four being a common choice. Nationally, the arrangements for the annual meeting of the MA, held in London during January, continued on a relatively modest scale. The details were discussed by the Council and normally finalized at its meeting in October of the previous year. From 1923 a small 'programme committee' of Council took on the responsibility of constructing a draft programme. (148) The inclusion of a publishers' exhibition became a regular feature from 1925.

In 1925 the MA took advantage of the fact that the IAAM had already made arrangements with publishers for an exhibition on the same site at the beginning of January. The MA invited these publishers to leave their mathematical books and apparatus on display during the annual meeting, and this proved to be a successful arrangement. (149) Around this time efforts were also made to include an exhibition of teachers' or pupils' work. Miss Punnett invited girls' schools to send in material for use at the annual meeting in 1926, but the response was disappointing. (150) Accordingly, the idea was dropped for 1926 but the Girls' and Boys' Schools Committees were both invited to consider the possibility of an exhibition in 1927. The response of the Boys' Schools Committee was distinctly unsympathetic and the matter was taken no further:

> an exhibit of work at the annual meeting of the M.A. did not seem to be a suitable activity of the general meeting as members attending would not have time to inspect an exhibit if it were sufficiently representative to be worth inspecting. (151)

In the 1930s the first day's programme for the annual meeting was extended to include an afternoon session, part of which was devoted to the MA's business meeting. The publishers' exhibition was now spread over the two days, and the other programme components – papers, discussions and the Presidential address – might be accommodated on either day. Discussions were carefully managed, with a view to publication in the *Gazette*. The topics for discussion up to the Second World War included: the teaching of various branches of school mathematics from arithmetic to calculus and mechanics, and, more surprisingly, statistics and probability; other aspects of the curriculum and pedagogy; examinations and their effects; and some non-school topics, including developments in technical, university and teacher education. (152)

From the time of Bryan's two-year Presidency, 1907–9, a pattern of two addresses by a President, one after a year of office and a second at the end of the two-year term, became established and lasted until 1934, when Neville became President for one year only. Thereafter, Presidents held office for one year and gave one address at the end of their term. Addresses were published as a major feature in the *Gazette*. Table 5.2 shows the range of topics covered up to 1939. With a small number of

Table 5.2 MA Presidential Addresses 1910-39

1910	H.H. Turner	Mathematics and 'general education'
1911	H.H. Turner	The outer satellites of Saturn and Jupiter
1912	E.W. Hobson	The democratization of mathematical education
1913	E.W. Hobson	On geometrical constructions by means of the compass
1914	A.G. Greenhill	The use of mathematics
1915	A.G. Greenhill	Mathematics in artillery science
1916	A.N. Whitehead	The aims of education - a plea for reform
1917	A.N. Whitehead	Technical education and its relation to science and literature
1918	T.P. Nunn	Mathematics and individuality
1919	T.P. Nunn	Astronomy as a school subject
1920	E.T. Whittaker	Some mathematical problems awaiting solution
1921	J.M. Wilson	The early history of the Association, or, the passing of Euclid from our schools and universities, and how it came about. A story of fifty years ago
1922	No address	
1923	T.L. Heath	Greek geometry with special reference to infinitesimals
1924	No address	
1925	G.H. Hardy	What is geometry?
1926	G.H. Hardy	The case against the mathematical tripos
1927	M.J.M. Hill	On the teaching of mathematics
1928	M.J.M. Hill	The logical eye and the mathematical eye
1929	W.F. Sheppard	Variety of method in the teaching of arithmetic
1930	W.F. Sheppard	Mathematics for the study of frequency statistics
1931	A.S. Eddington	The end of the world (from the standpoint of mathematical physics)
1932	A.S. Eddington	The decline of determinism
1933	G.N. Watson	The marquis and the land agent
1934	G.N. Watson	Scraps from some mathematical notebooks
1935	E.H. Neville	The food of the gods
1936	A.W. Siddons	Progress
1937	A.R. Forsyth	Applied mathematics in school training
1938	L.N.G. Filon	Mass and weight in Newtonian mechanics
1939	W. Hope-Jones	Simplicity and the truthfulness in arithmetic

exceptions – Nunn, Wilson, Siddons and Hope-Jones – the Presidents in this period were professional mathematicians. The subjects chosen for their addresses reflect a wide range of interests in mathematics, pure and applied, its history and place in education.

ADMINISTRATION, ACCOMMODATION AND THE LIBRARY

The central administration of the MA's affairs was conducted on a very small scale in the early twentieth century. There were normally two honorary secretaries, who were London-based, but this number was increased to three between 1908 and 1916, when the rules required that one of the secretaries should be a woman. Acting as one of the secretaries, Pendlebury provided continuity and efficiency from the late nineteenth century to the 1930s. He joined the AIGT in 1885 and became an honorary secretary in the following year, a position he held continuously for fifty years. H.D. Ellis, who joined the AIGT in 1887, acted as a fellow-secretary from 1900, and they were joined by Miss Greene from 1908, Miss Gwatkin from 1910, and Miss Punnett from 1912. (153) Accommodation for business and general meetings of the MA was first provided at King's College and then at the London Day Training College, where the link with Miss Punnett would have been helpful, but no permanent base or clerical support for the MA's administration was proposed until 1916. Ellis resigned as secretary at the end of 1915 and Pendlebury made a recommendation:

> the Association should secure the services of a paid clerk who would undertake the sending out of the *Gazette* and all circulars connected with the Association, should keep the Roll of Members, and should give help in the routine work to the Treasurer and Librarian as well as to the secretaries. (154)

This recommendation was agreed at a fee level not exceeding £20 per annum. At this time Pendlebury was also responsible for making the arrangements for the annual meeting but this work was handed over to a programme committee in the 1920s, when the timetable was extended to run over two days. (155) Pendlebury and Miss Punnett served together for twenty years as the secretariat of the MA, until Pendlebury's resignation in 1936.

Throughout much of Pendlebury's period of office the honorary treasurer of the MA was F.W. Hill of the City of London School, who took over the job in 1900 and held it continuously until his death in 1935. Honorary treasurers were not listed in the three-hundredth number of the *Gazette*, in which Siddons included lists of all the Presidents, secretaries and editors of the *Gazette* up to 1948. As Combridge has fairly pointed out, 'the Treasurer bears alone a considerable burden'. (156) Snell took over this burden as acting treasurer for 1935, and he served as honorary treasurer from 1936 until 1947, during which time the war and its aftermath made his work particularly 'laborious and troublesome'. (157) From 1936 the financial

MATHEMATICAL ASSOCIATION

Treasurer's Statement for the Ten Months Ending 31st October, 1936

RECEIPTS.

	1935 £ s. d.		1936 £ s. d.
Cash in hand, December 31st, 1935			357 5 1
Subscriptions received for the year 1936— £882 16 7			
Ordinary members	836 0 6		890 4 0
Junior members			
Subscriptions received for previous years	54 15 6		86 15 0
Subscriptions received in advance	72 0 0		24 10 0
Life compositions	68 6 5		47 11 4
Proceeds of sale of Gazettes	88 6 3		167 11 0
Proceeds of sale of Reports	57 1 0		73 15 0
Proceeds of Sale of Newton Book			8 4 0
Advertisements	38 10 0		19 11 2
Interest on Investments			
Subscriptions from Branches—			
North Wales	3 11 0		15 0 0
London	15 0 0		15 0 0
North-Eastern	15 0 0		15 0 0
Yorkshire	15 0 0		15 0 0
Manchester	15 0 0		15 0 0
Liverpool	15 0 0		15 0 0
Midland	15 0 0		15 0 0
Bristol	15 0 0		15 0 0
Cardiff	15 0 0		15 0 0
South-West Wales	15 0 0		15 0 0
North Ireland			15 0 0
Queensland			
Victoria			
Sydney	15 0		
	£1,227 18 1		**£1,688 15 7**

PAYMENTS.

	1935 £ s. d.		1936 £ s. d.
Deficit, December 31st, 1934	49 2 11		
Gazettes, Nos. 235—240 (October, 1935— October, 1936)—			
Printing	369 4 0		651 13 1
Postage	53 4 8		59 16 10
Grant to Editor	125 0 0		93 15 3
Printing Index			15 10 3
Reprinting Arithmetic Report			26 11 5
Printing List for School Libraries	25 0 0		108 3 0
Printing Library List			75 0 0
Expenses of Library			6 10 0
Greenstreet plate	87 16 1		55 18 0
Expenses of Committees	1 3 6		15 19 0
Expenses of Problem Bureau	5 14 0		15 10 0
Expenses of Meetings			
Grants to Branches—			
North Wales			
London	13 7 0		9 6 6
North-Eastern	2 8 0		7 19 0
Yorkshire	3 19 6		1 2 0
Manchester	12 12 6		2 3 6
Liverpool	1 15 6		2 8 0
Midland	1 18 6		1 10 6
Bristol			1 0 6
Cardiff	2 9 6		
South-West Wales	2 4 6		2 6 6
North Ireland	4 16 6		6 19 6
Queensland			5 4 6
Victoria			18 0 6
Sydney			10 0 6
Clerical Assistance	2 17 0		41 13 0
Stationary. Printing	30 0 0		66 19 0
Postage	22 5 11		32 19 0
Office Expenses	30 0 0		16 2 0
Sundries			1 0 0
Cash in hand, October 31st, 1936	357 17 0		365 16 5
Sundry Items	38 0 5		
	£1,227 18 1		**£1,688 15 7**

LIABILITIES.

	1935 £ s. d.		1936 £ s. d.
Subscriptions in advance	72 0 0		24 10 0
Life compositions	914 18 0		951 13 11
Balance of Assets over Liabilities	470 7 1		583 4 11
	£1,457 5 1		**£1,559 7 11**

ASSETS.

	1935 £ s. d.		1936 £ s. d.
Cash in hand	357 0 0		
War Loan	1,100 0 0		365 16 5
Due from G. Bell & Sons, Ltd., for sale of Gazettes, etc			1,100 0 0
Sundry Items			93 11 6
	£1,457 5 1		**£1,559 7 11**

In addition, £100 is due from members who have not paid their 1936 subscription, and £15 15s. 0d has been lost by members dropping out without paying their 1935 subscription. Assets also include Books in Library, Book Cases, and Stocks of Gazettes and Reports. The liabilities for Life Compositions has been increased by £47 5s. 0d., and decreased by £10 10s. 0d. owing to the death of one life member.

K. S. SNELL, Hon. Treasurer.

Audited and found correct W. M. ROBERTS,
November 18th, 1936.

Plate 5.4 Treasurer's Statement 1936

year end for the MA's statement of accounts was moved from December 31st to October 31st, thereby making a presentation of an audited statement possible at the annual meeting in January. (158)

Parsons replaced Pendlebury as an honorary secretary in 1936, and with 'new blood' in the positions of treasurer and secretary it is not surprising to find that the question of support for the MA's administration was again raised at this time. Parsons and Snell pressed for the establishment of a central office in London to bring together and co-ordinate the work and record-keeping of the secretaries and treasurer, with an appropriate level of clerical support. The Council had to admit:

> in view of the very large amount of time so generously given by Mr. Pendlebury to the work of the Association over a number of years, it was only to be expected that, on his retirement, fresh arrangements would need to be made and more expense incurred. (159)

Following the advice of Parsons, it was agreed to rent a room from the IAAM, at 29 Gordon Square, and to buy in clerical assistance from members of the IAAM staff. Up to £90 per annum was agreed for this purpose and a further £65 in capital expenditure was allowed for furniture, equipment and fittings. As Parsons pointed out, the links with the IAAM would bring economies in printing, stationery, etc., and 'other advantages of a less material kind might be expected to result from establishing friendly relations of this sort'. (160) All the arrangements were carried through and completed in 1937. In 1940 the MA moved from a top floor room to the basement, which provided a safe store for records, and in 1944 a room was rented from the Historical Association, which was also based at 29 Gordon Square. Apart from some early dislocation because of wartime bombing, the central office of the MA remained in the basement at 29 Gordon Square until 1965. (161)

The library of the association was also based in London. It started as small collection in the home of C.V. Coates from 1890. Ten years later arrangements were made to transfer the collection to the private room of Professor W.H.H. Hudson at King's College, where the MA's meetings were also held. (162) C.E. Williams was formally designated as the honorary librarian from 1908, and in 1911 plans were made to transfer the library to the premises of the Teachers' Guild: the MA was to pay £5 per annum, and Guild members were to have right of access to the books. (163) In 1921 this agreement was terminated by the Guild, and in 1922, with the co-operation of the IAAM, a similar agreement was secured to house the library at 29 Gordon Square. At the same time the Council set up a subcommittee to consider policy for the library and its future. (164) In the following year, Professor Neville took over as librarian and the collection was moved to his own very large house on Castle Hill, in Reading. Apparently, Neville had been persuaded by a near neighbour, Greenstreet, then editor of the *Gazette*, to take on this task, and Neville pursued his responsibilities with energy and enthusiasm for the next thirty years. (165)

Former associates of Neville have referred to him as 'a born bibliophile' for whom the development of the library was 'a life hobby'. (166) He

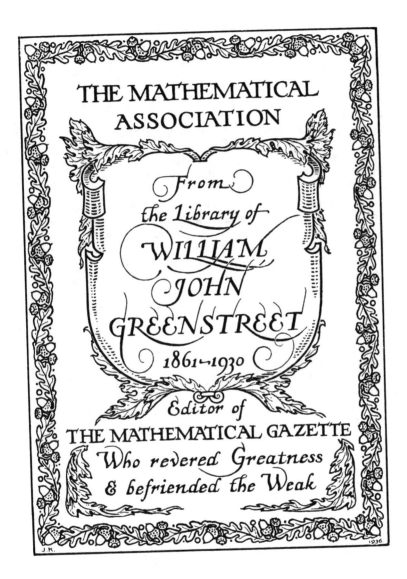

Plate 5.5 Commemorative Bookplate 1930

took over a collection of around one thousand books, plus various serial publications, and by the end of the Second World War the collection had grown impressively to around four thousand volumes. In addition to receiving the donations of others, Neville himself gave most generously to the library and was persistently searching out and obtaining relevant items at negligible cost to the Association. He also put much time and energy into the display and cataloguing of the collection. His production of a meticulous, hand-written and very detailed card index was a major feat of bibliography, and four lists of books and pamphlets were produced by Neville and published between 1926 and 1936. (167) Unfortunately, Neville's own unique card index has since been destroyed. In 1937, when Neville moved to the Red House, Sonning, the library moved with him; but the onset of wartime conditions necessitated a further move to a safer location in 1940, when the collection was stored at Douai School, Woolhampton, partly in inaccessible conditions in the Abbey, where it remained until 1948. (168)

In addition to Neville's, two other distinctive contributions to the library's growth between the wars deserve specific recognition. Godfrey was a leading spirit in the world-wide reform of elementary mathematics teaching in the early years of the present century and a leading member of the MA. On his premature death, in 1924, his entire collection of books was given to the library by his wife, each volume displaying a commemorative bookplate. The donation included a large and representative collection of school, college and university textbooks from the 1880s, together with a good number of early contributions to the literature in mathematics education and pedagogy. (169)

Greenstreet was another bibliophile, and one perhaps to surpass even Neville, who acknowledged him as 'the most lavish and most persistent of benefactors' of the library. Soon after the library was moved to Reading, Greenstreet 'unloaded his own shelves' on the new librarian whom he had helped to appoint. (170) By 1930, when Greenstreet made a final bequest of all his remaining mathematical books and periodicals other than 'modern' textbooks, he had contributed several hundreds of volumes to the library, among them many old and valuable items. In 1914 the MA distributed a catalogue of current mathematical journals, compiled by Greenstreet and including details of runs held in forty-nine libraries within the British Isles. The MA's and Greenstreet's personal library are listed, the latter because Greenstreet claimed 'to possess sets or long runs of several periodicals to be found, to his knowledge, in but one or two libraries or nowhere else in this country'. (171) These rare periodicals were also added to the MA's collection. His unique contribution was eventually recognized with a commemorative bookplate. Unquestionably, it was Greenstreet and Neville who were jointly the prime movers in bringing the library up to its post-war standard, in terms of scale and coverage.

Between 1948 and 1953 the MA's library was back in Reading, still under Neville, but now housed in the university library. Pressure on space led to the transfer of the collection to the University College, Leicester, in 1954, when Professor R.L. Goodstein (1912–85) took over as the new locally based librarian. (172) Building on the previous published lists and

Neville's card index, Goodstein, with some assistance, produced the most recent listing: *Books and Periodicals in the Library of the Mathematical Association* (1962). (173)

Both Broadbent, who edited the *Gazette* from 1931 until 1955, and Goodstein, who took over as editor in 1956, were colleagues of Neville during the long period of his professorship at Reading, from 1919, through the year of the University College's charter, in 1926, until 1954. Broadbent moved to the Royal Naval College, Greenwich, in 1935, when Goodstein moved to Reading, where he was to stay until 1947. Goodstein then took up a chair at University College, Leicester, which was chartered in 1957, and he remained there until his retirement in 1977. (174) It is clear that Neville's role and his personal connections at Reading were important not only for the care and development of the library but also for the editorship of the *Gazette*.

THE MATHEMATICAL GAZETTE

The international reputation of the *Gazette* as a minor mathematical serial became well established during the period of Greenstreet's editorship. Neville's assessment of Greenstreet's editorial policy and its consequences is generous but fitting:

> Greenstreet always desired to attain, and believed that all teachers benefit if they can attain, to such appreciation of current advances in mathematics as is possible without intensive study of special branches; he therefore encouraged ample notice of treatises, Continental and American as well as English, far beyond the range of school mathematics, until the review pages of his *Gazette* were admitted to be among the best in the world . . . In short, Greenstreet gave a character and a standing to a periodical which might have become nothing but a pedagogical mouthpiece . . . (175)

In his later years, however, Greenstreet's work suffered because of his illness; Neville stepped in as editor in 1927, and again for some numbers after Greenstreet's death in 1930, until a successor, Broadbent, was appointed, principally on Neville's recommendation. (176) A Russian assessment concurs with Broadbent's: the second half of Greenstreet's term as editor was 'a period of decline' for the *Gazette*. (177)

In 1931 the Council appointed a small subcommittee, including Neville and Broadbent, to consider both the form of the *Gazette* and the policy for its content. As a consequence, from 1932, the type size was increased and the number of issues per annum reduced from six to five, each of approximately eighty pages. (178) This was actually an increase in the number of pages per annum. The *Gazette* gained new impetus under Broadbent's editorship; the larger journal attracted a widening circle of contributors on an international scale, while the reviews section and the mathematical notes continued to be important features for the status of the *Gazette*. Neville was a 'welcome and generous contributor' of articles, reviews and notes as well as a wise counsellor in the new editor's early years. (179)

One feature of the *Gazette* – the inclusion of mathematical questions and their solutions – was not reinstated after it was phased out over the first decade of this century. However, a new service for members – a problem bureau - was first advertised in the *Gazette* in 1928. (180) The problems typically came from university scholarship examinations, particularly at Cambridge, and A.S. Gosset-Tanner of Derby School acted as secretary of the bureau from 1928 until his death in 1953. (181) Over its first seven years the bureau received problems from over a hundred members and some 350 solutions were supplied. (182) G.A. Garreau took over from Gosset-Tanner, working with existing staff from the bureau, and he directed the service until 1970, when he was replaced by R.H. Cobb. (183)

Although the mathematical reputation of the *Gazette* was firmly established by Greenstreet and maintained by Broadbent, questions were still from time to time asked about the balance – or rather the imbalance – between relatively advanced mathematical exposition on the one hand and material concerning education and pedagogy on the other. In his Presidential address of 1936, Siddons drew attention to 'grumbles that the *Mathematical Gazette* is too "high-brow" and does not perform the function for which it was started', as 'a journal of Elementary Mathematics, to be devoted entirely to such subjects as are usually taught in secondary schools'. (184) Siddons appealed for more articles concerned with elementary work, but pointed to one obstacle to advance in this direction:

> One more appeal, and that is to the 'highbrows' – do be kind to the writer of articles on elementary work. I am sure that the fear of highbrow criticism has, in the past, prevented some excellent teachers from giving to their fellow teachers ideas that would be valuable in the ordinary class-room. (185)

Broadbent, who was sympathetic to Siddons's point of view, confessed in an article for the *Gazette*:

> The suggestion that there is too much high-brow material in the *Gazette* causes me more anxiety. But some of the blame, if there be any, lies on the shoulders of members themselves, since it is not unreasonable for an editor to confess his inability to publish those contributions which he never receives. (186)

On the other hand, he added:

> Moreover, it has been said from the opposite side that the *Gazette* spends too much effort on points of routine teaching and has thus thrown away its chances of being recognised as a serious mathematical periodical. As long as both comments continue to be made, there is some ground for believing that we are not too far from the golden mean. (187)

The contents of the *Gazette* continued to reflect the relatively undeveloped state of mathematical pedagogy in England in comparison with other leading countries, particularly Germany and the USA. Up to the 1950s in England, textbook production and dissemination, together with informal discussions, dominated more critical efforts to articulate pedagogy, and questions about the *Gazette*, its audience and purposes, continued to surface in the post-war period. (188)

A NEW CONSTITUTION

The onset of war in 1939 inevitably affected the MA's level of activity both centrally and locally. Services and development work were not fully resumed until 1946. However, one major constitutional development was finalized in 1937 and this established a new pattern of working for the Teaching Committee in the post-war period. The matter was first raised in January 1936 by Miss Punnett, who drew attention to the fact that the work of the Girls' Schools Committee had essentially become marginalized by comparison with that of the Boys' Schools Committee, which had been responsible for the inter-war programme of major report production. A subcommittee was appointed to draw up new proposals and draft appropriate regulations, which were finalized before the end of the year. (189) The new regulations provided for one widely representative and relatively large committee, which would normally meet only once a year, the bulk of the development work being delegated to small subcommittees. The principle of wide representation was a central one and such representation extended not only to the universities, public and other secondary schools, teacher training institutions, and technical schools and colleges, but also to the elementary and central schools (which was relatively unfamiliar territory for the MA) along with the preparatory schools. Gender differentiation, with some bias towards men, was still built into the regulations.

The new Teaching Committee first met in January 1938, with Robson in the chair and Daltry as secretary, and in this first year five subcommittees were appointed. (190) The topics for development covered a wider range for the MA than hitherto: the teaching of children up to the age of eleven; the revision of the report (1926) on the teaching of mathematics to evening technical students; the presentation of the historical side of mathematics; the teaching of trigonometry; and examinations. In addition, two other topics were discussed and proposed as suitable for development through articles in the *Gazette*: teaching the 'complete duffer' (*sic*), and the contact of mathematics with other subjects. (191) The Teaching Committee met again in January 1939, when a subcommittee on sixth form mathematics was appointed, but the progress of all the subcommittees was seriously affected by the war and it was the *Gazette* which became the principal vehicle for necessarily limited progress and communication during the war years. (192) Elizabeth Williams acted as honorary secretary, 1939–46, and the *Gazette* was kept going through the 'constant and unwearying work of Snell, Parsons and Mrs. Williams'. (193)

To manage the wartime affairs of the MA, an Executive Committee of Council was set up and it met in October of 1939 to discuss a strategy.

This Committee presented a report jointly with the Council, for the perioc 1939–44, at the MA's first general meeting after war broke out, at King': College in April 1944. (194) In this same year, the new Education (Butler Act provided a basis for the post-war reconstruction of the education system. By coincidence, 1944 also saw the publication of the Jeffery Repor on alternative syllabuses for school certificate mathematics. Increasingly from the 1940s, new developments outside the confines of the MA were to have important implications for the scope, character and influence o the Association as it worked to improve mathematics education for the multitude. Post-war reconstruction, new educational initiatives, and the MA's response, will be considered in the next chapter.

CHAPTER SIX

EDUCATIONAL RECONSTRUCTION AND NEW INITIATIVES

> . . . the Mathematical Association is called upon to play a role that is at once constructive and integrating. It is important that we should hold in proper balance the work to be done in universities, training colleges, technical institutions and schools of all kinds. (1)
>
> (J.T. Combridge, 1962)

> The Reports issued by our Association have brought clarity and definition into our teaching; they have laid down principles which will remain valid long after matters of detail have been changed . . . the temptation is upon us to continue as a kind of comfortable club, fighting old battles which are losing their relevance, and dwelling on the memories and portraits of the heroes of the past . . . (2)
>
> (J.T. Combridge, 1962)

PRE- AND POST-WAR SCHOOLS AND CURRICULA

The reconstruction of the English educational system, following the widely dislocating consequences of total war, is bound up, as we shall see, with the ideology and provisions of the 1944 Butler Education Act: 'a Rolls Royce among statutes' according to one historian of educational administration. (3) It was to enjoy greater longevity than its three major predecessors: the Acts of 1870, 1902 and 1918. What is more, the effects of educational reconstruction after the Second World War were to be more widely and deeply felt than had been the case after the First World War.

The concept of partnership between the central and local authorities was a common theme linking the 1902 and 1944 Education Acts. In the words of one commentary on the educational system's development over the first half of the twentieth century:

> It is the story of a progressive partnership between the Central Department, the local education authorities and the teachers. To build a single, but not uniform, system out of many diverse elements; to widen educational opportunity and at the same time to raise standards; to knit the educational system more closely into the life

of an increasingly democratic and industrialized community: these are among the main ideas which, despite two major wars, have moved legislators and administrators alike. (4)

After 1944, the Board of Education and its Consultative Committee wer replaced by a new Ministry of Education together with Central Advisor Councils for England and Wales. Following the Act, LEAs were require to prepare development plans for the organization of public education i three progressive stages: primary, secondary and further. The provision o free secondary education as an option for all was the major advance i terms of educational opportunity. Before 1944, grant-aided schools wer classified as either elementary or secondary, and the former catered i various ways for children up to the age of fourteen. A third category o direct grant secondary schools – those receiving capitation direct from th Board – was introduced in a circular of 1926. The reconstruction of th system involved a clear break for all pupils around the age of eleven an transfer from a primary school to a secondary school of an appropriate type Previously only a narrow ladder had connected the elementary and second ary systems with progress up the ladder depending upon performance i the LEAs' selection examinations. The basis for a two-stage system fo all pupils was created by two gradual twentieth-century developments the upward striving of the elementary system towards the provision c quasi-secondary education for older pupils in separate central schools o in senior elementary schools; and the provision of selective post-primar education in separately provided junior technical schools.

The movement towards secondary education for all was helped forwar and consolidated in the inter-war period by two major reports from th Consultative Committee of the Board: the Hadow Report of 1926 on 'th education of the adolescent' and the Spens Report of 1938 on 'secondar education with special reference to grammar schools and technical hig schools'. (5) The notion of a tripartite system of secondary schools wit differentiated curricula – grammar, 'modern' and technical – graduall emerged and was strongly endorsed by the Norwood Report of 1943 which was produced by a committee of the Secondary School Examina tions Council, appointed by R.A. Butler in 1941. (6) Such a system, accom panied by arrangements for selection at eleven-plus, based on performanc in 'intelligence', arithmetic and English tests, became the basis for th post-war provision of secondary education by the LEAs. However, th ideal of parity of esteem across the tripartite divisions proved to b elusive in practice. The Norwood Report declared that the three type of education:

> should have such parity as amenities and conditions can bestow; parity
> of esteem in our view cannot be conferred by administrative decree
> nor by equality of cost per pupil; it can only be won by the school
> itself. (7)

The challenge for the secondary modern schools was an enormous one to provide a suitable 'secondary' education for the majority and growin number of pupils up to the compulsory leaving age, which was raised t fifteen in 1947. In relation both to parity of esteem and to curriculum development, the link with the long historical tradition of elementary schooling and its piecemeal or limited provision for older pupils was a major constraining factor. Looking back on the early years of secondary modern schooling *The Times Educational Supplement* commented:

> Secondary Modern: The name was part of the brave new world hoped for after 1944. Quite what 'modern' meant, no one was too certain, except that it was presumably more practical than 'grammar' and less technical than 'technical'.
> The schools themselves looked warily at the situation and did what they could. They had virtually everything against them . . . (8)

The grammar schools continued to provide *the* prestigious form of secondary education in the maintained sector and this prestige was only marginally affected by the development of secondary technical schools. Such schools struggled both to gain parity of esteem with the grammar schools and to develop their own distinctive ethos and curriculum. By 1952 there were only 291 secondary technical schools in comparison with 1189 grammar schools. (9) By 1961, the proportions of pupils in the tripartite types of post-1944 secondary school demonstrate both the limited advance of the secondary technical schools and, at the same time, the numerical importance of the secondary modern schools, catering for 'half our future': secondary technical, 3 per cent; secondary modern, 54 per cent; maintained grammar, 22 per cent. Other maintained secondary schools, including bilateral, multilateral and the first comprehensive schools, were accommodating 11 per cent of pupils at this time. (10)

Given the sweeping changes which are currently being felt as a result of the 1988 Education Act and subsequent legislation, it is important to recognize major differences between the 1944 and 1988 Acts in two key areas: school curricula and examinations. In relation to curricula, the 1944 Act provided no policy for the content of primary and secondary education. The curriculum was not regarded as an issue requiring legislation, with the isolated exception of religious education, which was made a statutory requirement as a school subject from 1944. The period from 1944 to the beginning of the 1960s has been described a 'the Golden Age of teacher control (or non-control) of the curriculum'. (11) For nearly twenty years the principle of partnership between the Ministry and LEAs, and the ideal of teacher autonomy in curriculum matters, remained unchallenged. However, the 'secret garden of the curriculum' continued to be the subject of educational debates, reports and recommendations, both before and after the 1944 Act. (12)

Between the wars, the major reports of the Consultative Committee did not neglect the curriculum, but the pronouncements tended to be necessarily rather general and somewhat visionary in character. There are sections on specific subjects in the post-primary school curriculum, including mathematics, in the Hadow Report of 1926, the Spens Report of 1938 and the Norwood Report of 1943. Subject associations, including the MA, were invited to respond to the enquiries of these committees. The Hadow Committee acknowledged both the Historical and Geographical

Associations for their production of detailed memoranda. (13) The MA also responded, with Miss Punnett taking a lead, though the minutes record that the submission was 'hastily drawn up after various unfortunate delays'. (14) But the Science Masters' Association made no submission to the Hadow Committee. (15)

In discussing the curriculum, the contribution of a small number of individual educationists, including Sir Percy Nunn, was acknowledged by the Spens Committee. (16) The section on mathematics is pure Nunn, combining progressivism with some evident frustration concerning the general state of secondary school mathematics. (17) The MA responded to the Spens Report in a letter which began:

> The recommendations with regard to the teaching of Mathematics contained in the Report are essentially sound. They are in no sense new. They have been advocated for the past twenty years by members and committees of the Mathematical Association and His Majesty's Inspectors. The views expressed in the Report are those of a former President of our Association, well known for many years as head of a Training College and as an advocate of modern methods. (18)

The MA questioned the controversial suggestion that the amount of time allocated to mathematics in the curriculum might be reduced by simplifying and unifying the treatment of the subject. Rather, it was felt that any saving in time might profitably be used to broaden the scope of mathematics, as Nunn and others had argued for over thirty years, to include elements of trigonometry and calculus as part of a general secondary education. In relation to unification, the MA was supportive but not optimistic, given the conservatism of teachers and textbooks, and the requirements of examinations. The MA added: 'It may be that new textbooks and new training in the training colleges (and not merely in one of them) are wanted.'

The Consultative Committee, under Hadow, also reported on the primary school (1931), and on infant and nursery schools (1933). (19) These reports were imbued with a progressive spirit and sought to provide blueprints for three identifiable phases in primary education: nursery, infant and junior. As H.C. Dent remarked some thirty years later, 'the history of the Primary school ever since the early 1930s has been largely a working out in practice of the ideals embodied in those reports'. (20) The Hadow Report of 1931 included sections on the full range of subjects suitable for the primary phase, including suggestions for arithmetic together with 'simple geometry', in the interests of broadening the narrow range of mathematical work traditionally treated in the elementary school standards, and reinforced by the requirements in arithmetic of free-place and scholarship examinations. (21) The effects of selection examinations on the junior phase, effects which persisted after 1944 through the eleven-plus, were identified as 'a sombre and dissonant feature' by Dent. who perceived that examinations still served to widen the gap between educational ideals and the reality of school curricula. (22)

The arrangements for and the effects of examinations at the secondary stage were a central concern of the Norwood Committee, which reported to Butler in 1943. In common with primary and secondary curricula, the effective control and detailed requirements of examinations were not issues addressed by the 1944 Act: the LEAs managed the eleven-plus arrangements and the university examining bodies continued to exercise their independence and powerful influence on secondary curricula through the school certificate and higher school certificate examinations. There is a striking contrast here with the 1988 Education Act and its provision for a national system of centrally controlled testing at the ages of seven, eleven, fourteen and sixteen.

Following the Spens Report's criticisms of the effects of the school certificate arrangements, the Norwood Report made radical proposals for the reform of the system in two main directions: the gradual transfer of responsibility for syllabuses and papers from external university boards towards a system of internal teacher controls; and the replacement of the single-certificate system by single-subject examinations, with no restrictions on the number or choice of subjects. (23) The second proposal was taken up by the SSEC in 1947, and new examinations for the General Certificate of Education (GCE) at ordinary (O) level, for sixteen-year-olds, and advanced (A) level, for eighteen-year-olds, plus a higher, scholarship (S) level, were introduced in 1951. The proposal for greater internal teacher control was not implemented at this time. However, the principle of teacher involvement in the development of the university boards' syllabuses and papers, particularly through the influence exerted by the professional or subject associations, was a long-standing one. In mathematics, major syllabus developments took place before the introduction of the GCE. The drift of the new proposals was flagged by the Norwood Report, which included short chapters on all the subjects of the secondary school curriculum.

In contrast to the views expressed by Nunn in the Spens Report, the Norwood Report presented a somewhat optimistic picture:

> Compared with the theory and practice of thirty years ago . . . Mathematics has reformed itself; the various branches of the subject have coalesced, dead matter has been pruned away; the course has gained in unity and embraces content which some years ago was reserved only for advanced students; progress has been accelerated and laborious formal proof and rigidly logical sequence have been replaced by shorter methods and by the demonstration of Mathematical principles and their practical application. (24)

But these remarks were not unqualified: 'Many teachers . . . would point to the changes already made as an earnest of others to come.'

The way forward was sketched by the Norwood Report along the following lines:

> This 'normal' course from 11 plus to 16 plus should include, we believe, parts of Arithmetic, Algebra, Graphs, Geometry and Trigonometry, treated not as isolated subjects but with the fullest measure of co-ordination. For the treatment of Mathematics now stresses frequent numerical illustration, and this change has affected not only Trigonom-

etry, making it more suitable for less able pupils, but also Algebra and Graphs . . . In Geometry formal proofs of geometrical propositions would give way to informal explanations and the use of algebraical and trigonometrical methods where appropriate. Solid Geometry would be touched upon in the first lessons and references to three dimensions would recur throughout the course . . . pupils would be taught to rely upon a few fundamental principles and their own power to use them. The process . . . of purging away old-fashioned topics . . . would be carried still further. (25)

ALTERNATIVE MATHEMATICS SYLLABUSES

The simplification, unification and broadening of the subject matter of school mathematics, which implied the rejection of the dominant nineteenth-century tradition of separate branches in mathematics, were identifiable pedagogical strands underpinning the Perry movement. The tendency towards simplification and unification facilitated broadening, and, indeed, Perry's scheme of practical mathematics was both ambitious in scope and a mixed treatment of elements taken from various branches of the subject. But textbooks in practical mathematics were designed for use by technical students and such books made no inroads into the secondary sector. The Perry movement had brought about some intermingling of the branches, including the spread of arithmetical work throughout the course, but, up to the Second World War, secondary mathematics continued generally to be discussed, taught, learnt and examined in its separate branches: arithmetic, algebra, geometry, trigonometry, calculus and mechanics.

The idea of general courses in mathematics was initially associated with technical education, and the possibility of transfer of this idea to secondary education was not seriously entertained. Given the character of the reactions to reform, general courses would have been regarded as too ambitious, diluted and mathematically inferior to the systematic treatment of the branches taken separately. The low status of general mathematics had parallels both with developments in the USA and in science education, where the 'general science movement' encountered fundamental value barriers. (26) However, isolated initiatives, which departed from the dominant trend, go back to as early as the 1900s.

A concern for fundamental ideas, connections and concentration of subject matter in the curriculum, which reflected the influence of the German educationist J.F. Herbart in England, is detectable in the early-twentieth-century writings of Whitehead, Nunn and Godfrey. (27) Whitehead's view of school mathematics came from a university standpoint, and Nunn was an idealist, but the latter's seminal book on the teaching of algebra ranged widely to consider links with trigonometry, complex numbers, calculus, statistics, astronomy and map projections. Nunn's accompanying textbooks for his ambitious scheme were predictably a commercial failure. (28) Godfrey was idealistically inclined but also a realist and he confined his very successful textbook writing to the separate branches. However, D.B. Mair of the Civil Service Commission produced an extraordinary unified textbook, *A School Course of Mathematics*

(1907). (29) Furthermore, Godfrey and Mair were instrumental in a very early breakthrough involving the examination requirements of the Oxford and Cambridge Joint Board, with which the public schools and Godfrey, who had links with both the HMC and the MA, were closely associated.

In 1919 the Joint Board raised the possibility of mixed examination papers for the school certificate, and Godfrey and Mair became involved in drafting new schedules for implementation from 1921. (30) Siddons opened a discussion on 'the best method of examining school mathematics' at the annual meeting of the MA in 1928, and he emphasized the benefits of the Joint Board's distinctive scheme of mixed papers, which was also commended by the SSEC in its report of 1932. (31) However, this innovation in examining was of little consequence in relation to the MA's major inter-war programme of reporting on the separate branches of school mathematics; and, with the exception of Durham University, the other university boards, which catered for the grammar schools, remained unmoved by the argument for mixed papers until the 1940s.

From 1928 Durham provided an alternative syllabus for the school certificate, which had much in common with the subsequent Jeffery syllabus. But Durham's influence was small; the alternative proved unpopular with the schools and was allowed to lapse in 1934. (32) In 1942, on the initiative of the Cambridge Local Examinations Syndicate, renewed efforts were made to promote unification and broadening through examination syllabus construction, at first in the restricted domains of geometry and trigonometry.

Towards the end of 1942 the Cambridge Syndicate informed the MA that it proposed to issue an alternative syllabus in geometry and trigonometry. In 1938 the Teaching Committee of the MA had established an examinations subcommittee, with Daltry as secretary, and this subcommittee had started to work in earnest until the outbreak of war. (33) Daltry judged it to be 'unfortunate that the Association was not asked to help in preparing this new syllabus until a late stage', but the thinking behind this initiative, and its essential features, were communicated through letters and notices in the *Gazette* during 1943. (34) J.L. Brereton, assistant secretary of the Cambridge Syndicate, apologized on behalf of the Cambridge committee for the short time given for consultation, but added:

> They hope that by hastening the issue of the syllabus and so making possible its experimental adoption in a few schools, they are providing concrete material for discussion among members of [the MA] out of which a new agreed mathematical syllabus may emerge after the war. (35)

The consequences of the Syndicate's initiative were to be swiftly and widely felt by other examining bodies and educational associations during the years 1943 and 1944, and the MA again became closely involved in the development of new examination syllabuses.

The Cambridge committee argued that the time was now 'ripe for a change' in school geometry, which had reached a stable state between the wars. The new Cambridge syllabus was designed to be more accessible to average pupils in grammar and independent secondary schools. It included much less memory work on theorems, more work in three dimensions, and further broadening to include more trigonometry alongside geometry. It was felt that unless such changes were introduced 'mathematical teaching may get more and more out of step with the times'. (36)

The MA used both the *Gazette* and the branches to promote discussion on the new proposals, and a questionnaire was circulated. The Teaching Committee held a special meeting in August of 1943 to consider the new possibilities, including the alternative of mixed papers. By this time the Cambridge Syndicate had also taken an important strategic step by setting up a widely representative conference which met in September to consider the Cambridge syllabus and the wider potential for reform that it raised. (37) Among the conference delegates were four representatives of the MA, including Daltry and Robson; there were also two representatives from each of the eight examining boards, and two each from the professional associations of headmasters, headmistresses, assistant masters and assistant mistresses.

The conference strongly supported the new thrust initiated by the Cambridge Syndicate and it was widely felt that 'the traditional divisions of mathematics at this stage were harmful and restrictive in teaching practice'. (38) A small committee of seven was set up, under the chairmanship of Professor G.B. Jeffery FRS (1891–1957), to prepare an alternative syllabus and specimen papers covering the whole range of elementary mathematics for the school certificate. Jeffery held a chair in mathematics at University College, before he became Director of the London Institute of Education, in 1945, and he was elected President of the MA for the year 1947–8. All seven members of the committee were members of the MA; Daltry, Robson, Parsons and Mrs E. Shuttleworth were also members of the MA's examinations subcommittee. (39) The committee was assisted by reports of discussions held in branch meetings of the MA, and its proposals were first discussed at a full meeting of the MA in April of 1944. Earlier in the same month the proposals were also considered by the representative conference. The Jeffery syllabus, as it became known, was issued with a recommendation from the conference that it should be considered for adoption by the examining bodies as an alternative to existing syllabuses, and with the aim of parity of esteem between the traditional and alternative syllabuses.

The Jeffery syllabus as such was never officially approved by the MA, but in 1944 resolutions were carried unanimously, on the need for a general revision and in support of the main lines proposed for geometry and trigonometry by the Cambridge committee. The need for reductions in formal algebra to allow further work in graphs and functionality was agreed with a very few dissentients. The radical proposal to introduce some optional, and largely graphical, calculus questions into the new papers was also carried, although with a much smaller majority. (40) Thus the principal aims of the Jeffery syllabus were supported not only by the representative conference but also by a large number of members of the MA, and leading members had played a very large part in the shaping of the syllabus. (41)

A 1973 report judged that the Jeffery syllabus had had 'a far-reaching influence on the deformalization of geometry and the integration of all branches of mathematics'. (42) It is important to recognize that the Jeffery syllabus, examined by means of mixed papers allowing complete freedom of method, was intended only as an alternative. It was not an attempt 'to use the syllabus of the examination to impose change upon teachers who may prefer to follow the more traditional line of approach'. (43) Within three or four years the alternative syllabus, with minor modifications, was made available by the various examining boards. (44) The pace and scale of adoption of the alternative now depended upon the development of suitable textbooks and upon the attitudes, motivation and capabilities of the teaching force. Many of the ideals underpinning the Jeffery syllabus had flourished during the Perry movement but had not come to fruition in that earlier period. The momentum for further changes had become lost in the inter-war years, and conservatism in curriculum development is understandable in the immediate post-war period of educational reconstruction.

Successful textbook writers within the traditional branches, such as Durell, were, not surprisingly, reluctant to start again from scratch and provide innovatory new textbooks in general or unified mathematics. It was much easier to produce textbooks for general mathematics by compiling individual chapters or sections from previously successful textbooks on arithmetic, algebra etc. (45) In spite of the Norwood Report's (1943) early optimism, some indication of the relatively slow uptake of the alternative syllabus is given by the fact that, by 1955, only about one third of sixty-three grammar schools in Northumberland and Durham were using the new syllabus, and it was not until 1962 that the alternative became more popular amongst the large number of schools taking the NUJMB's examination. (46) In addition, one important value-barrier to change persisted in the 1950s, in the form of the faint but still detectable shadow of Euclid.

It became the custom to appoint more schoolmaster-Presidents of the MA in the post-war period: Tuckey, 1944–5; Bushell, 1946–7; Robson, 1948–9; Snell, 1952–3; Parsons, 1955–6; and Langford, 1957–8. (47) The educational values reflected in their Presidential addresses are sometimes quite revealing. In 1953 Snell commented:

> the 'alternative syllabus' proposed by the 'Jeffery report', and now largely adopted, introduces new topics, and something has to be curtailed to make way for these; and this, unintentionally, has left little time for work on riders. (48)

Snell regretted the erosion of deductive geometry and, in 1956, Parsons was more outspoken on the same theme:

> This emphasis on rider work has led in some quarters to a development which I personally feel to be mistaken viz. the demand for the abolition of all set theorem work . . . I believe that it is not possible to know any geometry at all worth the name unless it is based on a logically coherent set of facts, that is on a body of theorems . . . Perhaps I am expressing a very reactionary point of view but one of the things I seem to have picked up in the course of 35 years' teaching is that old Euclid was rather a wise schoolmaster after all. (49)

Echoing the sentiments of Rollett, Parsons added:

All revolutions lead to a period of chaos in which all sorts of ideas about new freedoms and the breaking of old bondages naturally come to the fore. Perhaps the chaotic period resulting from the revolution in the teaching of geometry was to some extent prolonged by the intervention of two wars but it may not be out of place to express the hope that it may soon be ended. (50)

Langford, in 1958, was less pessimistic regarding the status of geometry, following:

the greatest change of all: the Jeffery Report and the acceptance by the schools and the Examining Authorities of the Alternative Syllabus. So far as can be judged after ten years' experience this revolution, far-reaching in its effect on the mathematical work in schools, has been entirely bloodless – for Euclid, if deposed, is neither exiled nor ostracised. (51)

Teachers starting or building their careers after the war were likely to be more favourably disposed towards the alternative (B) syllabuses. As Bill Brookes has remarked, the syllabus 'created sufficient of a change for a number of us to experiment in our teaching with different treatments of a variety of topics'. (52) A head of mathematics and physics at one of the first comprehensive schools recalls his adoption of London's syllabus B around 1948: 'I said, "Thank God for that." For the first time it did try to integrate . . . It was in the right direction.' (53) The progress of syllabus B was also helped forward by the growth of the single-subject O-level examinations from 1951.

Not surprisingly, the MA became involved in the discussions and representations leading up to the new O-level and A-level examinations. About 250 attended a discussion at the annual meeting in 1948, which was chaired by Professor Jeffery, when the subject was fully explored and specific resolutions passed. Fears that the abandonment of the single-certificate system might undermine the strong place of mathematics in the grammar and independent school curriculum were not seriously entertained. On the contrary, the importance of choice, with responsibility, was underlined by Jeffery, who had had a hand in the 1947 report to the SSEC:

the due balancing of the school curriculum of every child is a matter of the very first importance. Whether it should include mathematics or not include mathematics is not a trivial matter . . . But looking back over the experience of the group requirements of examining bodies, we came to the conclusion that this was not a problem that could be solved through the regulations of examining bodies. The responsibility should be placed fairly and squarely upon the teachers and the schools. (54)

Langford, of Battersea Grammar School, pointed to the potentially important role of the MA in the fine tuning of new syllabuses for the GCE, building on the existing school certificate syllabuses:

this Association is surely the only body in this country able to speak with authority on the syllabus for these proposed examinations. If we can do this at once our position will be immensely strengthened; it is one thing to be invited to work in consultation, it is quite another thing to take the initiative and to present a scheme in advance. (55)

Jeffery indicated that the SSEC would welcome representations from the MA concerning syllabuses. Over the next year, the examinations subcommittee of the MA prepared a detailed report on the arrangements for papers, together with recommendations for syllabuses in mathematics and mechanics at all levels; and the report was forwarded to the eight university examining bodies. (56)

In 1955, a newly established examining board for the GCE – the Associated Examining Board (AEB) – held its first examinations in technical and commercial as well as academic subjects. Uniquely, it was a non-university board, sponsored by commercial and technical institutions, and its range of subjects appealed particularly to secondary modern schools, which were beginning to enter candidates for small numbers of O-level subjects, normally after an extended course beyond the minimum leaving age. Between 1954 and 1964 there was a remarkable growth in the uptake of O-level examinations by secondary modern schools: the number of such schools entering candidates increased five-fold, from 357, and the number of candidates increased ten-fold, from around 5500. (57) This upward striving by secondary modern schools, particularly in areas where the number of grammar school places was limited, was one kind of response to the need to enhance the esteem of this sector of the tripartite system. But GCE work required these schools to follow the syllabuses which had been progressively developed to serve the interests of the minority of pupils in the selective schools. In mathematics, as we have seen, the MA had played a central role in the development of both school certificate and GCE syllabuses. The needs of the multitude in secondary modern schools was also one among a number of items on the Teaching Committee's agenda when it resumed its activities after the Second World War.

POST-WAR TEACHING COMMITTEE

Following the 1944 Education Act, the regulations for the Teaching Committee were revised to accommodate the new division of schools into primary and secondary. The breakdown for the representation from all sectors was now as follows: universities, 5 men and 3 women; teacher-training institutions, 3 men and 2 women; technical institutions, 3 men and 1 woman; secondary schools, 16; preparatory and primary schools, 6. In appointing the 22 school representatives it was stated that 'care shall be taken to secure adequate representation of all types of school and both sexes'. (58) Langford took over from Robson as chairman of the Teaching Committee in 1946. He was followed by Combridge in 1950, who was followed by Allan Riley (1901–83) from 1957 until the mid-1960s. (59)

Throughout the war years, some Teaching Committee business had continued, principally through the post and the *Gazette*. (60) There had been some collaboration, on the mathematical needs of scientists, with both the Science Masters' Association and the Institute of Physics, and a joint report with the Institute was published in 1944. (61) The principal other war-time business concerned examinations, which was one of eight areas chosen for development work by subcommittees when the Teaching Committee returned to full-scale activity in 1946. Some of these areas had been identified in 1938 and they were all now firmly on the MA's post-war agenda. (62)

The range of institutional concerns now included primary and secondary modern schools, along with preparatory schools and technical institutions. In relation to the branches of school mathematics, there were subcommittees for trigonometry and sixth form work. Furthermore, the existence of a visual aids subcommittee provides one indication of the developing post-war interest in methods of teaching and learning. The basic strategy was to delegate the responsibility for the production of reports to small subcommittees, whose drafts would then be considered in detail by the fully representative Teaching Committee. The final approval by Council was normally a formality. The principal aim was still to produce authoritative publications, for circulation to members and for wider dissemination, as appropriate. Here the MA had a well-established reputation in relation to the traditional branches of selective-school mathematics – arithmetic, algebra, geometry and mechanics – and Langford could report 'sensational' sales of its major reports by 1946; reprinting was already under way. (63)

The post-war challenge was, however, a broader one: to continue to produce authoritative reports on the substance of school mathematics but also to extend the range to new institutional contexts. The aim was to cover not only the technical field but also the needs of primary and secondary modern schools, where the MA's membership was scarcely represented. At the same time, the MA sought through its Teaching Committee to maintain quality control over a widening range of publications. In this process, as Douglas Quadling has suggested, the representative character of the Committee facilitated 'cross-dissemination between sectors of mathematical education which I think was quite an important feature of the Association's image'. (64) University representation on the Committee continued to be important for the status of its work in all fields, and particularly so in connection with the work on trigonometry and other more advanced branches, where a major programme of report production was implemented that continued into the early 1960s.

REPORTS ON THE BRANCHES OF SCHOOL MATHEMATICS

Robson was the prime mover in the extension of the MA's reporting upwards from the school certificate stage to the sixth form and university interface. This policy was discussed at a meeting in 1937 at Cambridge, and Robson and others soon became involved in some early drafting in the fields of higher geometry and calculus. (65) When Robson handed over the chairmanship of the Teaching Committee to Langford in 1946, work was resumed, and much of it was brought to fruition during the period of Combridge's chairmanship in the 1950s. (66) The full timetable for the publication of the post-war reports on the separate branches of school mathematics extended throughout the period 1950–65:

1950	*The Teaching of Trigonometry in Schools*
1951	*The Teaching of Calculus in Schools*
1953	*The Teaching of Higher Geometry in Schools*
1957	*Analysis Course 1*
1957	*The Teaching of Algebra in Sixth Forms*
1962	*Analysis Course 2*
1964	*A Second Report on the Teaching of Arithmetic in Schools*
1965	*A Second Report on the Teaching of Mechanics in Schools*

The trigonometry report of 1950 was the first of an impressive post-war line of major reports, following the second geometry report of 1938. Work on trigonometry had started in earnest in 1938 but it was only brought to fruition 'after many vicissitudes'. (67) Part of the difficulty was associated with the scope of the report, which was required to span the school certificate and more advanced stages of school work. At the school certificate stage, as we have seen, trigonometry was at the centre of moves to unify the treatment of elementary mathematics. The movement towards unification created some tensions in a report on trigonometry taken in isolation. At the more advanced level, the production of one chapter on vectors and complex numbers proved particularly troublesome and the mathematical expertise of Neville, Broadbent and Goodstein was called upon to resolve the difficulties: 'it seemed desirable to go rather more fully into the theory and to make more demands on the attention of the reader'. (68)

Neville's influence within the Teaching Committee was still considerable, even when he was not directly involved in drafting. Broadbent commented: 'On the battlefield from which the *Trigonometry Report* eventually emerged, he slew many attractive but unsound proposals.' (69) Tuckey, chairman of the trigonometry subcommittee, underlined the general difficulty of reaching a consensus on specific teaching points: 'you would perhaps be surprised to find out how much argument can centre round the question "which is the best proof of the addition theorem" or "which should come first, the sine or the tangent".' (70)

The calculus report of 1951 was the first of the specifically more advanced reports. The subcommittee was chaired by Snell, and Robson exerted a major influence as editor, drawing upon the specialist contributions of Broadbent, Goodstein and Ida Busbridge. Calculus was treated from its roots in graphical work up to differential geometry and differential equations; analysis was treated separately in two later reports. (71) The subcommittee's work in calculus appears to have been uncontroversial and production of the final report was relatively straightforward. The same cannot be said about the higher geometry report of 1953.

Neville chaired the higher geometry subcommittee and he was assisted, on the university side, by Combridge, Mary Cartwright, and a new recruit from Cambridge, Edwin Maxwell, who in 1963 took over the editorship of the *Gazette* from Goodstein. (72) Tuckey and Durell represented the schools' viewpoint, along with J.B. Morgan of Harrow (a subsequent MA President, 1963–4) and teachers from Christ's Hospital and Winchester College: the membership was exclusively public school, and not surprisingly given the level of work considered. (73) There is a clear link in philosophy between the 1953 report and the famous geometry report of thirty years earlier, which Neville edited. A prologue to the 1953 report began:

> A large part of this report is addressed to those teachers who are unfamiliar with the ideas of abstract geometry and much material is included which is not intended for the pupil. Unless this is realized . . . the contents will be dismissed as visionary and unrealistic. (74)

The report went on to place its aim in the broader context of MA report production:

> To a great extent this policy represents a change from that of previous reports of the Mathematical Association. With the exception of the 1923 Report on the teaching of geometry, these have been concerned mainly with methods of presentation. They have been based on extensive experience gained in the class-room and on the interchange of ideas between teachers at meetings of the Association and its Branches. A report has in fact expressed the considered opinions of the general body of teachers and has put on record various details of class-room procedure which have proved to be effective in practice. (75)

The 1953 report opened up the whole question of progression in geometry for the future specialist, from spatial geometry, based initially on physical observation and measurement at stage A, to abstract geometry, whether pure or analytical, based on formal and rigorous deductive methods. Here two twentieth-century discontinuities were identified. The first was a consequence of the tendency to move towards the spirit of the Jeffery syllabus and away from systematic, stage C geometry. The second was a consequence of the development of abstract geometry in undergraduate courses. The report – a big one of over a hundred pages – aimed to provide a bridge for teachers between spatial geometry and abstract, mainly algebraic, cartesian and projective geometry, in the interests of smoothing the passage of higher attaining pupils through a difficult field.

Parsons, in his 1956 Presidential address, used the pedagogical, three-stages model to point to discontinuities not only in geometry but also in calculus and analysis: 'it seems to me that the liaison between the various stages of teaching is weakest at the point where the sixth form mathematical student merges into the first year undergraduate'. (76) He appealed for 'the continuance of that happy liaison between dons and schoolmasters which has been such a beneficial feature of the work of this Association', and he hoped particularly for the co-operation of the younger generation of university teachers in this work at the sixth form and university interface. Certainly, the 1957 report on sixth form algebra is a good example of a 'happy liaison' involving some new blood in the MA's subcommittee work.

The algebra subcommittee was chaired by Professor M.H.A. Newman of Manchester University, who also drew in a colleague, W. Ledermann, a writer in the field of modern algebra for undergraduates. Robson, who had retired from Marlborough College, was also a member, until his death in 1956. Robson had been an acquaintance of Newman before the war and was probably responsible for involving him in the MA. Robson also played a part in getting Douglas Quadling, of Marlborough College, involved in the 1950s work of the Teaching Committee, and, in particular, on to the algebra subcommittee as editor. Quadling was joined by two other experienced Teaching Committee members from the schools, Langford and Morgan. (77)

Newman underlined a major purpose of the report, which was to raise the status of 'higher algebra', as a study restricted to finite processes, by advancing:

the thesis that algebra is not to be regarded, even in school work, as a collection of oddments left over from other branches, but as a well-defined and unified subject particularly well suited for giving school pupils a taste of rigorous argument comfortably surrounded by the jam of formal manipulative work. (78)

Inevitably, the question arose of including material from modern or axiomatic algebra, which was now a feature of many English undergraduate syllabuses. Newman had raised some of the possibilities for schools as early as 1937, and the MA's report included an appendix on the subject. (79) But the passage of twenty years had made Newman 'a shade less sanguine':

It is to be feared that some will think we are proposing that school algebra should henceforth be rigorously developed from a stated set of axioms; and then we shall be hot on the trail of those countries . . . whose lofty aims leave us so far behind. Indeed our aim has been just the opposite, to resist premature academicism by providing, *for the teacher*, the means of convincing himself that he is justified in using some simpler and older methods of introducing the concepts of algebra, avoiding complicated constructions; and also in separating algebra from geometry and analysis when he wishes to. (80)

The report on higher geometry had been wide-ranging and forward-looking. The algebra report articulated a more well-tried and consolidated position, and contained only a hint of the more radical possibilities for schools, which were to become much more widely broadcast, on an international scale, over the next five years. (81).

With the publication of the second part of the MA's report on analysis, in 1962, there remained only one further branch – mechanics – to complete the series on sixth form work 'as hitherto understood'. (82) As early as 1950 Cambridge had raised the possibility of a second report on mechanics, to replace the report of 1930, but the considerable challenge was not taken up until 1958 and a report was not published until 1965. (83) Combridge replaced Snell as chairman of the subcommittee in 1961. As for trigonometry, the full school progression of the branch was covered, in the by-this-time well-worn three stages, and the report culminated in an ambitious treatment based on vectors 'for the teacher who may wish to give pupils the opportunity to read further'. (84) Not surprisingly, deeper questions about the relations between mechanics, applied mathematics and physics, which had come to prominence before the First World War, remained unresolved. As Trevor Fletcher has pointed out, 'when we speak of the long tradition of teaching applied mathematics in English schools we are thinking chiefly of pupils in the age range 16–18, and we are also thinking very largely of *theoretical mechanics*'. (85) Despite the cartoon on its front cover, this report was firmly located within this long English tradition.

The appearance of a report on arithmetic, in 1964, seems oddly out of place in the context of the fast-moving swell of 1960s innovation in school mathematics curricula. Work on the second arithmetic report had started in 1958 under the chairmanship of Tuckey, who had also led the work on the first report, which was published in 1932. The second report was focused primarily on the needs of pupils of grammar-school ability. Furthermore, despite the growing tendency towards the unification of elementary mathematics and the introduction of new mathematical topics such as simple descriptive statistics (which was only very briefly treated in the report), the focus was on only one traditional branch of the subject. (86) The general relevance of this report was seriously questioned during a discussion at the annual meeting in 1965, at which some members of the MA were pushed to adopt a distinctly defensive posture. (87) With hindsight, it seems to have been a case of 'one too many' in a long line of major reports on the separate branches of school mathematics, stretching over forty years, from the geometry report of 1923.

MATHEMATICS IN TECHNICAL EDUCATION

The MA first turned its attention to technical education in the 1920s, and new developments, culminating in the 1944 Education Act, led to further work in this field. Since the 1940s the MA has continued to have some stake in 'technical mathematics' – at different levels and with varying interpretations – and has been able to call on individual members with the necessary expertise and energy to promote this side of its work. Furthermore, the MA's branches and annual meetings, and the work of the Teaching Committee, have given the opportunity for teachers and lecturers in the technical field to mix with secondary schoolteachers, university mathematicians, and teacher trainers. Quadling's own personal experience serves to emphasize the importance of this point:

> It was through the MA that I, as a young teacher, became aware of the 'technical stream' of education: first through hearing men like Lowry . . . at the London branch . . . and then through the reports

on mathematics in technical schools and colleges . . . In those days every report was debated in full committee before being approved for publication. Then, following publication and distribution, reports were discussed in open forum at a conference and an account of the discussion published in the *Gazette*. The result was a cross-dissemination between sectors of mathematical education which I think was quite an important feature of the Association's image. (88)

In Britain, deep-rooted questions of status and definition have been a persistent problem in the development of technical education and its relations with a liberal education, the latter emphasizing broader 'academic' values against the narrower 'practical' values of the former. The problem has also persistently been linked with claims of 'declinism' in Britain's industrial and economic performance when compared with that of its competitors, a 'British disease' in the judgement of some historians. (89) In mathematics, as we have seen, the Perry movement and reactions to it brought many underlying values and assumptions to the surface, with the spotlight on 'practical mathematics' in relation to a general education at various levels. W.G. Bickley, of Imperial College, highlighted the broader historical and cultural context in a paper on mathematics for engineering students, which was published in the *Gazette*, in 1939:

Technical education grew as an appendage of the 'school' system of education, and was in some quarters – and to-day still is – regarded as a cancer or as a foreign body in that system . . . in a piecemeal, haphazard, and uncoordinated way technical schools and colleges have multiplied, but there are few signs that either the authorities or the public have yet attained a sane and well-thought-out attitude to technical education. (90)

In particular, the Spens Report's plans for the development of secondary technical schools, to be on a par with the grammar schools, were viewed with some scepticism by Bickley: 'The report will not kill at once the idea that lawyers and stockbrokers are so much more respectable than engineers and other craftsmen!'

For Bickley there were two sides to the challenge of developing an appropriate mathematics curriculum for technical students and particularly for the important group of future engineers:

any course in mathematics for technical students must be planned with their particular needs and interests constantly in mind . . . If the course is also to be educative, it must become clear to the students that the mathematical topics are closely inter-related and fit together into a coordinated structure of knowledge. (91)

As he was forced to admit, 'All this . . . doesn't sound particularly easy. It isn't!' Thus, in relation to the realized curriculum, the supply and training of suitable teachers was again a key factor.

In the efforts towards educational reconstruction after the war, the supply and training of teachers for all sectors of the educational system was the major concern of the McNair Committee, which reported in 1944. The MA was not in a position to prepare a full response for the McNair Committee but Bickley produced a memorandum on technical teachers of mathematics which was largely accepted as the MA's submission. (92) After the war, the technical subcommittee also drew upon Bickley's memorandum as a basis for a short report, published in 1949, on mathematics teacher training for the secondary technical schools and technical colleges. The early post-war provision for secondary technical education had exacerbated the 'considerable difficulty' already experienced in providing sufficient, suitably qualified, mathematics staff for technical institutions. Furthermore, the character of the preliminary education of such staff in mathematics was largely dictated by the twentieth-century dominance of pure over applied mathematics in the universities and by the 'pure' bias of the latter:

> The place where change of outlook would be most effective, and where it is most needed is, unfortunately, just where change seems least likely, and where it would be most difficult to enforce, namely in the departments of mathematics in the universities. Not every university has a separate department of applied mathematics, and . . . they are usually smaller than the corresponding departments of pure mathematics. Where they do not exist, the combined department is, more often than not . . . in the charge of a 'pure' mathematician . . . until the outlook changes, or other steps are taken, the majority of those who enter the teaching profession as mathematical specialists will have been taught 'pure' mathematics and abstract mechanics, in an atmosphere largely indifferent to technical (if not scientific) applications. (93)

The problem was, again, a deep-rooted and persistent one.

The whole question of 'technical mathematics' was discussed at the 1946 annual meeting of the MA. The discussion was opened by H.V. Lowry, of Woolwich Polytechnic, who began by clarifying the three major categories of work involved: mathematics for pupils up to sixteen in technical schools; mathematics as part of a degree course in science or engineering, from matriculation, through intermediate, to final degree level; and mathematics within part-time courses leading to ordinary national certificates – numerically the largest category of work – and higher national certificates. During the discussion, the possibility of collaboration between the MA and the engineering institutions was considered, with a view to the production of an authoritative report on technical mathematics. A precedent had already been set by the Institute of Physics, which had approached the MA during the war. Now the initiative would need to come from the MA, and one member suggested that a lead from a body such as the MA was badly needed in this field:

> It was necessary to elevate technical mathematics in this country to as high a position in engineering education as it had on the Continent. If Great Britain was to keep pace with other countries, from the viewpoint of modern technical developments, technical mathematics must be well to the fore. (94)

The MA's technical subcommittee first turned its attention to the needs of secondary technical schools, and a short report was published in 1949. Francis Kellaway chaired the first post-war technical subcommittee, and, following Parsons, from 1949 he also acted as honorary general secretary of the MA. He continued in this office until 1969, and was MA President for the year 1966–7. Kellaway looked back on his wealth of experience in technical education and acknowledged the influence of Whitehead:

> All my associations with technological education make it appropriate to remind you of Whitehead's affirmation that 'the antithesis between a technical and a liberal education is fallacious. There can be no liberal education which is not technical: that is, no education which does not impart both technique and intellectual vision.' (95)

The MA's technical subcommittee, under Kellaway, included members representing a full spectrum of relevant interests: Riley, an LEA inspector, as secretary; C.W. Tregenza, a staff inspector from the Ministry of Education; Lowry and H.A. Hayden, from Woolwich and Battersea polytechnics; Bickley from Imperial College; plus representatives from the technical colleges and secondary schools. The recommendations for secondary technical schools were necessarily somewhat tentative in the 1940s. The aims for mathematics teaching in all types of secondary school were broadly classified under three headings: 'social', which relates to the general needs of everyday life; 'vocational', insofar as a variety of career requirements can be generally accommodated; and 'cultural', where the emphasis is on aesthetic values and on mathematics placed in its historical context. The proposed syllabus for a very broad, and integrated, thirteen-plus course has much in common with the Jeffery syllabus, but even less emphasis on theoretical geometry, and further broadening in trigonometry, including the general functions, plus some introductory work on vectors and statistics. There are striking similarities with Perry's fifty-year-old syllabus for elementary practical mathematics. Differences between grammar school and technical mathematics were envisaged in the relative emphasis placed on the three broad aims, and in the consequent treatment:

> The cultural interest will be strongest in the specialist streams of the grammar school. The interests and abilities which have brought pupils into the technical school will point towards the vocational and utilitarian aspects of their work . . . Much will depend on the teacher . . . The environment of the pupils and the technical interests drawn from it must serve to illustrate and enrich the mathematics. Only in this way will the interest of the pupil in the subject as a whole be sustained. (96)

But the general aspirations of secondary technical schooling were never realized on a large scale, and in the 1950s the MA's work on mathematics for technical colleges proved to be of considerably greater significance.

The subcommittee on mathematics for technical colleges started work in 1948 under Kellaway's chairmanship. A number of MA members from technical colleges were co-opted to undertake this work, and representation from the Institutions of Civil, Electrical and Mechanical Engineers was also secured. (97) A major report was published in 1954. In the introduction to the report the Perry legacy was still much in evidence:

> one may hazard a guess that Professor Perry might view with approval a good deal of the work done in the mathematics classes in technical colleges to-day. It cannot be gainsaid, however, that there are some lecturers who either ignore the practical applications, or else teach nothing but applications without explaining the mathematics. (98)

The MA's earlier report of 1926 was judged to have had some effect on the consolidation of a common core syllabus at national certificate level, and the bulk of the new report was devoted to details of mathematical presentation which, it was emphasized, needed to be read in conjunction with the MA's reports on the separate branches. Two broad aims for the teacher were identified:

> He must try to illustrate the topic of any particular lecture by applications to engineering topics . . . He must also try to relate the various branches of mathematics that he has to teach . . . This integration of the various branches of mathematics is of prime importance to all technical students. (99)

The report concentrated on the work for ordinary national certificates, but it also included some discussion of higher and post-higher national certificate courses, which overlapped degree-level work, although it was admitted, 'It is not the general practice of the Association to report on the teaching of mathematics of University Standard.' (100) Mathematics in lower-level trade courses, linked with City and Guilds syllabuses, was also considered.

The publication of the MA's report was timely, given the great expansion of technical education and the rationalization of its provision, at various levels, after the 1944 Act. Progress was stimulated by Government White Papers on technical education, in 1956 and 1961, and followed the blueprint in the Percy Report of 1945. At the highest level, ten colleges of advanced technology (CATs) were established, and a new diploma in technology was instituted. Such developments paved the way for the general expansion of further and higher education in the 1960s; and, on the recommendation of the Robbins Report (*Higher Education*, 1963), the CATs became universities in their own right. The national certificate system was also reorganized from 1961, and it had expanded greatly: the number of ordinary national certificates gained in 1963 was almost seven times as many as in 1938; and the figures for higher national certificates show a ten-fold increase over the same period. (101)

The MA's report was reprinted in 1964 as it was 'so much in demand', at a time when 'the place of technical education in the public esteem is higher than ever before'. (102) A new report was planned, to accommodate the changes in the courses for national certificates, although this never materialized. But the 1954 report was a valuable contribution to the teaching of mathematics in a burgeoning sector of the educational system.

MATHEMATICS IN SECONDARY MODERN SCHOOLS

The MA was not able to draw upon the strength of its membership in selective schools and the universities to shape detailed blueprints for the teaching of mathematics to the multitude of pupils in primary and secondary modern schools. In 1946 two subcommittees were established, and they first met jointly, 'but the attendance was very small; only preliminary discussion has been possible and progress is hindered by the lack of members able to speak with authority and experience in the work of these schools'. (103) It should be added that, during the inter-war period, some early efforts had been made to extend the range of the MA's links and influence outside the selective schools.

A differentiated tradition of mathematics in post-primary education has roots going back to the work of the higher grade board schools in the late nineteenth century. The dominant and persistent question concerning the mathematics curriculum for the mass of post-primary pupils was how to broaden the scope of the subject beyond arithmetic, which had traditionally dominated syllabuses for the standards in elementary schools. Some of the earliest and most ambitious experimentation had started before the First World War, in the central schools, particularly in the London area. A further push to develop varieties of 'senior school mathematics' followed the raising of the school leaving age to fourteen and the reorganization of elementary schools after the Hadow Report of 1926. The degree of broadening, in principle and in practice, varied to include elements from mensuration, practical geometry, graphical work, the beginnings of algebra, and even some numerical trigonometry. A course in deductive geometry was generally not entertained, and this marked an important difference between non-selective and selective school mathematics. The approach to the former was typified by such keywords as 'non-academic', 'practical', 'useful' and 'relevant'. Indeed, the notion of 'practical mathematics' was resurrected between the wars to denote a differentiated mathematics curriculum for the embryonic secondary modern schools. (104)

In 1929 HMI Carson stressed the importance of the developing concept of a post-primary 'modern school', for which an alternative, less academic, mathematics curriculum was required than the paradigm for public and grammar schools. He added, 'The subject (or method) known as practical mathematics, which thirty years ago did so much for teaching in this country, is in mind in this connection.' (105) In 1935 the Board of Education published a pamphlet entitled *Senior School Mathematics*, which encouraged LEAs 'to provide courses for teachers in Practical Mathematics'. (106) Such courses could ignore both the constraints of the school certificate examination and 'the need for academic or conventional treatment', and a unified approach to the subject was advocated. (107)

In the 1930s the MA started to show some interest in the work of the central schools, which provided four-year courses for more able pupils from the elementary schools. In 1930 the Boys' Schools Committee co-opted two representatives from central schools, and plans were made to circulate a questionnaire and produce a report, drawing on relevant experience within the branches. (108) The Board of Education's policy at this time was to subsume central and senior schools, and the MA's efforts to gain the co-operation of HMI in the preparation of a report on central school mathematics were unsuccessful. But this subject was discussed at the annual meeting of the MA in 1934, a year before the Board's own report on senior school mathematics was published. Two teachers from central schools contributed to the MA's discussion, and Bushell revealingly remarked: 'A great many members of the Mathematical Association had been for some little time very curious indeed to know what mathematics was being taught in the Central Schools . . . ' (109) Branches were encouraged to pursue the matter, although the local involvement of elementary and central school teachers was minimal. In 1946 the needs of secondary modern schools brought a renewed response from the MA.

Although the MA could not call upon largely non-specialist teachers to provide the necessary lead in mathematics for primary and secondary modern schools, there were members of the MA with relevant experience from the fields of both teacher training and school inspection. Miss Adams, a member of HMI from 1925, was a leading figure, with sympathies for and wide experience of mathematics in popular education. In her MA Presidential address she looked back with some optimism to the evolution of senior schools and their approach to the curriculum:

> They were indeed Secondary Modern Schools in all but name, privilege and one year of age, fourteen to fifteen [from 1947]. They were for the most part staffed by teachers whose experience was with the children of the elementary school. Many teachers had themselves been so educated up to fourteen, so that they understood their pupils' background as though they were fellow scholars. Many of them had a real interest in Mathematics even though not highly qualified . . . To these old hands were added young teachers interested in a new venture and perhaps better qualified as subject specialists. The combination was often a strong one . . . the best of these schools tried to suit the curriculum to their pupils' world: to the rural community, to the life of an industrial town or to the kind of folk living in a dormitory area of a city . . . I think that scant justice has been done in our thoughts to the pioneer efforts of Senior Schools and indeed the top classes of many unreorganised schools of the pre-war period. The best of them took advantage of their freedom and showed flexibility and powers of adaptation controlled by a knowledge of circumstances which was the fruit of long experience. (110)

But the war had a serious effect on the staffing of these schools in both mathematics and science, particularly for boys, and Miss Adams commented: 'I consider it a tragedy that the natural evolution of mathematics teaching through the development of Senior Schools was almost obliterated by the war.' (111) Alongside the effects of war, there were also long-standing problems of large classes, poor facilities, inadequate professional training for teachers, and pupils' early leaving.

The field was certainly a challenging one for the MA in the post-war period. The place of mathematics in secondary modern schools was discussed at the MA's annual meeting in 1946. (112) A training college lecturer, formerly from a grammar school, opened the discussion, and a number of teacher-trainer members of the MA became involved in the work of a new subcommittee; other members included Miss Adams and, as secretary, Allan Riley, an LEA inspector from Wolverhampton and formerly a head of a central school. The subcommittee was chaired by Elizabeth Williams, who had moved from Goldsmiths' College to become first principal of the new City of Leicester Training College. (113)

The inevitable lack of contributions from secondary modern school teachers to the MA's discussion was a limiting factor, but Bushell emphasized the potentially important role for the MA:

> The history of the Association over the last forty years . . . revealed that what the Association had achieved was of a very high order. Now it had something else before it, namely to try to develop the teaching in the modern secondary schools on similar orderly, good and useful lines. He most earnestly hoped that the Association would in no way abdicate the position which it had won for itself after forty years of effort. (114)

But, as the discussion clearly revealed, there was no consensus about secondary modern school mathematics at this time and grammar school perspectives tended to narrow the debate. The starting point for the MA's subcommittee was a very different one from that of the many subcommittees charged with reporting on the branches of selective school mathematics.

The subcommittee produced a brief interim report for circulation in 1949. The report firmly emphasized the need for a differentiated curriculum for secondary modern schools:

> the mathematics which will emerge will not be the classical mathematics which has proved a well-marked and safe path for so many teachers of School Certificate forms. For Modern School children traditional academic standards and methods, appropriate as they may be to the needs of Grammar School children, lead only to failure; in the child the sense of failure leads to frustration and distaste for the artificial culture of the schools. (115)

The need for variety of provision was stressed: 'there can be no one certain recipe'; and some general principles were laid down, including the values of both teaching based on interest and 'activity' methods: 'activity involves self-directed search for knowledge through personal experience and experiment; obviously it can arise only in an environment which the child finds interesting'. (116) Detailed recipes were not provided; a much longer report, produced over 'several years more', would be required. (117) The interim report concluded with a reference to the most vital ingredient of all, the teacher:

> The work is undoubtedly more difficult for the teacher than the work
> with parallel age groups in Grammar and Technical Schools: it calls
> for mathematical knowledge of no less depth, but greater breadth, for
> first-class teaching ability, and for unlimited initiative and appetite for
> hard work . . . it is work for pioneers. (118)

The needs of average and below-average pupils in secondary schools were prominent in formal discussions at the annual meetings of the MA in 1949 and 1950. The subjects for discussion reflected important developments outside the MA: the plans for the new GCE O-level examination and the early development of comprehensive schools. The annual meeting at Birmingham University, in 1949, was the first such meeting outside London, and it was organized by the Midlands branch. Mrs Williams introduced a discussion on 'non-certificate mathematics' and sketched her vision by identifying a number of key ideas: structure and pattern in number; generalization in number; measurement, ratio and approximation; relationships; and choice and chance. She posed a key challenge: 'Can they be conveyed to children as a unified course with arithmetic, algebra, geometry, trigonometry and mechanics all welded firmly together?' (119) No doubt, such fundamental considerations were also driving the work of the secondary modern subcommittee at this time, and Mrs Williams suggested the use of practical and interesting starting points, e.g. in modelling or 3–D construction, as a major step towards unification in mathematics for the multitude.

During the annual meeting of the MA in 1950, at the Regent Street Polytechnic, a discussion on mathematics in the comprehensive school was led by two teachers with relevant experience from the experimental West Norwood Secondary School, one of whom also had had previous experience of speaking from the front at the annual meeting. He began:

> It is always with feelings of awe and wonder that I face the distin-
> guished audience of brilliant mathematicians and/or brilliant teachers
> of mathematics which gathers for the Annual General Meeting of this
> Association . . . To-day, it again falls to my lot to plead the cause of
> the *ordinary teacher* of the *ordinary child*. (120)

He was ably supported in this cause by his colleague, Miss Y. Giuseppi, who became a founder member of the Association for Teaching Aids in Mathematics (ATAM) two years later. Daltry, from the London Institute of Education, Riley, and another inspector, for London Schools, contributed to the discussion, when it turned to ways of helping the 'ordinary teacher' to develop the mathematics curriculum for the 'ordinary child'. Here a role for the MA was envisaged, in that its branches might involve such teachers and encourage them to share their experiences, e.g. through discussion or study groups. The London branch had already shown a possible way forward by inviting teachers from secondary modern schools in London, Middlesex and Surrey to make contact with the branch:

> Seventy replies were received, and at the first meeting . . . it was
> astonishing what enthusiasm was shown amongst these people. It had

been found in subsequent meetings, at which the average attendance was not less than fifty, that by far the best way of discussing these points was not to have a formal paper, but to get together, and after opening up some particular aspect, to break up into small groups of ten or so, have group discussions, and then all come together again . . . There are a number of people who are afraid to get up and talk in a large body but are not afraid to talk in a small group . . . there was a tremendous job in front of the Branches of the Mathematical Association in getting these people together in that way. (121)

The Branches Committee resumed its work in 1946, and, by the end of that year, branch activity had largely returned to its pre-war level. (122) The first of the new post-war branches, the Leicester and County branch, was started in 1947. There were now two active branches in Wales – Cardiff and the South West – and ten in England: London, Yorkshire, Bristol, Manchester, Midland, North-Eastern, Liverpool, Sheffield, Southampton and District, and Leicester and County. There was very little expansion in the number of branches in England and Wales until the 1960s, but the MA, through its branches, continued to act as a major provider of professional support for teachers and lecturers. By 1950 the London branch could claim to have almost five hundred members including a 'fair percentage' from secondary modern schools. (123) Apart from London, other branches too were actively involved in mathematics for secondary modern schools.

In 1946 the Liverpool branch produced a common syllabus for the first two years of secondary education, which was being trialled in a number of local schools. (124) Miss Adams was a prime mover in efforts to extend the MA's influence in the Bristol area:

she made great efforts to draw into the Association local primary and secondary modern teachers and strongly advocated making more provision for their interests, believing that their needs were not at that time being met in any way. This was an innovation in those days and the more recent success of the Association of Teachers of Mathematics and of their publication *Mathematics Teaching* shows how right she was in this belief. (125)

In 1951 the annual meeting was hosted by the Bristol branch, and one new feature was an exhibition of work from secondary modern schools. E.J. James, from Redland Training College, was closely involved, and in 1954 he joined the MA's subcommittee. He acknowledged that 'the real inspiration and drive behind the work came from Miss Adams', who, for many years, had been involved with teachers' courses. (126) Work in such areas as surveying, navigation and technical drawing was strongly featured in the exhibition and summarized in the *Gazette*.

Progress on the production of a major report on mathematics in secondary modern schools was slow and Miss Adams took over from Mrs Williams as chairman in 1954. Miss Adams had experience of senior work in elementary schools going back to 1925. There were also other changes in the composition of the subcommittee, and James took over from Riley as secretary in 1956. A final report, running to over two hundred pages, was not published until 1959. (127) One obvious difficulty was the lack of consensus in this area of mathematics teaching. The illness of Mrs Williams, towards the end of 1951, didn't help at a time when she also moved from Leicester to become principal of Whitelands College. Alongside her heavy commitments in teacher training, she was also secretary of the primary subcommittee. (128) Here a clear priority was established: to produce a major primary report first, and then to build upon its foundations in a secondary modern report. The work on primary mathematics was completed in 1955 and Miss Adams saw the 1959 report through to publication ('a project about which Miss Adams cared deeply'). Mrs Williams acknowledged the strong influence of Miss Adams:

> It was her clear view of the mathematical potentialities of ordinary boys and girls that was the main factor in producing a document which has prepared the way for the substantial developments now reflected . . . in C.S.E. [Certificate of Secondary Education] syllabuses [after 1963] . . . (129)

The shaping of the report was assisted by feedback from teachers in secondary modern schools. Members and non-members of branches were invited to meetings, often led by a subcommittee member, to consider aspects of the work. (130) The report certainly captured much of the best thinking about secondary mathematics for the multitude, building on a wealth of experience from the senior schools of the 1930s to the secondary moderns of the 1950s. But it was soon to be overtaken by other developments of major consequence: the introduction of modern mathematics syllabuses, the development of the CSE, and the spread of comprehensive schooling. The report was a subject for discussion at the annual meeting in 1959, but 'unfortunately [this] did not lead to the spirited debate which the discussion of Reports has so frequently provoked in the past'. (131) Inevitably, the report was soon to appear backward-looking.

MATHEMATICS IN PRIMARY SCHOOLS

The task of penetrating the world of primary education poses distinctive challenges for a specialist subject association with its roots in the selective schools and universities. As in its work on secondary modern school mathematics, the MA could make an effective start in the primary field only by drawing on the experience and expertise of members who were school inspectors, local or national, or teacher trainers. The inter-war years saw the gradual emergence of the notion of a 'primary' education in three distinct phases: nursery, infant and junior. Progressivism in educational thought and practice has a long history of close associations with nursery and infant education. (132) At the junior stage, however, the long tradition of educational administration based on the standards, and the demands of the competitive selection examinations for secondary schooling, which encouraged streaming of pupils by ability, persistently served to inhibit progressive tendencies in the curriculum. In mathematics such pressures inhibited the broadening of the syllabus beyond arithmetic and constrained the range of teaching methods employed. As Miss Adams remarked as late as 1960, 'the art of reckoning is still in popular estimation the *only* evidence of progress to be sought, and soundness in this art is impeded by obscuring fundamentals and usefulness under pile upon pile of rules'. (133)

From 1905 until 1944, the Board of Education endeavoured to promote good practice at the primary stage, both through the publication of successive editions of its handbook of 'suggestions' for teachers, and through the efforts of HMI in the field. (134) In 1931, the Consultative Committee, under Hadow, reported on a wide range of aspects of education for the seven-to-eleven age range, and a further report on infant and nursery schools was published two years later. (135) The often-quoted principle, from the Hadow Report of 1931 – 'the curriculum is to be thought of in terms of activity and experience rather than of knowledge to be acquired and facts to be stored' – symbolized the generally progressive line in official publications concerning the primary curriculum between the wars. (136) But, as a note to the revised edition of 1948 cautioned, 'though few would challenge the general validity of its conclusions, the practical effects of the Primary School Report have not been anything like so general or so strong as those of its predecessor, "The Education of the Adolescent"'. (137) The latter had major administrative consequences – the Hadow reorganization of elementary schools – but the former was primarily concerned with educational ideals and the curriculum: 'more depended with the Primary School Report on a wide acceptance and appreciation of principles differing greatly from those familiar to many teachers trained in an earlier tradition'. (138) Miss Adams summarized her own experience of the Hadow dictum in relation to practice:

> It was least well understood in its application to Mathematics. Attempts to give juniors things to do, often at too low a level of experience, and to let them 'progress at their own rate' in arithmetic (a slogan of the 1930's) were so often time-wasting that they brought the theories themselves undeservedly into disrepute. Arithmetic text books . . . are amongst the dreariest of school books. They deal only with limited aspects of learning the subject; even the best of them cannot provide a substitute for discussion with the teacher and fellow pupils or deal adequately with the need for experiment and experience. (139)

The Hadow Reports of 1931 and 1933 clearly exhibit the early influence of educational research on policy making, particularly in connection with the physiological and psychological aspects of child development. In 1933 Susan Isaacs was appointed as head of the department of child development at the London Institute of Education. Her work on young children's social, emotional and intellectual development, and the related work of her colleagues and successors at the Institute, became 'a major force in the development of child-centred education' from the 1930s. (140) An exceptional contribution to the *Gazette*, from Mrs Williams in 1934 – on the geometrical notions of young children – clearly reflected the influence of contemporary educational thought and research, and its developing links with teacher education. (141)

Mrs Williams had the particular good fortune to come under the early influence of Nunn in her initial training. In her own words, 'Nunn was a joy' and 'This was for me the start of a valued lifelong friendship. It was in . . . individual encouragement that Nunn's wide influence was spread. Yet it was his educational philosophy that gave depth to our thinking.' (142) At an early stage she encountered the ideas of Herbart, Froebel and Montessori, and she was also directly influenced by the innovatory work of Margaret Macmillan, who developed the use of simple, everyday objects, within a Montessori framework. Mrs Williams's school teaching experience spanned the full five-to-eighteen age range, and she was helped by Nunn, in the early 1930s, to secure a teacher training post at King's College. It was work for a master's degree at King's which led to the article in the *Gazette*, following a paper on the subject given to the London branch of the MA in 1933. (143)

Mrs Williams acknowledged the major influence of Professor Cyril Burt in the general field of psychometrics and test design, and Burt had recently contributed to the London branch programme. She commented, 'I need only refer to the way he has traced the development in complexity and the growth in sustaining power of the child's capacity for reasoning and the excellence of his graded tests.' (144) But she also added, 'Piaget of Geneva has taken a different line of investigation', involving the clinical technique of individual interviews, to explore children's own patterns of reasoning about matters within their experience. Such work had stimulated Mrs Williams to undertake her own investigations into the capacity of children to understand the spatial properties of objects. She added:

> we need a *genetic* study of the growth of geometrical ability. We all know how much the teaching of reading and elementary arithmetic owes to our utilising the child's natural method of approach and his normal stages of development, and it is one of the aims of the researches into special aptitudes that are now being conducted at the Institute of Education (with the co-operation of the Education Department of King's College) that they may lay the foundation of a scientific as opposed to an empirical study of methods of teaching. (145)

Thus, as well as reflecting the influence of the psychometric school in educational psychology, Mrs Williams was clearly leaning towards the use of developmental psychology, grounded in empirical evidence about learning, as a basis for curriculum planning in mathematics. But her interest in such a programme was exceptional at this time, and Piaget's influence was not to be generally felt until after the war. (146)

Mrs Williams joined the MA in 1932 and she moved to Goldsmiths' College in 1935. Her experience of mathematics in primary education, as a teacher, researcher and teacher trainer, was to prove invaluable when the Teaching Committee first chose to add primary mathematics to its new agenda, which it did in 1938, following a suggestion made two years earlier that a subcommittee on junior school mathematics might be formed. (147) Riley acted as convener of the subcommittee and Mrs Williams was involved from the outset. There were some understandable early difficulties in securing the involvement of primary teachers: 'the Committee felt that it did not adequately represent those who were actually teaching children up to the age of 11, and it had proved difficult to find such teachers to serve as co-opted members'. (148) But some early progress was made, and co-operation was secured from HMI, before the war interrupted the work, which was not resumed until 1946.

The work up to 1946 was largely consistent with the conventional range of expectations for MA reports, and particularly those aimed at preparatory and girls' schools, where sympathetic, step-by-step advice on teaching an approved mathematics syllabus, in clear stages, was the principal identified need. Riley and Mrs Williams continued to serve on the Committee from 1946, but the work now began to take a different tack:

> the members discussed children's approach to number and play and the use of apparatus; much time was spent on grading the steps of a new process and considering the apparatus through which it should be learnt. This led to deeper inquiries into the nature of the processes themselves . . . (149)

This paradigmatic shift of emphasis from teaching to learning appears to have been partly caused by the co-option to the subcommittee of two new members, Miss Adams of HMI, and Caleb Gattegno (1911–88), who had been recently appointed at the London Institute of Education. Of Miss Adams, Mrs Williams recalled:

> In 1946 she joined the reconstructed Primary Sub-committee and at once its purpose was deflected from the consideration of *what* should be taught to younger children to the more fundamental problem of *how* pupils could be brought to understand and to learn for themselves the remarkable properties of number and space. (150)

According to Mrs Williams, Gattegno's involvement was timely and fundamental in relation to the subcommittee's developing interests:

> There were two main influences which inspired our new start: first the freedom that had developed in nursery and infant schools and in art, English, etc. at the junior stage; secondly, the investigations into children's modes of thought which were being conducted by the Piagetian school in Geneva. We knew of Gattegno's lectures and the new ideas he was advancing, having just returned from work with Piaget, and we invited him to come [and join the committee] and give us his views on what we were attempting. We thought we had brought ourselves up to date; he told us that we were entirely old-fashioned, and were ignoring vital new concepts. (151)

Dick Tahta, a student of Gattegno's work, has suggested a challenging historical line of enquiry, which will not be taken up here: 'why it is that the educational establishment has so massively ignored the work of this fertile pioneer'. (152) He came to England after the war and he followed Nunn's lead at the London Institute by exerting a profound influence on mathematics education through personal contacts, not only in this country but on an international scale. His first article for the *Gazette* was published in 1947, with a striking focus on 'mathematics and the child'. (153) He obtained a London master's degree in the following year, with a thesis on 'the mathematical definition of education'. At this time he argued:

> There must be a world-wide investigation:
> (i) of what are the ways used by children to get their truths;
> (ii) of whât are the substitutes for the truths we want to hand to the child in the field of mathematics, substitutes which will use the logic present at the stage in which the child is, which will build the next logic as a tool. (154)

Such an emphasis – on *child logics* as opposed to *mathematical logic* – would probably have disturbed the mental sets of many of those readers of the *Gazette* who tried to make sense of Gattegno's provocative, wide-ranging and pithy article. Further contributions to the *Gazette* followed in 1949 and 1954: one on the *use* of mistakes in the teaching of mathematics – another mind-set breaker – and a final *Gazette* contribution, relegated to the mathematical notes section, on the use of dynamic patterns in geometry, including reference to the films of J.L. Nicolet. (155)

Miss Adams and Gattegno continued as co-opted members when a third subcommittee was appointed in 1950, with Riley as chairman and Mrs Williams as secretary. The other members were largely from training colleges, and by this time 'it was clear that while they would be indebted to the earlier committees for the work they had done, a new doctrine had emerged and must be embodied in a completely re-written report'. (156) There was still much work to be done, twelve years after the first subcommittee had been appointed. The passage of the draft report through the full Teaching Committee further delayed the eventual date of publication.

In 1953 the draft primary report came under the critical eye of university mathematicians in the full Teaching Committee, including Mary Cartwright, who opened a lively discussion which extended over two days. A major bone of contention was the introductory chapter on psychological principles, which it was thought might be off-putting for primary teachers. Robson's remarks underlined the point: 'he thought [the chapter] would be more intelligible if written in English instead of "psychologese". He had experienced great difficulty in understanding this chapter himself.' (157) Some major rewriting was clearly required and the subcommittee spelt out the principal challenge: 'technical terminology was needed when talking about the psychology of learning – difficulties with English language had delayed production somewhat – simple language was needed in view of the wide audience envisaged'. (158)

The primary report was eventually published in November of 1955, and complimentary copies were sent to LEAs and training colleges, together with a covering letter about the MA itself. (159) The preamble to the report well summarized the seminal thinking of the final subcommittee:

> children, developing at their own individual rates, learn through their active response to the experiences that come to them; through constructive play, experiment and discussion children become aware of

relationships and develop mental structures which are mathematical in form and are in fact the only sound basis of mathematical techniques. The aim of Primary teaching, it is argued, is the laying of this foundation of mathematical thinking about the numerical and spatial aspects of objects and activities which children of this age encounter. The justification of this theory and its implications for the day-to-day work of the teacher form the subject matter of this Report. (160)

The report's emphasis on mathematics and not just arithmetic was important, as was the attention paid to unpacking the fundamental ideas and relationships in number, measurement, space and graphical communication. Here a balance was advocated between the development of understanding, grounded in practical and environmental experiences, and the accumulation of knowledge and skills though practice, particularly in arithmetic. A chapter was included on 'material aids to teaching', classified in four categories: realistic materials, e.g. money; tools, e.g. measuring instruments; explanatory and experimental apparatus, e.g. sectioned rods or coloured rods (the latter 'less familiar in this country') and pegboards; and aids for practice, e.g. tables and charts. (161) The last chapter was devoted to a survey of research on the teaching of arithmetic. Here it was admitted:

Unfortunately research has itself been restricted by the paucity of the facilities made available for such work, and in this respect it must be recognised that greater scope has been afforded to investigators in America than to those in Great Britain, where surveys were often made in such a limited field that the results could only be described as tentative and sometimes inconclusive. (162)

The related bibliography, largely of American work, included one exceptional entry: Piaget's *The Child's Conception of Number* (1952), first published in 1941, in French, and subsequently translated by Gattegno and Frances Hodgson. There had been other translations of Piaget's work, published in the inter-war period, but this was the first English translation of a book with important implications for *mathematics* education. As Tahta has reasonably concluded, 'one of Gattegno's achievements was the dissemination of Piaget's work among mathematics educators in the 50s'. (163)

The second half of the 1950s saw a significant growth of interest in the development of primary mathematics, among teachers, advisers and teacher trainers. A 1959 Ministry of Education report judged:

There is no subject in the primary school curriculum which gives rise to more thought at the present time than mathematics. It is significant not only that it is the theme of discussions and conferences in all parts of the country among primary teachers themselves, but that mathematicians are increasingly giving thought and attention to the development of their subject in the minds of young children. (164)

In connection with the interest of 'mathematicians', the MA's primary report was specifically mentioned, and the Plowden Report (1967) also acknowledged it to be 'a tremendous encouragement to change'. (165)

Talk of 'revolution' in primary mathematics was not to come until the 1960s, but, from 1950, the theoretical underpinning had been well laid by the MA's subcommittee. Hilary Shuard's assessment of the primary report's historical significance is fitting: 'in its time it was an enormous breakthrough' and 'a single-handed move into practical maths'. (166)

TEACHING AND LEARNING AIDS

As we have seen, the paradigmatic shift of emphasis from the teacher to the learner in the emerging ideology of primary mathematics brought with it a renewed and growing interest in material aids as part of the learning environment. Gattegno was a prime mover in this field from the 1950s, but his and other contributions in mathematics were only part of a developing general interest in material aids – audio, visual and tactile – for educational purposes. The pressing need to equip military personnel for the technical demands of war certainly helped forward the movement towards greater variety in teaching methods, including the development of material aids. As Bill Brookes has pointed out, 'the war had resulted in people realizing that far more people could cope than the theories beforehand had supposed'. In the cases of the RAF and the Air Training Corps, Wilf Flemming has drawn attention to the strong stimulus of practical need in reforming the teaching of established parts of the mathematics curriculum, such as trigonometry for aspiring airmen, and the renewed interest in correlation between mathematics and other subjects. (167) Roland Collins, who became a founder member of the ATAM, has emphasized the importance of his RAF experience for his educational work, both in school and with other teachers, after the war:

> I had to teach these people, and their lives depended, in part, upon how they were taught. I had to work out the best way of making sure they understood it in case they had to modify it; and it was no good just giving them a rule, they had to work it out for themselves . . . (168)

Evidence of a general movement associated with visual aids in education is provided by the formation, in 1946, of the National Committee for Visual Aids in Education and the Educational Foundation for Visual Aids, and the appearance of a new monthly periodical, *Visual Education*. National activity was accompanied by local activity, involving working groups of teachers, and the movement was not confined to this country. In mathematics, the American National Council of Teachers of Mathematics devoted a complete yearbook, in 1945, to the subject of 'multi-sensory' aids in the teaching of mathematics. The introduction to this yearbook began:

> TEACHING AIDS in mathematics are not new. The last hundred years have brought us the telephone, the phonograph, the radio, television, the silent and sound motion picture, the stereoscope . . . and motion pictures in color. These inventions and developments are being used in many forms in our schools at the present time. It

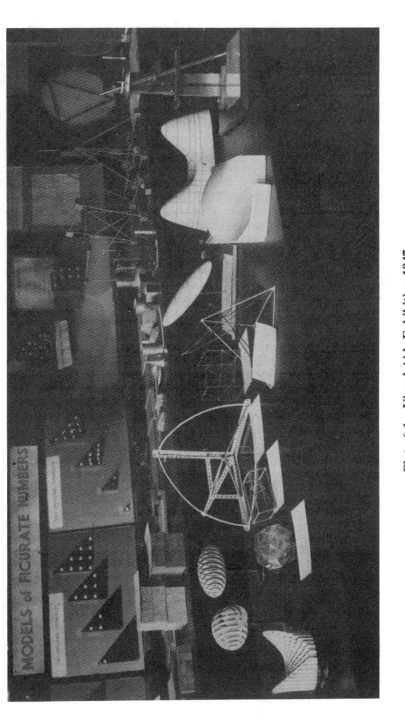

Plate 6.1   Visual Aids Exhibition 1947

is only natural that mathematics teachers, too, consider the possible adaptation of these materials to the improvement of instruction in their field. (169)

In England, the early interest in mathematics was focused on the uses o models, filmstrips and films, and the MA was not slow to take notice o these new developments.

Brief references to mathematical films started to appear in the *Gazette* from 1936, and in that year a subcommittee led by Miss Punnett wa appointed to investigate the new developments and report back, which it did, briefly, in the following year. (170) After the war, the Teaching Committee chose visual aids as one new area for subcommittee work and an early effort was now made by the MA to raise the profile of this aspect of mathematics teaching. The focus on visual aids lent itself to a new initiative from the MA, in 1947: the mounting of a major exhibition at the annual meeting, in addition to the normal publishers' exhibition. A discussion on the place of visual aids in mathematics teaching was opened by I.R. Vesselo, chairman of the visual aids subcommittee and the leading spirit in bringing the idea of an exhibition, with some fifty to sixty main exhibits, to fruition. Pioneering films by R.A. Fairthorne – on unforced and forced vibrations and on hypocyclic motion – were included, along with some filmstrips produced for the British and American navies.

Static and dynamic geometrical models were featured prominently a the exhibition, and the list of contributors included Martyn Cundy, whose 'home-made harmonograph attracted much attention'. (171) The names of Cundy and Rollett became closely linked through their joint authorship of *Mathematical Models*, a very successful reference book first published in 1952. (172) Another major contribution to the exhibition came from a Leicester group, led by W.W. Sawyer, from the local college of technology and including Collins, who had started to develop the use of working models and demonstrations in his teaching at the Gateway School, a technical high school for boys where facilities for construction in wood, metal, plastic and plaster of Paris were readily available. The potential of material aids helped to further the mission of those teachers seeking to make more of the substance of mathematics more accessible to more people. Lancelot Hogben's *Mathematics for the Million* (1936) and his companion volume, *Science for the Citizen* (1938), symbolized the general thrust, and the works of popularization by Sawyer, beginning with his *Mathematician's Deligh.* (1943), shared the same spirit. (173)

By the late 1940s, visual aids had become a fashionable topic in education, and, following the report of the NCTM, the MA clearly saw a need for some kind of report focused on English mathematics teaching. But this was a relatively new field, in which both tradition and consensus were lacking. As late as 1957, a report of the IAAM judged:

> The material available for the teacher of mathematics is very limited and is likely to remain so for some time. Commercial manufacturers and producers are reluctant to enter such a hazardous field. It rests largely with the enthusiastic amateur not only to produce his own material, but also to bring it to the notice of other teachers. (174)

The MA's attitude to the commercial dimension was clear: there would be no endorsement of any commercial products, this refusal to endorse being 'in keeping with the policy of the Teaching Committee of the Mathematical Association'. (175) But efforts to produce a major report proceeded, and by 1950 drafts of several chapters had been prepared under the general guidance of Vesselo, the bulk of the detailed writing being undertaken by co-opted members with relevant experience. (176)

There was an unfortunate lack of continuity in the Teaching Committee representation on the visual aids subcommittee, pre- and post-1950, and the draft of the report ran into difficulties when it was put to the full Teaching Committee in 1952. The major bone of contention was that the report ranged too widely beyond specifically mathematical concerns and, in parts, was not well matched to the parallel work of the primary and secondary modern subcommittees. (177) Given that much of the work had been done by co-opted members, who were out of direct touch with the Teaching Committee, this is not surprising. The upshot was a very modest pamphlet, put together by an *ad hoc* subcommittee under Vesselo and finally published in 1954. (178) All consideration of the wider and more general application of visual aids was left to the 'appropriate bodies'.

The MA's pamphlet included annotated lists of filmstrips and films, in which the work of Fairthorne and Nicolet of Lausanne featured strongly. (179) Photographs from the 1947 exhibition were included and also plates from two English films – plucked strings and the Simson line – produced by Trevor Fletcher at the Sir John Cass College. Fletcher had attended the 1947 annual meeting and he joined the MA in that year. But, from 1953, he became very actively involved in the national work of a new association, the ATAM. There is a passing reference in the MA's pamphlet to the formation, in 1952, of an Association for Multi-Sensory Aids for the Teaching of Mathematics, with Collins named as secretary. (180) Gattegno has been referred to as the 'principal founder of the ATAM and the mainspring of its early work'. (181) The circumstances leading up to the formation of a new mathematics teaching association in England, and its connections with the related work of the MA and its members at this time, warrant a closer investigation.

A new branch of the MA was established at Leicester in 1947 and this gave Collins an early opportunity to disseminate his work on demonstration models, displays, including historical material, and filmstrips. He contributed to the MA's 1947 exhibition and gave talks and demonstrations at MA branch meetings, including one at Sheffield in 1950. Here it was suggested that the Gateway School's and other ideas for what was essentially the popularization of school mathematics might be disseminated in the form of a regular, 'cottage-industry' publication. (182) As a result, a new, cheap – it started at 1d for 4 pages – and user-friendly periodical was launched under Collins's editorship, with the title *Mathematical Pie*. The links with the MA branches helped Collins rapidly to build up an impressive mailing list of contacts, principally in grammar schools, through the very successful marketing of *Pie*, and he also started a newsletter. (183) Through the *Pie* network, Collins came into contact with other innovative teachers, such as Ronald Fielding and Miss Giuseppi, both of whom had established links with Gattegno through his work at the London Institute. (184)

From 1950, Gattegno had been instrumental in the development of an international network in mathematics teaching under a somewhat inflated title: the International Commission for the Study and Improvement of the Teaching of Mathematics (ICSITM). He acted as general secretary and clearly saw the potential for a group of like-minded British activists to be linked with the work of the ICSITM. Through his existing contacts and *Pie* network, Collins was well placed to take an organizational lead and he was brought in as an 'import' for an informal meeting with Gattegno at the Institute. As a result, a first circular was sent out by Collins in February 1952, inviting co-operation in the establishment of a new association. (185) A testimonial from Gattegno was attached:

> I welcome the initiative taken by Mr. R.H. Collins, a member of our Commission, to form in this Country, a Committee of all those who wish to contribute to the visual side of Mathematics Teaching. I am confident that this Committee will find the adequate response among teachers and will contribute a great deal to clarify the ways in which our pupils improve in their learning processes. (186)

Collins's early work with visual aids had, not surprisingly, also attracted the attention of the MA's visual aids subcommittee. However, his overtures were not well received. Independently, Collins was making an early impression through the dissemination of visual aids at prices teachers could afford. Mathematical Pie, as a 'cottage industry', became a limited company and registered charity. The success of *Pie* helped to subsidize these efforts. Collins's initiative in helping to start a new association was driven by a strong sense of pedagogical mission and was clearly intended to bypass the MA. (187)

Twenty-four respondents to Collins's circular indicated their willingness to become involved at committee level in what was named the Association for Teaching Aids in Mathematics, at the meeting held at the London Institute in June 1952. (188) There was an attendance of twelve at this meeting, and Gattegno was elected as chairman as well as 'director of studies', with Collins as secretary and Miss Giuseppi as assistant secretary. (189) About half of those involved at this stage were also members of the MA. A first full list of contacts was sent out as part of a second circular in July 1952, and it included 164 names grouped in regions, including Scotland, Ireland and an overseas group. Thus a solid basis upon which to build a new national association was readily established, and the ATAM progressed from strength to strength through the 1950s and 1960s.

Early members of the ATAM shared a general sense of mission: to further the development of mathematics for the multitude. As Brookes has remarked, 'if human beings couldn't do it, it was something else which was turning them off not the mathematics', and the development of ways forward 'was part of what the Association was about'. (190) Obviously, individual members' perceptions and priorities differed. In particular, as Fletcher has succinctly put it, Gattegno was 'very much the founding father' and 'the idealist', and Collins 'very much the pragmatist'. (191) Oral ccounts suggest that Gattegno was a guru-like figure and a challenge to work with, in more ways than one. He was junior to Daltry, at the London Institute, and personal hostilities existed between the two lecturers. (192) Daltry was an MA stalwart, in the London branch and nationally, and Gattegno was viewed with some suspicion not only by Daltry but also by other MA stalwarts such as Rollett and Combridge. (193) Collins and Gattegno would have been united in the belief that the MA was not the appropriate organization within which to pursue their respective missions. Furthermore, Gattegno's championship of the use of Cuisenaire rods was clearly out of step with the MA's policy to isolate commercial from professional interests, both in textbook and visual aids production.

From the outset, the ATAM was a very different kind of organization from the MA. The latter had a long-standing and well-established link with the independent schools and the universities which they fed. The ATAM was not strongly associated with one particular sector of education, and its leading members in the 1950s came from various occupational locations: grammar, technical, secondary modern and comprehensive schools, and teacher training institutions. (194) The ATAM enjoyed the benefits of youth and enthusiasm in its membership, and, within a relatively small organization, innovators and activists soon made a significant impact. Fletcher has recalled that in 1953, after an initial letter to Collins, he was swiftly drawn into the central committee's work; in the following year he also took over the editorship of the *Bulletin*. (195)

Communion was central to the ATAM's work and influence on a growing membership, which had reached a thousand by 1958. On a small scale, residential meetings, initially held at Brazier's Park, a retreat in the Chilterns, provided an opportunity for in-depth reflection and personal development under the guidance of Gattegno himself, as 'director of studies'. His behaviour was, by all accounts, most guru-like in such a setting. On a larger scale, exhibitions, including lectures and demonstration lessons, were mounted in various parts of the country and they made a considerable early impact. (196) The pattern was established at a first meeting in London, early in 1954, and, later in the same year, meetings in Manchester and Exeter attracted around 300 and 250 people respectively. Typically, Gattegno demonstrated the use of Cuisenaire 'briquettes' (coloured rods) or the geoboard, which comprised a five-by-five square grid of pins on a wooden board designed for use with thread or elastic bands. Collins specialized in filmstrips and Fletcher led the early work involving films. Lists of models, films and filmstrips were distributed through the growing ATAM network.

The first *Bulletin* of the ATAM was edited by Collins and distributed in duplicated form in January 1953. (197) Fletcher took over from the third issue; the size of the journal increased and the quality of production was improved. From 1955 the journal was printed and distributed under the title *Mathematics Teaching*. It served to disseminate news about developments in teaching and learning mathematics, both in England and abroad, at a time when the *Mathematical Gazette* was hardly fulfilling this function. It also served to publicize the work of the ATAM and to enhance the new association's reputation.

In 1956 Gattegno resigned as chairman of the ATAM, but he wa then elected to the special position of President. He left the Institut in the following year and took up a post abroad. But he continued to act 'at a distance', and to maintain links with individual member of the ATAM, particularly through the ICSITM, as the movement for modernizing the content of school mathematics gained momentum from the late 1950s. Collins took over from Gattegno as chairman for a short time, but complications developed over the links between the ATAM and Collins's limited company. From 1959, a new secretary, David Wheeler and a new chairman, Ian Harris, helped to secure the ATAM's independen constitutional and financial position in good time for the expansion of its activities in the 1960s. Collins's influence on the ATAM faded – he moved to a new headship in the Midlands, which brought new curriculum development opportunities in the 1960s – but the influence of Gattegno wa a deep and lasting one. The spirit of his inspiration was well summarized in a message to the ATAM in 1958:

> When in the committee we learnt to work together as a team, the obvious thing was to know that we had to learn a great deal and that the best way for us to grow was to go to the teachers and the students where they are. Our humility and our enthusiasm gave us the chance of appearing what we were: keen students of the science of teaching mathematics. Because we learnt by observation, by studying pupils' mistakes and tracing them to the mental structures and the techniques we used, we struck the right direction and all over the country first, in several countries afterwards, our Association became known as formed of a group of earnest workers; practical people who had ideas and a great love of truth . . . Our membership is international because our problems are simply human . . . There is so much for us to discover in our activity and so much improvement to bring to our work in order that the joys that we receive from our success shall be the everyday feature of our function, that *Hope* is the sign under which we can now work. Indeed, when we think of the smiles and the bright eyes of so many who formerly were condemned to remain untouched (or even disgusted) by mathematics and now enjoy and even love it, we can see our work as providing spring-boards for the young generation, and no longer straight-jackets. (198)

CHAPTER SEVEN

MODERNIZING SCHOOL MATHEMATICS

The schools and industry are both short of mathematicians. The fact of the shortage and its gravity has been recognized in the educational world for some time. We know that the quality of mathematics teaching could and should be improved, the curricula brought up to date, and above all the number of mathematicians with good qualifications increased. (1)

(Sir David Eccles, Minister of Education, 1961)

. . . we shall not remain in the van of the improvement of mathematical teaching unless young members come forward constantly and make their ideas known to the Association and through the Association to all teachers in the country . . . Have we taken a sufficiently strong lead in the new projects about the teaching of mathematics which are exciting so much interest? Is it for the Association to commend or condemn? Ought we to explore more than we have done the relation of mathematics to other subjects? Should we prepare a recommended syllabus? (2)

(T.A.A. Broadbent, 1965)

The MA's report on sixth form algebra (1957) and the reports on secondary mathematics by the Assistant Masters' Association (1957) and the Ministry of Education (1958) all regarded the potential for modernization of school mathematics as little more than a peripheral matter. Within only five years the situation had changed dramatically. One early survey report on international developments and initiatives in the United Kingdom concluded:

It is a measure of the success of the reformers that, whether or not one agrees with their particular proposals for reform, one cannot today avoid considering the bearing of modern mathematics on the basic mathematical curriculum and the methods of teaching it. (3)

As in the case of the Perry movement from 1900, the MA became caught up in a curriculum reform movement which was driven by forces largely beyond its control. Broadbent's questions of 1965 were very pertinent but problematic for the MA. Such questions also suggest some parallels with the concerns of the AIGT in the 1870s and 1880s. As we shall see, there is again a sense of inevitability about the MA's limited influence in the 1960s.

In the 1950s the MA's work had proceeded on two principal fronts: extension of its reporting to the more advanced branches of selective school mathematics; and broadening of its institutional concerns to include major work on defining the scope and possibilities for mathematics in primary schools, secondary modern schools and technical institutions. One sector of education is conspicuous by its absence from the MA's main agenda: teacher training. By 1960, as Sir David Eccles implied, the solution of the problem of mathematics teacher supply was linked with the need to modernize school mathematics. But, from the 1940s, educational reconstruction as a whole was closely bound up with questions concerning teacher supply and teacher education, to serve the needs of a rapidly expanding educational system.

MATHEMATICS TEACHER EDUCATION AND SUPPLY

Between the wars the administratively separate elementary and grant-aided secondary school systems were served by separate systems of teacher recruitment and training. For elementary school teachers the norm was a two-year training college course, including general academic, professional and practical teaching elements. For secondary teachers the norm was academic specialism leading to a university degree, which might or might not have been followed by a one-year professional course in a secondary training department. In 1931, of all the men teaching in grant-aided secondary schools, 83.6 per cent were graduates and 44 per cent were trained graduates. For women the corresponding figures were 65.5 per cent and 39 per cent. (4) In 1938 over 75 per cent of newly qualified mathematics graduates entered teaching. (5) Furthermore, in public and direct grant schools the need for professional training to supplement good academic qualifications was generally less strongly felt.

By contrast with the period of expansion up to the First World War, questions of mathematics teacher supply and education attracted very little attention between the wars. (6) In particular, the American National Council of Teachers of Mathematics (NCTM) concluded in a comparative report of 1939 that the MA had not 'pressed for reform in this direction with the zeal with which it has attacked the problems of improving mathematical instruction in the schools'. (7) The MA was, however, able to call upon the expertise of a very small number of leading members who were teacher trainers: Nunn and Miss Punnett of the London Day Training College, Milne of Leeds University and two leading students of Nunn, Daltry and Mrs Williams. Nunn's influence was seminal and long-standing, as is evidenced by the fact that a statement on teacher training which he produced for the MA in 1919 was reprinted in the *Gazette* in 1951. (8) The NCTM found that the London Institute (formerly Day Training College) provided a sixty-hour 'mathematical methods' (pedagogy) course, four times the average length for twenty-two secondary training departments in its survey. (9)

Between the wars elementary teacher training was a major concern of the Training College Association (TCA), predecessor of the Association of Teachers in Colleges and Departments of Education (ATCDE). There was an active Mathematics Section of the TCA, and its early work has been charted by Frank Land. (10) Both Land and Mrs Williams became involved in the Section's work, before the outbreak of war abruptly halted its activities. But at least work on an arithmetic report for primary schools was saved for publication after the war, and the Mathematics Section (of the ATCDE) was revived in the late 1950s. By this time developments in teacher education were growing apace, following the implementation of the Butler Act and the recommendations of the McNair Report (1944), *Teachers and Youth Leaders*.

Post-war educational reconstruction and expansion involved a number of strands with implications for the supply and training of teachers. The depleting effects of war, particularly on male teacher numbers, and the raising of the school leaving age to fifteen in 1947 led to the development of an emergency scheme for the teacher training of ex-service personnel. Between 1945 and 1951 over fifty 'emergency colleges' provided fourteen-month courses, and over 30,000 additional teachers for primary and secondary schools were trained in this way. Another direct consequence of the war brought further pressure, initially on the need for primary teachers: the bulge in the birth rate. Live births peaked at around 880,000 in 1947 from a low of around two-thirds this figure in 1941. (11) There was also the pressing need to staff new courses for the growing number of pupils in secondary modern schools. In terms of sheer numbers the expansion of the output of trained teachers from permanent establishments was remarkable: by comparison with 1939 the total had doubled by 1951 and trebled by 1964. (12)

After 1944 the form and control of courses in teacher education depended principally upon the implementation of the recommendations of the McNair Report. The status of courses of initial training was enhanced by the development of a system which brought colleges into a professional relationship with a neighbouring university, through the work of Area Training Organizations established within newly designated Institutes of Education. Another recommendation of the McNair Committee – the extension of initial training courses from two to three years – brought further respectability but put new pressure on the system. The introduction of three-year courses was finally announced in 1957, for a start to be made in 1960. A shift in terminology in the 1960s – from 'training college' to 'college of education' – was indicative of the growing respectability and professionalism in this sector of education, for which the ATCDE acted as the principal mouth-piece. The development of the four-year Bachelor of Education (B Ed) degree course was soon to follow. (13)

Post-war expansion in the provision for primary, secondary and teacher education was paralleled by major growth in further and higher educational opportunities. Of the universities and university colleges only Reading was chartered between the wars. But some early expansion in student numbers is evident between 1939 and 1947: Manchester and Sheffield doubled in size, Southampton trebled and Oxford went up by 50 per cent. (14) Between 1948 and 1957 five university colleges – Nottingham, Southampton, Hull, Exeter and Leicester – received charters. By 1965 these universities had been joined by a number of new foundations: Sussex (1961), Keele (1962; a university college from 1950), Newcastle (1963), East Anglia (1963), York (1963), Essex (1964), Lancaster (1964), Kent (1965) and Warwick (1965). (15) Further expansion followed the publication of the Robbins Report in 1963, the chartering of the Council for National Academic Awards (CNAA) in 1964, the granting of university status to colleges of advanced technology and the subsequent growth of a national system of polytechnics. (16)

Despite the general post-war expansion of educational opportunities at all levels, concern over mathematics teacher supply mounted in the 1950s. Difficulties were being experienced in two major respects: the supply to training colleges of suitably qualified entrants and staff; and the recruitment of mathematics graduates for specialist secondary teaching. Candidates for college entry were being attracted to other occupational fields such as nursing, secretarial work, commerce and local government. Furthermore, a pre-war legacy of disadvantage in secondary mathematics education for girls persisted. Their relatively low qualifications in mathematics and the consequences for the teaching of this subject in primary schools were particular concerns. In an ATCDE survey of 1956 only 44 per cent of women college entrants possessed an O-level pass in mathematics; a third of seventy-five women's colleges had no full-time graduate mathematics lecturer on the staff; and over two-thirds had nobody on the education staff with suitable qualifications for 'methods' work in mathematics. (17)

The recruitment of full-time mathematics lecturers to all training colleges did improve greatly between 1955 and 1962: from 64 in 1955 to 159 in 1960 and 248 by 1962; and the number doubled again between 1962 and 1967. (18) During the period 1955–62 the move to three-year courses and the near-doubling of the number of students specializing in mathematics provided the major stimulus for improvements in staffing. (19) But the demand here for mathematics graduates only served further to exacerbate the staffing problems in secondary schools. This expansion of the work in mathematics teacher education was also accompanied by another development of considerable significance: the growth of specialist professional organizations with a particular stake in English mathematics education.

As we have seen, the teaching aids movement embraced from 1952 the growth of a new association in mathematics education, the ATAM. Within ten years two more mathematics education associations had emerged: the ATCDE Mathematics Section and the University Departments of Education Mathematics Study Group (UDEMSG). The year 1956 brought two important initiatives in mathematics teacher education: a conference convened by HMI Rollett at Whitelands College, where Mrs Williams was the Principal; and the publication of the ATCDE's report on mathematics and science teacher supply. As one consequence the ATCDE Mathematics Section was revived, and at a fitting time to respond to the challenge of expanding opportunities in mathematics teacher education. (20) Within ten years Mrs Williams could report:

> It is . . . particularly valuable that the Association of Teachers in Colleges and Departments of Education has a strong mathematics section that makes recommendations about main courses and is now actively planning a policy for the B.Ed. courses that will soon be supplying the schools with the first graduates in Education with mathematics as one of their degree subjects. (21)

Furthermore, the link with HMI has continued through the joint organization of annual conferences.

Some early efforts had been made to cater for the specific needs of the University Departments of Education (UDEs) – principally concerning the one-year postgraduate training courses – within the ATCDE Mathematics Section. But a survey (1959) by Flemming of around twenty UDEs revealed that much needed to be done to develop the work in mathematics. With the co-operation of Daltry an exploratory meeting was held in 1960 at the London Institute of Education. The formation of the UDEMSG followed, and early meetings were held in Leicester. (22) By 1966 Mrs Williams could report: 'Mathematics tutors in Departments of Education now form an organized and vigorous group which discusses policy for the professional training of graduate teachers of mathematics.' (23) Thus, by the time the ATAM changed its name to the ATM, in 1962, there were four organizations with a particular stake in English mathematics education. There were overlaps in membership, but the organizations were wholly separate and catered for distinctive needs at a time when the world of mathematics education was growing in scale and complexity.

In the expanding secondary school sector, the shortage of suitably qualified mathematics and science teachers was an intractable problem in the 1950s and through subsequent decades up to the 1980s. This 'chronic condition' and its persistence are bound up with burgeoning claims, from a widening range of vocations, on the potential of mathematics and science graduates. (24) A proportion of over three-quarters of all mathematics graduates entering schoolteaching in 1938 had dropped to almost a quarter by 1964 and to only 8 per cent twenty years later. (25) As early as 1946 the growing call of other occupations was identified by Professor Chapman in his MA Presidential address:

> large manufacturing businesses, insurance companies, and Government departments need statisticians; industrial firms need mathematicians for design departments; research organisations, both in industry and in Government scientific departments, need mathematicians for special branches of their work . . . Large government scientific organisations like the National Physical Laboratory and the Meteorological Office need mathematicians . . . In biological work also the need for help from mathematicians is increasingly recognized. (26)

During its first two years the National Advisory Council for the Training and Supply of Teachers (NACTST), formed in 1949, pointed to shortages of mathematics and science teachers for both grammar and secondary modern schools. By the mid-1950s the matter had attracted the attention of MPs, the

Federation of British Industries (forerunner of the Confederation of British Industries), the Science Masters' Association, the British Association for the Advancement of Science and the Association of Headmistresses, as well as the ATCDE. (27) Both Langford and Combridge represented the MA at a conference convened by the CBI early in 1954 'to discuss the shortage of mathematicians and other scientists in industry, in the schools and in the universities'. (28) Two years later Langford was a member of a UK delegation at an international conference in Geneva. Seventy-four nations were represented, and a wide-ranging survey of secondary school mathematics was conducted. He reported on the results in his Presidential address to the MA in 1958 and noted:

> About two-thirds of the countries concerned experience difficulty in recruiting sufficiently qualified teachers of mathematics for schools . . . They all point to the immense technical developments of recent years bringing with it increased opportunities for graduates in science and mathematics, and many of these new appointments carry greater material rewards than can be expected in teaching. (29)

Langford pointed to 'the disastrous situation which is now prevalent in most of our grammar schools' and he presented figures from his own survey of public, direct grant and grammar schools to support this conclusion. (30) Predictably, the greater public schools were least affected by the deteriorating situation. Langford's conclusions were reported in *The Times*, and his related contribution to a meeting of the British Association was also reported in *Nature*. (31) From 1957 the issue of mathematics teacher supply became intertwined with the growing movement to modernize school mathematics.

Three major and well-publicized conferences – at Oxford (1957), Liverpool (1959) and Southampton (1961) – provided important platforms for the movement to modernize English school mathematics. (32) These conferences were not mounted by existing organizations from the industrial, commercial, academic or educational spheres but were spearheaded by leading individuals with roots and connections which embraced these different spheres of interest in curriculum reform. (33) The first conference was the brainchild of J.M. Hammersley, a fellow of Trinity College Oxford, a statistician with industrial and research connections, and a champion of the teaching of mathematics in the context of its wide-ranging contemporary applications.

These conferences broke new ground by bringing together representatives of industry, commerce and government-sponsored organizations, research mathematicians, lecturers in further and higher education, and teachers from selective secondary schools. The involvement of the country's users of mathematics in these conferences brought with it two consequences: sponsorship for delegates (and subsequently for curriculum development) and recognition of the important role of applications in shaping new directions for English school mathematics. The conferences also enjoyed the advantage of significant media coverage, notably through *The Times* newspaper, which also sponsored the full publication of the proceedings at Oxford and Liverpool.

Hammersley was quick to deploy 'declinist' arguments, as Perry had done sixty years earlier in his championship of 'practical' over 'academic' mathematics. As Cooper has adumbrated, Hammersley argued at Oxford 'from national decline to a national interest in producing scientists to the schools' current failures to the need for reform to the holding of the conference'. (34) The worsening situation concerning the supply of mathematics teachers served to heighten this sense of crisis at both Liverpool and Southampton. The Liverpool conference – on the general theme of 'mathematics in action' – was chaired by Professor L. Rosenhead, a university applied mathematician, with Land, a teacher trainer, as vice-chairman. The pattern at Liverpool followed that at the Oxford conference but involved a wider representation of delegates from further education colleges and selective secondary schools.

The architect of the conference at Southampton was Professor Bryan Thwaites, an applied mathematician with a national reputation, wide-ranging contacts, and the potential to exert a major influence on the course of events. He made the most of the groundwork prepared by the two earlier conferences, involving both Hammersley and Rosenhead on his advisory committee, and wide representation of around 130 delegates from schools, universities and industry. Thwaites acknowledged a debt to Hammersley for opening up the possibilities for reform through the conference at Oxford. (35) But in 1961 there was a much greater sense of urgency about the need for curriculum change. Whilst sharing Hammersley's declinist view, Thwaites's argument was now more sharply focused on the 'national crisis' of mathematics teacher shortage, at a time of major expansion: 'Bulge, Trend and Swing . . . the growing numbers of children, the widening desire for higher education, and the shift from the Arts to the Sciences'. (36) Thwaites also devoted his inaugural lecture in the same year to 'a definitive statement concerning the vital dependence of good mathematics on the supply of good teachers'. (37)

It is remarkable that the Southampton conference report of over a hundred pages was written within the space of just seven days. It also included a foreword from a leading politician, Eccles, which highlighted the need for reform (as in the opening quotation of this chapter). But Thwaites also had a mission to move from rhetoric to the reality of curriculum development, drawing on the model of existing projects in the USA. The conference was organized to produce a 'body of opinion' on school mathematics which led directly to the establishment of what was to become the most successful of all the modern mathematics curriculum development projects of the 1960s in England: the School Mathematics Project (SMP), directed by Thwaites himself. (38)

Thwaites's reference to 'Bulge, Trend and Swing' reflected the 1950s expansion in the age-participation rate in sixth-form education and in the numbers of pupils taking O-level and A-level examinations in mathematics. Between 1951 and 1961 the numbers taking O-level increased from 84,798 to 203,281; for A-level the increase was from 12,329 to 44,395. (39) Over this same period the number of passes at A-level almost trebled, from around ten thousand, but the number of honours degrees awarded in mathematics increased from 412 to only 738. (40) By around 1960 the spotlight was also beginning to focus on the universities themselves.

At a time of general growth in the university sector there were two major barriers to growth in the production of mathematics graduates: the requirements and arrangements for university entrance; and the range and difficulty of university mathematics courses. (41) Furthermore, the best qualified mathematics graduates were increasingly being recruited by the universities themselves, for research and teaching, thus putting further pressure on the supply to selective secondary schools.

By comparison with the high profile conference at Southampton, the MA's annual conference in 1961 passed by largely unnoticed, although the early warnings of Langford were followed up by Maxwell in his Presidential address, and a discussion on the state of school mathematics was opened by Rosenhead. (42) Langford himself chose to work through organizations other than the MA, principally the Incorporated Association of Headmasters (IAHM), to exert particular pressure on the universities.

A working party on mathematics teacher shortage was set up early in 1961, with Langford and Rollett as members, and one major recommendation was that heads of university mathematics departments should meet with headmasters and others to explore the problem. Such a meeting was convened by the Committee of Vice-Chancellors and it took place in September 1961 at the Royal Society. Almost all universities were represented at this Conference of Professors of Mathematics, which was, according to Rollett, 'the first of its kind to be held in this country'. (43) One focus was on what the universities might themselves do to alleviate the situation, by increasing both the access to and the range of mathematics courses.

At committee level, under the chairmanship of Professor Sir William Hodge of Cambridge University, co-operation continued between representatives of the university mathematics departments, the schools and the Ministry of Education (the Department of Education and Science from 1964). (44) In the short term, successful efforts were made to extend the provision of university courses on modern mathematics and its applications for teachers; and a booklet providing details of all university honours courses in mathematics was prepared by Rollett. (45) Furthermore, as we shall see, there were other concomitant institutional developments in the early 1960s, arising from the growing professional and political consciousness among university and industrial mathematicians: the establishment of the Joint Mathematical Council of the United Kingdom (JMC) and the Institute of Mathematics and its Applications (IMA).

In connection with the supply and training of mathematics teachers, the MA became involved in the production of a joint report with the ATCDE Mathematics Section, which was published in 1963. (46) Some initial stimulus for such a report had come from the revival of international activity in mathematics education during the 1950s. The International Commission (ICMI) again identified mathematics teacher education as a major topic for reports to the ICM at Stockholm in 1962. (47) The MA and ATCDE prepared a joint memorandum for the Stockholm ICM and there was a 'spirited discussion' of its substance at the MA's annual conference in the same year. (48) It was agreed that the work should be continued by a joint subcommittee, to produce a major report under the chairmanship of Mrs Williams, now retired from Whitelands College. Wilf Flemming as deputy chairman provided another personal link between the two associations involved. (49) Riley (the chairman of the Teaching Committee) pointed out that the published report of forty-six pages was:

> a departure from the standard type of report of the Association in that it was a 'tract for the times' rather than a teacher's desk-book; it is aimed at an audience much wider than our own membership. The report has been produced with speed in order that its findings may make a contribution towards solving some of the present problems of shortages of staff and changing syllabuses. (50)

The report was wide-ranging but necessarily speculative at a time of rapid change. It encompassed three major areas: mathematics teacher supply; the implications of new developments in both university and school mathematics for the mathematical preparation of teachers; and the provision for professional training, both initial and in-service. The case for professional training to supplement adequate academic qualifications – a case first argued in the nineteenth century – still had to be pressed. As Riley pointed out:

> There has been sharply divided opinion on this point. Mutual mistrust and criticism not noticeably constructive have made it difficult to shape a positive policy of developing co-operation between schools and training institutions in securing the most effective and practicable ways of preparing new teachers for their professional tasks. (51)

Mrs Williams was prompted to remark:

> It seems to me that the status of the teacher of mathematics in this time of development and change demands an end to the old controversies and the beginning of a period of combined effort in establishing a unified professional approach to the modes of training new teachers of mathematics. (52)

In his 1964 Presidential address to the MA, Morgan was conservative but realistic about the scope and limits of what the MA itself might achieve:

> I come to a major problem, the recruitment and training of teachers, to assist with which the traditional form and organisation of the Association were quite unsuitable . . . I refer to social influence and political power which the Association has never sought to acquire. Certainly attempts were made to draw the attention of those in authority to the vastly increased demand for mathematics and mathematicians which had arisen since the War. The Association regarded the position so seriously that, in 1961, it became for the first time an examining body, and awarded its Diploma in Mathematics to 50 teachers and students who had taken special courses in technical colleges and training colleges in order to become qualified in mathematics. (53)

The joint report with the ATCDE was the first and last of its kind involving the MA directly in the field of mathematics teacher education. Subsequently, professional support was provided in various ways by either the ATCDE Mathematics Section or the UDEMSG, and, from 1965, wider policy making and influence was also exercised through the JMC, the IMA and the Royal Society. But the development of a Diploma in Mathematics was a distinctive contribution of the MA to the teacher supply problem.

MATHEMATICAL ASSOCIATION DIPLOMAS

The decision to extend the range of the MA's work to the field of mathematical examinations for teachers was both bold and timely. Land spoke on teacher shortage at the Oxford conference in 1957 and drew attention to some of the disturbing findings of the ATCDE's 1956 report. In particular he compared the qualifications of teachers of mathematics and arts subjects: three-quarters of the latter had 'good honours' degrees but only one-quarter of the former. (54) In the short term the need was identified for a 'top-up' qualification, to bring emergency or two-year trainees up to the equivalent standard of one year of full-time study beyond A-level and thereby to equip them to teach O-level and some sixth form work. At the Oxford conference Miss Cooke asked whether the MA should explore this possibility and initial reaction to the idea was positive. At the Liverpool conference Land returned to the same theme and could now point to two 'palliatives': 'the Ministry of Education's one-year supplementary courses and the diploma, mooted at Oxford, which the Mathematical Association was arranging to provide'. (55)

Following meetings of a small group, including Combridge, Langford, Kellaway and B.J.F. Dorrington, the MA Diploma regulations were framed and circulated to all members as well as colleges, UDEs and LEAs. (56) Specimen papers were prepared and a Diploma Board was set up with Langford as chairman and Dorrington as secretary; the latter handled all the arrangements with the printers, Hodgson. (57) Combridge, Maxwell and Busbridge were the other members of the first Board. Examiners were appointed and the first examination took place in November 1961 at twelve centres. (58) The papers covered pure mathematics, applied mathematics, statistics and 'history and ideas of mathematics', for which Daltry acted as the first examiner. (59) Commonly, technical colleges provided courses for the MA Diploma, and the standards demanded for the award were high. Fifty passed the first examination, fifty failed and twenty-two were referred.

From 1962 the MA also took steps to develop a second Diploma in Mathematics (Technology) award, to serve the need for technical college staff to boost their qualifications in two stages: the equivalent of a higher national certificate, in two parts, and a more advanced award. (60) However, the IMA was established in 1964, and, as Combridge pointed out, 'the pace is not set entirely by our Association'. (61) The first examinations for the Diploma in Mathematics (Technology) were held in

THE MATHEMATICAL ASSOCIATION

This is to certify that

having in the year .... satisfied the Examinations Board of

the Association at an Examination in

Pure Mathematics
Applied Mathematics & Statistics
History & Ideas of Mathematics

has been awarded the

𝔇iploma in 𝔐athematics
(Teaching)
of

THE MATHEMATICAL ASSOCIATION

Chairman

Secretary

Signature of Holder

Plate 7.1 Diploma in Mathematics (Teaching)

June 1964, but the MA continued to act as examining body for this award only up to 1967. (62) As Combridge explained:

> The Institute [IMA] can benefit the profession by providing an examination that will enable non-graduates to qualify for graduate membership. Our Association took the first step by its examinations for its Diploma in Mathematics (Technology). This was a temporary measure, and we shall be ready to end it when the Institute has its own exam. (63)

Subsequently, the IMA provided its own scheme for the award of a graduate-equivalent qualification, but the Diploma in Mathematics (Teaching) continued to play a part in extending teachers' mathematical qualifications. (64)

In 1967 the Diploma in Mathematics (Teaching) was first recognized by the DES as sufficient to warrant some salary enhancement (£50 per annum). From the mid-1960s alternative papers were provided on a modern mathematical syllabus, and the whole syllabus was modernized by the end of the decade. Quadling and Shuard acted as first examiners for the new syllabus, and modernization helped to sustain the Diploma's currency value for teachers. Busbridge, a Diploma Board member under Dorrington as a new chairman, opined that 'the diploma should make a substantial contribution towards the development of modern mathematics in Britain'. (65) Another new departure, in 1969, was a special conference for course providers, focusing on the new pure mathematics syllabuses. Over thirty colleges were still running Diploma courses at this time. (66)

By the mid-1970s the Diploma in Mathematics (Teaching) had largely served its purposes; the number of candidates was declining and only twenty candidates passed in 1974. (67) Modern mathematical topics had become generally disseminated and there were now alternative educational opportunities: established three-year teacher training courses and the four-year B Ed degree; the provision of university diplomas; and the start of distance-learning opportunities through the work of the Open University, which awarded its first degrees in 1973. (68) By this time candidates were finding it difficult to gain day release, evening courses were proving hard to sustain, and the MA's financial involvement was becoming a burden. The scheme was wound up before the end of the decade. Since its inception nearly eight hundred teachers, including some from overseas, had been awarded this Diploma. The Council paid a particular tribute to Dorrington, who had been involved with the Diploma from its germination to its demise. (69)

ROYAL SOCIETY, JMC AND IMA

The institutional world of mathematics education had grown more complex in the 1960s. In addition to the coexistence of the MA, ATM, ATCDE Mathematics Section and UDEMSG, the co-ordinated involvement of university, industrial and commercial mathematicians in educational matters was another new development from the late 1950s. In a recent book on physics education, 1960–85, Woolnough has shown how educational activity 'in the courts of the mighty' multiplied through the efforts of both the Royal Society and the Institute of Physics. The latter became the single professional body for physicists from 1960, through amalgamation of the Physical Society, founded in 1874, and the original Institute, set up in 1918. With its roots going back to the seventeenth century, the Royal Society was the obvious scientific institution with potential educational influence, but in 1960 as Woolnough points out 'it had virtually no formal contact with, or interest in schools'. (70)

In the case of physics, co-ordinated educational work through joint committees of the Royal Society and the Institute grew through the 1960s, with a particular concern for the health of physics in selective schools. In the case of mathematics, institutional developments were less straightforward. Educational matters were at most a peripheral concern of the London Mathematical Society – the major British learned society for mathematics – and, up to the 1950s, it was the MA that provided common ground and an effective platform for teachers, college lecturers, professional mathematicians and interested amateurs to address questions concerning school mathematics.

In connection with international activity in mathematics education, when the ICMI was briefly revived in the 1930s it was the MA itself that took over from the Board of Education and represented UK interests. Three of its members, including Neville and Nunn, served as the UK subcommission. (71) After the Second World War international mathematical links were resumed, and, in 1949, the Royal Society established the representative British National Committee for Mathematics (BNCM), which subsequently became linked with a newly created International Mathematical Union (IMU). (72) The MA had a single representative on the BNCM, initially Broadbent, and, from 1952, the ICMI was revived as a subcommission of the IMU. In turn the BNCM established its own representative Mathematical Instruction Subcommittee (MIS) to link with the ICMI. (73) Thus the Royal Society took over the UK responsibility for formal international links with the IMU in both mathematics and mathematics education. At home the institutional activity which had been initially stimulated by the problems of teacher supply led to calls for a measure of co-ordination of professional interests in both mathematics and mathematics education, 'to make our collective voice heard', as Combridge subsequently put it. (74)

In his 1962 Presidential address to the MA Combridge drew attention to the growing number of 'unco-ordinated activities' in mathematics education and added: 'But there was no over-all strategy whereby all these activities could be co-ordinated and brought to bear on the problems which were pressing on our mathematical world.' By this time a letter had already been drafted proposing the formation of a Federal Council 'to meet the need for co-ordination and general strategy'. (75) The letter was signed by Combridge, as the President of the MA, Mary Cartwright, President of the LMS, and Hodge, Physical Secretary of the Royal Society and also associated with the follow-up work of the Conference of Professors of Mathematics. A meeting followed at King's College, in July 1962, at which it was agreed to set up the Joint Mathematical Council (JMC) with a wide-ranging institutional membership: the Royal Society (BNCM), LMS, Conference of Professors, MA, Royal Statistical Society, Edinburgh Mathematical Society, Glasgow Mathematical Society, ATM, and ATCDE Mathematics Section; and the UDEMSG joined in the following year. (76) Hodge was appointed chairman of the JMC, which held its first meeting in January 1963; Professor J.G. Semple and Combridge, both of King's College, were elected secretary and treasurer respectively. By this time a scheme was also being developed to establish an Institute of Mathematics, to work along the lines of the existing Institutes of Physics, Chemistry and Biology. (77)

Given the existence of the prestigious London Mathematical Society, which was granted a Royal Charter in 1965, it is perhaps surprising to find concerted efforts arising as late as 1959 to establish a professional institute for mathematicians. However, in the post-war period, it is important to recognize the differentiated nature of professional needs in the development of mathematics both as an academic discipline – pure and applied – and in its growing range and scale of applications. Two principal movements leading to the formation of a new professional body for mathematics are distinguishable. On the one hand, a committee largely composed of representatives from colleges of technology and government research organizations, acting under the chairmanship of A. Geary of Northampton College of Advanced Technology, London, had been campaigning from 1959 for the establishment of a new body to represent the growing interests of mathematicians in industry, technology, government research and commercial organizations. (78) On the other hand, a British Theoretical Mechanics Colloquium had been set up in 1959, initially as an informal annual gathering. By 1962 the potential for a new institute of applied mathematics was clear, and, in the following year, a small committee led by M.J. Lighthill FRS, of the Royal Aircraft Establishment at Farnborough, was empowered to secure such an outcome. The two movements came together in 1963 with a united proposal to the new JMC for the establishment of an Institute of Mathematics and its Applications. (79) A Provisional Council was set up with Lighthill as chairman and Combridge as convenor. The IMA was formally incorporated in April 1964 and, by the end of its first year, had nearly one thousand members of various grades. (80)

Combridge is conspicuous by his involvement in the establishment of both the JMC and the IMA. As Kilmister has fairly noted, 'Combridge has, perhaps, had less than due recognition for his work and inspiration here; if so, it is just as he would have wished.' (81) As a leading figure within the MA at this time, Combridge was also able to lend the support of the MA to these new institutional developments. At the same time, such developments raised fundamental questions for the MA itself, both regarding its scope and influence in mathematics education and its relationships within the professional world of mathematics and its users.

From 1961 three MA stalwarts – Combridge, Kellaway and Langford – all became involved in the discussions stimulated by the Geary Committee. At an early stage Combridge was optimistic concerning both the possibilities raised and the potential of the MA to accommodate the users of mathemat-

ics by extending its services, initially in four main areas: diploma examinations, periodicals, conferences, and accommodation and administrative
support. He added:

> I feel strongly that we are in a position to begin gradually . . . that no
> other body has our facilities or experience for this task, and that if we
> are to adventure on it we can ultimately achieve a unity – a unity of
> the subject and a unity among mathematicians – that is both desirable
> and essential. (82)

But in his 1962 Presidential address he added a note of caution concerning
the limits of the MA's capacity to adapt:

> It is at present no part of our terms of reference to set up a professional
> institute, to create a closed shop, or to interest ourselves as a body in
> matters of professional status, grades and salaries. (83)

A clear tension is identifiable at this time between Combridge's vision
and the realities of the situation which, in the event, reflected some of
his fears:

> if we hold back we shall be left as an association of school teachers,
> with a few altruistic university men and women taking a kindly interest
> in us, and other voices will speak to the Government and Industry for
> mathematics and mathematicians. (84)

As we have seen, the MA's Diploma in Mathematics (Technology) was
only a short-lived venture, which the IMA took over. In the case of
periodicals, plans were laid to develop a new MA journal for mathematical
applications but the MA's *Newsletter* reported:

> The Bulletin that was authorised for our Association also as a tempo-
> rary measure in the first instance has never materialised, and is likely to
> appear first (but with the same editors) as the Bulletin of the Institute
> [IMA]. Instead we have issued sundry occasional papers . . . (85)

Combridge urged MA members to apply for membership of the new IMA,
which also became a constituent member of the JMC. The IMA's first
President was Lighthill, with Geary as one of two Vice-Presidents and
Kellaway as one of two honorary secretaries. During 1964–5 Combridge
acted as registrar, and clerical work was done in the MA's office at Gordon
House, until the IMA moved to Maitland House, Southend-on-Sea, and a
permanent registrar was appointed: Norman Clarke. Both Combridge and
Langford resigned from the Council of the IMA at this time but Kellaway
continued as secretary. (86)
Clarke was well known in the world of physics and physics education. He
served for many years as deputy secretary of the Institute of Physics and

also became closely involved with the educational work of the Royal Society and the Nuffield Foundation. In a recent history of physics education he is described as 'an energetic, influential, man who . . . "knew all the right people"'. (87) He clearly had all the right credentials to help establish the IMA's reputation and to further its principal aim, which was 'to promote the advancement of mathematics and its applications'. But this did not exclude specifically educational work, and here some of the IMA's subsequent actions served further to complicate the institutional world of mathematics in relation to education. Indeed, oral evidence clearly points to the development of a schism between the IMA and the four mathematics teaching associations. (88) Furthermore, the Royal Society also extended the range of its influence in mathematics education through association with the IMA from the late-1960s.

Following the publication in 1963 of the MA and the ATCDE Mathematics Section's report on mathematics teacher supply and education, the JMC chose in-service training as a major focus for a first report, which was published two year later. (89) The JMC's report was presented at a major conference convened by the Royal Society to discuss in-service training in both mathematics and science. By this time Joint Committees for Education had been formed by the Royal Society and the Institutes of Biology, Chemistry and Physics, and their reports were also presented. The proceedings of the conference were published in 1966. In mathematics the IMA chose to take a lead itself, from 1967, with the focus again on mathematics teacher supply and education. *The First [sic] Report on the Shortage of Teachers of Mathematics* was not published until 1969, following some consultation with the JMC and its four constituent mathematics teaching associations, and a meeting with the Minister of State for Education and Science, Shirley Williams. (90) But Combridge judged that 'something more was still needed to make our collective voice heard' in mathematics education. (91)

Not surprisingly, mathematics followed the other sciences: a Joint Committee for Mathematical Education was set up by the Royal Society and the IMA. It included one representative from the LMS and one from each of the mathematics teaching associations, as well as one from the JMC itself. Combridge was optimistic about the Joint Committee's potential:

> This Joint Committee has two advantages. In the first place, it should be able to lend an ear to the opinions of all the mathematical bodies in the country. This, admittedly, the J.M.C. can also already do, but, in the second place – and this is for me its most impressive feature – the Joint Committee can give voice to these opinions in the quarters where national decisions are taken. This is something the J.M.C. has never yet been able to achieve. (92)

Thus, by the end of the 1960s, the MA was not only pursuing its own objectives, working independently of the ATM, the UDEMSG, the ATCDE Mathematics Section, and the IMA and its branches, but was also represented, as were these same bodies, on the JMC, the Royal Society's two committees (the BNCM and MIS), and the Joint Committee of the Royal Society and the IMA. From 1966 the annual report of the Council of the MA included a new section on 'representation'. (93) In his capacity as President of the MA in its centenary year (1971), Lighthill referred somewhat generously to 'the developments of the last decade that have enabled the Mathematical Association to exert an ever expanding influence on educational policy at national level'. (94) Certainly, leading members of the MA – notably Combridge and Kellaway – had been instrumental in these institutional developments. But, at the same time, developments in relation to school mathematics curriculum reform were growing apace. Early inspiration here came from the major conferences in England and also from international contacts and influences. The burgeoning of modern mathematics for schools put further pressure on the MA and its leadership in the 1960s.

INTERNATIONAL DEVELOPMENTS

The revival of the ICMI in 1952 was unimportant in the early stages of international activity focused on the reform of school mathematics. In the 1950s it was the International Commission (ICSITM), inspired and driven by Gattegno, which provided a unique forum for the exchange of new ideas. Polyglot meetings attracted innovative teachers from various countries, including France, Belgium, Spain, Poland and Greece, and English participation developed through links with the ATAM. In Fletcher's view it was 'an astonishingly good international group' and it helped to underpin the ATAM's early work in developing methods of teaching modern mathematics adapted to English conditions. (95) Partly as a consequence of the war, the Germans were not involved in this early international collaboration, and the American reform movement started independently in the 1950s.

These early European efforts notwithstanding, Hughes's survey of 'new trends', which was published by the MA in 1962, underlined the importance of the initial developments in the USA:

> The initiative in formulating new school programmes in mathematics, and indeed in physics and chemistry also, has unquestionably been American and the pioneering activities undertaken in mathematics go back at least ten years. (96)

University pure mathematicians played a leading part in the early American movement during the 1950s, and further impetus for a concerted national effort directed at curriculum reform came from the Soviet launching of Sputnik in 1957. The realization of Soviet technological advances galvanized public opinion and stimulated the provision of major government funding for curriculum development, notably in the case of the School Mathematics Study Group (SMSG) project from 1958. By 1962 the total sales of SMSG texts was approaching half a million volumes. (97)

Cross-fertilization between America and Europe was facilitated by the Organization for European Economic Co-operation (OEEC), whose membership included eighteen European countries and the USA and

Canada as associates. A major OEEC seminar was held at Royaumont, France, in the autumn of 1959, at which the radical French 'Bourbaki'-inspired proposals in pure mathematics were disseminated alongside the pioneering American efforts. Major publications and further international co-operation followed. (98)

A major collaboration resulted in the publication of an international consensus by the OEEC in 1961: *Synopses for Modern Secondary School Mathematics*. This provided further stimulus for leading ATAM activists to crystallize their thinking concerning both new content and methods of teaching. In the words of Fletcher, the *Synopses* acted as a 'beacon': 'We were not alone in what we were trying to do. It was a message. It was a prophecy.' (99) An English collaborative writing venture followed, in the form of a concentrated effort by ATM members during a week at Leicester in 1962, culminating in the publication two years later of *Some Lessons in Mathematics,* edited by Fletcher. (100) Both the mode of production and the form of this publication – a collection of individual contributions describing innovative practices – were different from the long-established pattern for MA reports. Neither consensus nor authority was a concern of the ATM at this time. But the publication was timely and influential, and it provided a stimulus for further experimentation and the production of new teaching materials.

Over the period 1952–62, international links were clearly more important for the ATAM than the MA. Maxwell of Cambridge University, who joined the editorial board of the *Gazette* in 1962 and took over as editor from Goodstein in the same year, had links in the 1950s with the ICMI and also played a part in the Royaumont seminar. (101) But the OEEC's *Synopses* was subjected to a critical review by Goodstein in the *Gazette*, where he concluded: 'Proposals as extreme and eccentric as those under review can I fear only serve to damage the case for reform.' (102) Maxwell was President of the MA for the year 1960–1, and in his address he made a passing reference to the MA's role in the rapidly developing scene:

> many activities of general mathematical interest are taking place with which the Association is not directly involved. Members of the Association sit, in private capacity, of course, on most of the Committees concerned with school mathematics at all levels; and, again, representatives are even now preparing reports for submission to the Congress of Mathematicians to be held at Stockholm in 1962. (103)

He concluded by underlining the challenge for the MA at this time:

> The crisis in the teaching of mathematics is now upon us, heavily but, as yet, by no means overwhelmingly; and it is to the members of the Mathematical Association that the public ought to look for guidance. (104)

By 1962 the ICMI was becoming more active in relation to new developments. Three educational topics were chose for discussion at the 1962 ICM: modern mathematics for secondary schools, correlation between arithmetic and algebra, and mathematics teacher education. (105) As we have seen, both the MA and the ATCDE Mathematics Section participated in the international work on mathematics teacher education, and a major report was published in 1963. The MA was also drawn into the international discussions concerning modern mathematics at this time. A subcommittee was set up under the chairmanship of Newman, who had had a major hand in the MA's 1957 sixth form algebra report; and a brief report was prepared and approved for presentation at Stockholm. Understandably, the MA's stance on modern mathematics was neither progressive nor definitive at this early stage but cautiously encouraging. By contrast, the newly named ATM was wholeheartedly embracing modern mathematics and starting a network of study groups to help forward the movement in this country. (106)

Both the MA and the ATM were officially invited to contribute to the work of the ICMI leading up to the 1966 ICM in Moscow. The ATM's involvement was indicative of its developing status as a professional association. For the British contribution, and following the ICMI's new agenda, the MIS invited the MA to prepare a report on the use of the axiomatic method in secondary teaching, and the ATM was given a notably child-centred focus: the development of mathematical activity in children. (107) An MA subcommittee under Quadling's chairmanship duly presented its report, which was published in the *Gazette*. (108) On the question of systematization, the MA's moderate position, by comparison with that of some innovators from abroad, drew strength from the long-established three-stages view of geometry teaching. As Hughes emphasized:

> It is hard to believe that any mathematical reformer reared in this tradition would wish to plunge into Stages B and C without a careful approach to the topic concerned via Stage A.

He added the following caveat:

> Even in geometry the systematizing Stage C has hardly been more than an aspiration and to-day it seems extremely unlikely that mathematics teachers in Britain would easily succumb to the arid formalism of premature rigour. The great danger is probably of not getting beyond the experimental and intuitive Stage A in the new topics which are brought into the curriculum . . . (109)

The ATM took full advantage of the opportunity to draw in a wide range of contributions to another major publication in a topical field close to many of its leading members' interests. As a springboard for the ATM's contribution, a widely representative meeting was held in London early in 1965. An impressive range of papers was submitted by individuals and groups to provide a basis for the final report. (110) Despite these British efforts, a report on the actual proceedings at the Moscow ICM of 1966 claimed that 'discussions on the topics prescribed for the Education Section had been desultory'. (111) Two developments followed a meeting of the ICMI at Utrecht in 1967: the launch of a new international journal,

Educational Studies in Mathematics, in 1968; and the first International Congress on Mathematical Education (ICME), held at Lyons, France, in 1969. (112)

The first ICME was attended by over six hundred delegates, including around fifty from the UK. Howson reported in the MA's *Newsletter* on the arrangements and the outcomes. In Lyons the ATM again took the opportunity to present a high and distinctive profile and thereby to enhance its international reputation:

> the ATM, with the financial assistance of several industrial and commercial bodies, produced a booklet, liberally illustrated in colour, describing its aims and methods of working. Even more important it established a workshop, complete with children, materials and teachers, to show its philosophy in action. A demonstration lesson led to an interesting discussion concerning the teacher's objectives and methods. (113)

But, generally, Howson concluded: 'What is needed is a closer study of how the interchange of ideas can be facilitated.' The decision to hold the next ICME at Exeter, in 1972, gave British enterprise an opportunity to flourish in the organization of a large and prestigious international congress.

Lighthill was President of the MA in its centenary year and he also took over as President of the ICMI in 1971. In preparing for the Exeter ICME, the MA was invited by the ICMI to contribute to the organization of particular working groups, and Mrs Williams, now in her 'retirement', energetically chaired the local organizing committee. A programme committee was also appointed, with seven British representatives, including Howson, who had replaced Kellaway as an honorary secretary of the MA from 1969, and nine representatives from other countries. (114) The published proceedings of the congress were edited by Howson, and the MA also chose to mark the occasion by inviting four international figures to become honorary life members: Edith Biggs, a leading figure in English primary mathematics reform; George Polya, a Hungarian-born mathematician who had also made major contributions to the literature on mathematical thinking and creativity; Warwick Sawyer, a leading figure in the popularization of mathematics; and Bryan Thwaites, who had by this time completed ten years as director of the SMP. (115) The SMP was one of a number of projects which played a major part in the modernization of British school mathematics in the 1960s.

MODERN MATHEMATICS EXPERIMENTS AND PROJECTS

In primary mathematics the MA had provided an important early lead in the 1950s, principally through its major and visionary report of 1955. Subsequently, it was Edith Biggs, acting not through the MA but in her capacity as an HMI, who did much to disseminate child-centred and more practical methods of teaching. Wilf Flemming recalls: 'She was

Plate 7.2   Second Primary Report 1970

running these courses all over the country and her car was absolutely loaded with little bits of equipment; and the courses were all practical. (116) Her thinking was embodied in an important publication from the newly established Schools Council for the Curriculum and Examinations: *Mathematics in Primary Schools* (1965).

In 1964 the Nuffield Mathematics (5–13) Project started under the direction of Geoffrey Matthews. Through close collaboration with LEAs, the involvement of teachers in working groups and courses, the develop ment of teachers' centres, and the production of a wide range of visually stimulating teachers' guides, the project exerted a considerable national influence, and it laid a foundation for subsequent published schemes which included children's materials. (117) In 1967 the ATM produced its own contribution to the development of primary mathematics teaching, *Notes on Mathematics in Primary Schools*. By this time HMI judged:

> at least a majority of schools have been influenced by the developments
> of the last five years and . . . a substantial minority, something between
> ten per cent and 20 per cent, have completely rethought and reorgan-
> ised their mathematical syllabus and teaching methods. (118)

Criticism of the MA's relative neglect of primary mathematics surfaced at the annual conference in 1965. (119) Around this time two developments helped to improve the situation. Matthews was now chairman of the Teach ing Committee, which was starting to implement a more flexible policy in relation to publications; and Mrs Williams was elected President of the MA for the year 1965–6. The primary subcommittee was reconstituted, and efforts were made to disseminate the new thinking, including the work of the Nuffield Mathematics Project, through the annual conference and the branches.

A substantial further report on primary mathematics was produced by the MA's subcommittee and rushed from the printers to the annual conference at Newcastle in 1970. No doubt reflecting the influence of the Nuffield Mathematics Project, the visual impact of this report was an important feature, and production had involved a heavy investment. As Thurston remarked, 'no report ever *looked* like this before, with gay cover in colour and illustrations throughout'. (120) The report's aim was to consolidate and disseminate the new thinking:

> the sub-committee re-affirms the principles set out in 1955 and presents
> [its report] to place before teachers an account of the ways in which
> children are being led to learn mathematics and of the mathematical
> ideas which the children now encounter in the new kinds of experience
> that primary schools are beginning to provide. (121)

In secondary mathematics some of the earliest British experimentation with the teaching of modern topics was undertaken by individual teachers. Drawing on his wealth of experience and connections as an HMI, Rollett surveyed a sample of such initiatives in a paper read at the annual meeting of the MA in 1963. He concluded: 'The property common to all these activities is that of spontaneity; all are independent of any organization here, across the Channel or across the Atlantic.' (122) Through publications and international contacts, American and continental influences were in fact helping to shape such experimentation in Britain, but on the question of intuition versus rigour the British approach was typically a moderate one. Cockcroft and Land summarized their impressions from the 1962 Stockholm ICM:

> both French and American mathematicians were in a majority amongst those who mistrusted intuitive ideas and vigorously attacked associating concrete experiences with mathematical arguments and . . . amongst those who thought in terms of mathematical ideas being abstracted from practical examples and concrete situations, a majority were from Britain, Germany and the Netherlands, there being some important exceptions on both sides. (123)

The shortage of mathematics graduates and the problem of teacher supply, the growing involvement of industrialists and professional mathematicians in the educational arena, the organization of major conferences focused on school mathematics, innovations by individual teachers, and influences from science education and abroad, all contributed to a more organized and better resourced approach to British reform through curriculum development projects of various kinds, focused principally on mathematics up to O-level standard in the GCE examinations.

In terms of status and resources, the early involvement of independent schools was significant, as was their independence. The SMP initially involved four public schools, and the Contemporary School Mathematics (CSM) Project had its roots in St Dunstan's College, Catford, under the guidance of Matthews, before he became director of the Nuffield Mathematics Project. However, independence was not a necessary condition for involvement in these new developments. The Midlands Mathematical Experiment (MME), with which Roland Collins of the ATAM became centrally involved, started with a group of eight lower-status secondary schools: two grammar, four technical and two modern. (124)

No central government funding was forthcoming for the early projects in England and Wales, by contrast with Scotland, where a single national project, the Scottish Mathematics Group (SMG), was supported by the Scottish Education Department. But some funding was forthcoming from industry for the SMP and the Mathematics in Education and Industry (MEI) Project, and LEAs also provided some support for local projects. Typically, projects devised their own materials, including teachers' guides, and established links with publishers. Ideas and materials were also disseminated through single meetings, conferences or short courses. In addition, a major factor in the success of the three principal O-level projects – the SMP, CSM, and MME – was the use of the examining boards' special syllabus provision to gain the acceptance of alternative project syllabuses and papers, alongside the existing alternatives A and B (the Jeffery syllabus). (125)

The SMP rapidly became the most successful of the modern mathematics projects in England and Wales, and by 1968 the SMP examinations were available through all the examining boards. By this time it has been estimated that of around 3500 schools involved in modern mathematics programmes probably about 3000 were involved in some way with the SMP. (126) The unrivalled success of the SMP is also indicated by the fact that, from 1967, when the examining boards started to provide alternative modern (C) syllabuses, which were not associated with a particular project, the SMP alternative persisted. Furthermore, the number of SMP O-level entries nearly doubled between 1968 and 1970. (127)

The MA had played an important role in the development of alternative B syllabuses in the 1940s. But the development of modern mathematics projects and syllabuses in the 1960s was multilateral. The new challenge for the MA was spelt out by Broadbent in the quotation at the start of this chapter. The developments of the 1940s, however, were a measured progression from the thinking and consolidation of earlier decades, whereas the 1960s was a period of major discontinuity in the school mathematics curriculum, comparable to that of the 1900s.

In the development of the SMP, Thwaites had no need to develop any links with the MA in the pursuit of his educational ambitions. (128) But some leading MA members did become, quite independently, associated with the SMP's early work: Quadling of Marlborough College, Cundy of Sherborne School, who was an assistant editor of the *Gazette*, and Langford of Battersea Grammar School, one of the first non-public schools to become involved with the SMP. (129) Howson also joined Thwaites at Southampton University in an appointment which was linked with the SMP from the outset. In addition, when the SMP extended its range to A-level mathematics, a powerful advisory group of university mathematicians included Busbridge from Oxford and Maxwell from Cambridge. Despite these personal links between the MA and the SMP, no official support for the SMP was offered by the MA, although brief details of the project's first year were provided by Cundy in the *Gazette*. (130) The SMP was also included along with eleven other British projects in an informative survey published by the MA in 1968; a syllabus analysis of all the projects was undertaken, but no comparative judgements were made. (131) Furthermore, oral evidence points to a less than sympathetic view of the SMP among some of the MA old guard, and antipathy towards such projects was evident within HMI, after Rollett had retired in 1963. (132) Links with one project, however – MEI – involved the MA itself as an agent in modern mathematics curriculum development.

Industrial involvement in conferences on the teaching of mathematics and science was taken a stage further by British Petroleum, late in 1961, when this firm sponsored a series of three conferences, on mathematics, chemistry and arts teaching, in successive weeks. Steven Mullaly, a personnel manager at BP, was instrumental in this initiative, and Combridge, President of the MA but acting in an individual capacity, was drawn in as chairman of the mathematics conference, which again involved industrialists, university staff and schoolteachers. (133) The two-day conference deliberations were again driven by a general concern about the shortage of mathematicians, but the need for better communication between schools and industry, for their mutual benefit, was also highlighted. Among a number of strategic recommendations was the following:

That a committee should be formed, with representatives from industry and schools, to make representations regarding the content of the mathematics to be taught in schools at all levels; to promote discussion of topics of mutual interest; to explore the field of opportunity for closer liaison between local representatives of industry; to sponsor regular meetings between these to discuss the introduction of modern mathematics into school curricula and to encourage and initiate further pilot experiments in this direction. (134)

Through Cambridge the MA was empowered to take the initiative, which led to the establishment of the Schools and Industry Committee. This was an officially designated committee of the MA from 1963, but it included non-MA representation and managed its own industrial fund, with some pump-priming from BP itself. (135)

From 1962 Mathematics in Education and Industry (MEI), the theme of the first conference, became associated with two fundamentally different developments. On the one hand, various MEI projects were initiated, beginning with some schools in or near North London and followed by a project centred on the Bristol branch of the MA. The principal aim was to give teachers an opportunity to gain first-hand industrial or commercial experience out of which better mutual understanding and new content and methods in mathematics teaching might be developed. On the other hand, the pioneering North London Schools project, which was concentrated in the independent sector, took this work a stage further by developing its own alternative modern syllabuses for O-level additional mathematics and A-level pure and applied mathematics. They became known as the MEI syllabuses, but as Combridge took pains to point out:

the production of official alternative syllabuses is no part of the aims of the MEI work stimulated by the Schools and Industry Committee, and neither this syllabus, nor any works that may be published in which reference may be made to it, have any kind of M.A. *imprimatur.* (136)

This possibility of a direct link between the MA and experimental syllabuses was clearly a sensitive issue for the leadership, but at least the North London Schools project adopted the policy of not producing its own tailor-made series of MEI textbooks. However, as MEI projects developed, so the original syllabuses gained in popularity and various books were subsequently published with MEI A-level specifically in mind. (137) In addition, the pioneering St Dunstan's O-level syllabus also became associated with the MEI scheme of school examinations in modern mathematics.

MEI projects helped both to promote the early use of mainframe computers, with batch processing supported by BP in particular, and to develop the potential of numerical methods, supported by computers or mechanical 'desk calculators'. (138) Developments in this field in the 1960s were sufficient to warrant the production of a substantial MA report *Computers and the Teaching of Numerical Mathematics in the Upper Secondary School* – published in 1971. (139) The growing attention paid to applicable mathematics in the 1960s was also reflected in the production by the MA of two compendia covering applications of 'elementary' and 'sixth form' mathematics respectively. (140)

The Schools and Industry Committee helped to stimulate and dissemi nate the work of MEI projects through conferences, reports and the finan cial support provided by its industrial fund, which was separate from the MA's general account. Early progress was surveyed at a major, three-da conference held at Brighton in 1966. Twelve local groups were now active Combridge identified the promotion of 'numeracy' in a broad sense as a major strategic aim of the committee:

> 'Numeracy' is not just getting sums right in arithmetic – nor even in algebra.
> It is the ability to deal mathematically – though the mathematics may be of the simplest – with everyday situations, and to understand others who speak or write about them in mathematical terms . . . And this is why [the Committee's] work concerns every level of school teaching – because it is concerned with the education of the average child for citizenship. (141)

The Committee's strategic objective became 'the achievement of the greatest possible degree of numeracy in the greatest possible number of school leavers'. (142) This was a particularly fitting objective in the 1970s, as a general concern about standards of numeracy gained momentum, and such concern was echoed by the Committee itself in 1975:

> The . . . Committee . . . is deeply concerned with the too-high proportion of school leavers who are not numerate, and believes that Education and Industry have complementary parts to play in reducing this proportion . . .
> The aim of the Committee is to bridge the gap between the abstract world of school mathematics and the real world by giving substance to the subject through its applications and so enlivening its impact upon pupils. (143)

In its submission to the Cockcroft Committee of Inquiry into the Teaching of Mathematics in Schools, which was set up in 1978 as a political response to the climate of concern about standards, the Schools and Industry Committee summarized its past achievements in relation to the growth of MEI projects and GCE examination syllabuses, and highlighted its more recent concern for different types of school leaver and corresponding vocational destinations. By this time two new initiatives were under way: a Bath University survey of mathematics projects involving education and employment, and the development of a 16+ School Leaver's Attainment Profile of Numerical Skills (SLAPONS). (144) The Bath project was supported jointly by the Schools and Industry Committee and the Schools Council Mathematics Committee, and it identified some seventy local groups. (145)

Combridge had been instrumental in the establishment of the Schools and Industry Committee and he acted as its energetic chairman until 1972. Writing in 1971, Combridge acknowledged the important role of Rollett in connection with another new committee of the MA, which was established in 1964: 'We have . . . strengthened our ties with the Universities by means f the Universities and Schools Committee with which the name of Mr A.P. ollett will always be associated.' (146) Thus, in addition to the work of aison between schools and industry, the MA also took a lead in developing aison between sixth forms and university mathematics departments.

Two major priorities were identified from the outset: widening the access) university courses and defining a minimal sixth-form core for intending ndergraduates. (147) A further concern of the 1960s was how to accom- odate new undergraduates who had experienced modern mathematics in eir school courses. (148) A collection of suggestions for sixth-form work pure mathematics was published in 1967, together with a suggested utline core syllabus in the following year. (149) But in 1968 the Committee uffered a 'severe set-back': the death of Rollett, its first chairman. (150) e was replaced in 1969 by Frank Smithies of Cambridge University. The constituted Committee set up a survey of first-year undergraduate courses nd the results were published in the *Gazette*. (151) Before it was disbanded 1975 the Committee also produced a booklet aimed at sixth formers tending to study university mathematics. (152) Over a period of some n years the Universities and Schools Committee had undertaken valuable ork at the interface, with which Rollett had become notably involved at early stage through the establishment of the Conference of Professors f Mathematics in 1961.

The institution of the new MA Diplomas, the work on liaison, both etween industry and education and between universities and schools, ere all significant contributions of the MA to mathematics education in e 1960s. We have also seen how the leadership of the MA became closely volved with the establishment of both the JMC and the IMA. However, in onnection with the development and dissemination of modern mathemat- s for schools, the 1960s was a very difficult period for the MA. Unlike e young ATM, the much older association was understandably reluctant lead at the cutting edge of classroom innovation. The Perry movement the 1900s was unilateral and pervasive but modernization in the 1960s as controversial and piecemeal. In the absence of a consensus, the ATM tively promoted debate, classroom experimentation and dissemination. luch of the MA's twentieth-century work had been evolutionary and onsolidatory in character, and it carried the stamp of professional author- y. As Elizabeth Williams pointed out in her Presidential address of 1966:

> today's situation is different from anything we have known. Fundamen-
> tal changes are proposed which are by no means acceptable to every-
> one . . . many teachers look to the Association for early assess-
> ment of the current changes . . . What is needed is better public-
> ity, more material with a wide appeal and new means of making it
> known. (153)

p to 1961 the content of the *Gazette*, under Goodstein's editorship, and e tenor of Presidential addresses revealed no sense of mission in the early ages of reform. (154) The growing pressures on the MA were highlighted the BP conference and in Cambridge's Presidential address of 1962, when e pointed to the need for improvement in the means of communication as major priority. (155) Changes in the MA's policy for publications soon followed. From 1962 Combridge was instrumental in the production of a regular *Newsletter* in addition to the *Gazette*. The *Newsletter* helpfull provided concise, up-to-date information about a wide range of strategi developments in mathematics education. Under Maxwell as its new editor the *Gazette* from 1963 also gave more prominence to modern mathematic and its teaching, including a special number – a symposium – on th subject. (156) In addition the MA sponsored an informative booklet *Modernising School Mathematics* (1962). (157) But the long-standing rol of the *Gazette* as a minor mathematical serial, which had been reinforce in the case of pure mathematics under Goodstein's editorship, continued to act as a barrier to its use as a major means of communication in the reforr of school mathematics, particularly at the less advanced levels. Maxwe confessed:

> I receive complaints from time to time that there are not enough articles on the very elementary levels . . . It is no part of policy to neglect the first stages; they are vital, and the Association has always seen them to be so. But the problem of printing non-existent manuscripts continues to baffle me. (158)

The range of work of subcommittees of the Teaching Committee an their published output provide further indicators of the strength of th MA's response to the reform movement. Applications and statistics wer two new areas on the agenda from 1958. (159) From 1962 the agenda als included the eleven-plus examination, new trends in mathematics teaching sixth form mathematics for non-specialists, and the development of the ne Certificate of Secondary Education (CSE). (160) The corresponding outpu of published reports in the 1960s was as follows:

1964   *Transfer from Primary to Secondary Schools*
1964   *Applications of Elementary Mathematics*
1965   *Experiments in the Teaching of Sixth Form Mathematics to Non-Specialists*, pamphlet no.1
1965   *The Teaching of Sets in Schools*, by K.R. McLean
1967   *Experiments in the Teaching of Sixth Form Mathematics to Non-Specialists*, pamphlet no.2
1967   *Applications of Sixth-Form Mathematics*
1968   *Mathematics Projects in British Secondary Schools*
1968   *A Report on Mathematics Syllabuses for the Certificate of Secondary Education*
1969   *The Same but Different*, by D.A. Quadling

Riley resigned as chairman of the Teaching Committee in 1963 and hi successor was Matthews, who made a rapid rise to 'new blood' prominenc within the MA:

> [Rollett] wrote saying that he was chairman of the local branch of the Mathematical Association, and would I come and give a simple talk on matrices at Crediton in Devon? The talk went down well . . . In April 1962 I delivered 'Matrices for the Million' at the Annual Meeting of the Mathematical Association. The venue was King's College, London,

and the audience was 400 strong . . . Things moved fast. My paper was published in the *Mathematical Gazette*; no sooner had I joined the Teaching Committee of the Mathematical Association than I became secretary of the Modern Trends sub-committee. This led on to being chairman of the full Teaching Committee. (161)

Matthews was well placed to lead a more flexible policy for MA publications from the mid-1960s. As Morgan pointed out in his Presidential address of 1964:

Clearly there is not yet sufficient authoritative information from practising teachers to justify a major report on classical lines, and it is good news that the Teaching Committee intends to produce comparatively brief pamphlets . . . (162).

The 'modern trends' subcommittee took the lead by sponsoring individual contributions to the *Gazette*, beginning with Tammadge's article on 'stage A topology', (163) and the separate pamphlets by McLean on sets and Quadling on equivalence. The committee which produced the survey pamphlet on modern mathematics projects was set up by the Standing Committee of Council; the committee included Bob Lindsay, who subsequently compiled a fully revised guide (1976). (164) In the 1960s the MA provided further advisory pamphlets, on books for a school library, compiled by Rollett, on the provision of mathematics laboratories, and on the introduction of SI units of measurement and decimal currency – 'D-Day' arrived in 1971. (165) Two compendia of applications of school mathematics were also published, but a report on statistics and its teaching is conspicuous by its absence, although the possibility was first explored by the MA as early as 1957.

TEACHING OF STATISTICS

The potential of statistics and probability as part of modern mathematics for schools was raised at the major conferences involving school and university mathematicians and personnel from industry. Further endorsement for some teaching of statistics and probability throughout the secondary school came in the reports of the OEEC, following the Royaumont seminar of 1959. But in England there were fundamental practical and ideological barriers to progress, associated with the long-established tradition that restricted school 'applied mathematics' to theoretical mechanics.

Although examining boards were by 1960 making some provision for statistics and probability at both O- and A- level, always as an option, the take-up was very small and understandably so, given the IAAM's observation in 1957: 'Most present-day teachers of mathematics had no opportunity of studying statistics in their formal training . . .' (166) Physical applications continued largely to exhaust the possibilities for 'applied mathematics' courses at undergraduate level, and a broader conception, embracing statistics, probability and other branches of mathematics applied to such diverse fields as the natural and social sciences, engineering, economics, management and the humanities, was very slow to develop.

The relatively late development of statistics as an independent academic discipline, not rooted in university mathematics departments and having its own professional support mechanisms, has been sketched by Bibby. He draws attention to the post-war boom in the general pursuit and teaching of statistics. Stimulus came from the war itself, the burgeoning demands of industry and the championship of the Royal Statistical Society. (167) From the 1930s the *Gazette* reflected some of these developments by publishing occasional articles on probability and statistical applications. In relation to school work, Hope-Jones's plea in 1924 for probability teaching was an isolated one, though the possibilities for statistics in school was a topic for discussion at the annual meeting of the MA in 1933. (168) B.C. Brookes, a contributor to the MA's annual meeting in 1947, went so far as to claim that the case for (some) statistics teaching in schools had 'already been fully discussed at previous meetings of this Association, and in other places'. (169)

The Royal Statistical Society gave an early lead through its own Committee on the Teaching of Statistics in Schools, whose report was published in 1951. In the same year a textbook by Brookes and W.F.L. Dick appeared which a reviewer in *Nature* claimed was 'the first textbook of modern statistics planned for and suitable for school use'. (170) However, as late as the 1960s, the MA's two pamphlets on elementary and sixth form applications of mathematics restricted the scope of the applications to the traditional mathematical branches: algebra, geometry, trigonometry and calculus. (171) By this time modern mathematics projects were helping to disseminate work up to O-level on data representation, averages, dispersion and introductory probability. (172)

In 1957 the MA asked Alec Penfold of Battersea Grammar School to convene a small group to consider the advisability of issuing a report on the teaching of statistics. (173) This was at a time when the IAAM reported: 'There is as yet little experience of teaching statistics in schools . . .' (174) Both teacher education in statistics and the provision of suitable school teaching materials were still far from adequate. Penfold himself was soon to become involved in the trialling of the first SMP materials and he subsequently moved from Battersea to join Daltry at the London Institute of Education. (175) In 1958 the Teaching Committee agreed to embark on the production of a major report on statistics teaching. The first small subcommittee for this purpose included Penfold, Vesselo, who had pressed for such a report six years earlier, and Brookes, who acted as the first chairman. (176) Daisy Penfold, a lecturer in educational statistics at the London Institute, was soon co-opted to join her husband in what was to prove a very difficult and protracted project.

To quote Alec Penfold's view over thirty years later: 'It would require some-one with the wisdom of Solomon to disentangle the web in which the Teaching Committee's subcommittee activities were enmeshed from 1957 to about 1970.' (177) Early links with the Royal Statistical Society and some contact with developments in the USA were pursued, but the subcommittee was short of practical, first-hand experience concerning statistics in schools. (178) Furthermore, the co-option of an HMI with strong views in relation to probability theory did not help in the efforts to shape a consensus in the report's mathematical treatment of its subject. As Penfold has explained, the subcommittee's broad aim encompassed much more than pedagogy: 'Our task was unique in so far as it would have been the *first* [Teaching Committee] Report which would have *instructed* the recipients rather than just broaden their horizons in a prescribed area of mathematics education.' (179) But a minute of November 1961 clearly exposed the subcommittee's early difficulties: 'opposing views on the sub-committee had brought the work to a halt for the moment . . . Mr. B.C. Brookes felt that he must resign'. (180)

With Daisy Penfold as a new chairman, work was resumed in 1963, and other co-options were made in an effort to keep the subcommittee abreast of current developments in statistics teaching. (181) In 1966 Matthews expressed the Teaching Committee's thanks for the work to date and to the Penfolds in particular 'for the strenuous efforts they have made to overcome great difficulties'. (182) The work continued into 1967, by which time seven chapters had been drafted and given the Teaching Committee's general approval. (183) There was still much editing to be done, and further delays occurred during the period of Bailey's chairmanship of the Teaching Committee, which he partly attributed to financial difficulties and competing priorities for publication. (184) The report reached the stage of galley proofs, still with some work to be done, but then it fell at the last fence: the stage of Council approval, which was normally a formality. The minutes of the Council meeting of October 1970 reported:

> It was agreed that an independent opinion of the report should be sought. If, as a result of this, the Teaching Committee is advised not to publish, then Council should be asked to rescind its permission to publish and the report would be referred back to the Teaching Committee. (185)

The upshot was effectively the demise of the report, which the Council explained in its annual report for 1970:

> it was decided with regret to reconsider the Statistics Report. So much time has passed since the writing of this Report was completed that it has been overtaken by events, and the Council agreed that the Association ought not to publish a Report which does not reflect the experience gained in teaching this subject over the last six years. (186)

Oral evidence hints that there may also have been some misgivings about the report on mathematical as well as pedagogical grounds. (187) Lack of consensus concerning the details of mathematical exposition, particularly within the domain of probability, had bedevilled the production of this report from start to finish. (188)

In the MA's major post-war programme of report production on the branches of elementary and sixth form mathematics, statistics was clearly a special case and the only branch for which the MA had failed to deliver an authoritative overview. The nature and history of statistics and its relations with mathematics and other disciplines, and its ill-defined and shifting place in education, had proved to be insurmountable barriers to the achievement of the consensus necessary for a major MA report. Efforts were made in the early 1970s to gain the support of the DES in the preparation of a joint report, but this fell through, and the MA had to content itself with a more modest piece of salvage work. (189) An exploratory pamphlet on sixth form statistics and probability was eventually published in 1975:

> Despite a serious fire at the printers the long-awaited pamphlet on statistics was distributed to members in November and December. We would prefer not to call it a Report; as its title indicates it suggests an approach to probability and statistics at A-level which we hope teachers will find helpful. (190)

Major developments in statistics teaching over the period 1960–80 have been surveyed by Barnett, who quotes a 1976 report which indicated that over 80 per cent of secondary schools in England and Wales claimed to be teaching some statistics. (191) In parallel with the widespread adoption of some statistics in mathematics syllabuses during the 1970s, statistical ideas and methods were also being widely introduced into other subject syllabuses, particularly in biology, economics and geography. The report of the Cockcroft Inquiry, 1978–82, made some specific references to the teaching of statistics but noted: 'Surprisingly few of the submissions which we have received have made direct reference to the teaching of statistics.' (192)

Statistics teaching was, however, the principal concern of three submissions from organizations whose existence is indicative of growing professionalism in the field of statistics education: the Committee of Professors of Statistics, the Joint Education Committee of the Royal Statistical Society and the Institute of Statisticians, and the Schools Council Project on Statistical Education 11–16 (POSE). (193) In the 1950s a major concern had been the dearth of teachers with sufficient statistics in their own education. For the 1980s the Cockcroft Report pointed to the 'considerable need for in-service training courses on the teaching of statistics not only for mathematics teachers but also for teachers of other subjects'. (194)

Professional support for statistics in education was forthcoming from POSE, which from 1975 was based at the University of Sheffield (subsequently the location of a Centre for Statistical Education). A new journal – *Teaching Statistics* – for teachers of pupils aged nine to nineteen was also started, with sponsorship from the Royal Statistical Society, the Institute of Statisticians, the International Statistical Institute and the Applied Probability Trust. (195) Another indicator of growing professionalism in statistics education is the development of international activity, supported by an *International Statistical Education Newsletter* and International Conferences on Teaching Statistics (ICOTS), from 1982. (196) These developments were part of a pattern of growing specialization within mathematics education, which brought with it greater complexity in the forms of professional organization and support. As Barnett concluded in 1980:

> Perhaps the one overriding obstacle to progress in the near future is the lack of any *coordination* of effort. Many well-meaning and

informed individuals and organisations are working hard to improve the statistical education scene. But they do so in isolation. (197)

The MA could do no more than play its own small part in the developing and increasingly complex world of mathematics (including statistics) education.

'CIRCULAR 10/65 AND ALL THAT'

In 1960 the MA conducted a survey of LEAs' arrangements for the testing of arithmetic in eleven-plus examinations, and the data was used in a report on transfer from primary to secondary schools, which was published in 1964. (198) By this time, however, the movement to end both the eleven-plus examination and the associated prevailing pattern of rigid streaming for children in junior schools was gaining considerable momentum. (199) At the same time, comprehensive reorganization of secondary schools was about to take off, with the initial support of both Conservative and Labour governments. Prior to the early 1960s the movement to establish comprehensive schools had been a grass-roots one, concentrated in a small number of LEAs. (200) Edward Boyle gave cautious encouragement to the movement as the new Conservative minister, from 1962, and his Education Act of 1964 legitimized middle schools (nine to thirteen or eight to twelve), which helped to ease the transition in some LEAs. In 1965 Anthony Crosland's DES Circular 10/65 established comprehensive secondary education as national policy, and the Labour government asked LEAs to submit plans for comprehensive reorganization. (201)

The resulting change in the shape of the secondary school system from its tripartite divisions was dramatic. The percentage of pupils in comprehensive secondary, including middle, schools in England grew apace between 1965 and 1980: 1965, 9.9 per cent; 1970, 34.4 per cent; 1975 68.8 per cent; 1980, 82.5 per cent. The change to a Conservative government, with Margaret Thatcher as Secretary of State, 1970–74, failed to arrest the pace of change. The number of comprehensive schools in England and Wales increased from 130 in 1960 to 1250 in 1970, and to 3538 in 1980. (202)

Structural changes in the school system from the 1960s were accompanied by internal developments in the comprehensive schools themselves. Teachers of mathematics and other subjects were now having to cope with a wider range of abilities taught in streamed, banded, setted or mixed-ability classes. Grammar school teachers were having to cope with less able pupils – the Newsom Report's (1963) 'half our future' – and secondary modern school teachers were now being challenged by pupils of grammar school ability. The adoption of systems of selection within individual comprehensive schools – the streaming, banding or setting of pupils and, it should be added, their teachers – alleviated the difficulties of transition, but the comprehensive movement embraced a wider objective: the undermining of the process of selection itself. There were pressures to introduce mixed-ability teaching, particularly in the lower secondary years, which brought further challenges for secondary teachers, in terms of organization, teaching styles and resources for learning. (203)

For older secondary pupils and their teachers there were also major developments in the system of examinations, which up to 1965 had been dominated by the O- and A-level single-subject examinations, designed for pupils of grammar school ability. Pressure from secondary modern schools, which in the 1950s were increasingly entering pupils for O-level examinations, led to the appointment in 1958 of a subcommittee of the SSEC under Robert Beloe. Their report in 1960 proposed the establishment of what became the CSE examinations for sixteen-year-olds, intended initially for the 40 per cent of pupils below the top 20 per cent for which O-level catered. The CSE was introduced in 1962 and pupils sat the first examinations in 1965. As Brian Simon has pointed out, the resulting system was an anomalous one in relation to comprehensive ideals:

> Just at the point when the drive towards comprehensive education became almost a nationwide consensus, with government support, a new examination was established which, while embodying certain progressive features, imposed a threefold division within comprehensive schools. Students, at least between the ages of thirteen or fourteen and sixteen had to be categorised and taught in three main groupings comprising those aiming at GCE, at CSE, or at nothing (in terms of an examination). (204)

A major 'progressive feature' was the built-in potential for schools to develop their own syllabuses and modes of examination, often including a coursework element, all of which provided an important incentive for school-based curriculum development and co-operation between schools, in the interests of pupils of 'average' ability.

One other major change in secondary schooling – the raising of the minimum school leaving age to sixteen – was promised by Boyle in 1964, but the planned implementation in 1970 was postponed until 1972 on economic grounds. Teachers in the 1960s were at least spared the additional pressure of this particular reform. The first cohort of pupils to be affected by the change completed their period of compulsory schooling in 1974. The challenge of developing full five-year courses for pupils of all abilities was a major one for the 1970s, leading to further developments in the system of secondary school examinations. (205)

Thus the movement to modernize school mathematics was soon to be caught up by the comprehensive school movement. The early period of coexistence for these two movements was an uncomfortable one. The major conferences on school mathematics from the late-1950s, and the early-1960s projects such as the SMP, MME, CSM and MEI, focused squarely on the reform of O- and A-level mathematics for grammar and independent schools. (206) As Howson has remarked, 'I don't think any of us had caught up to quite what the effects of comprehensivization . . . would actually be' and this 'took everybody by such surprise'. (207) The growth of comprehensive schools, CSE examinations and mixed-ability teaching brought fresh demands for new syllabuses and teaching materials suitable for a wider ability range. In the case of the SMP, a top-down response was made, to cater specifically for pupils of CSE ability. New textbooks were produced, based on the schemes of work originally trialled in public schools, and the new 'course' gained rapidly in popularity, in the absence of serious competitors. (208)

A second wave of projects, from the late-1960s, included the Mathematics for the Majority Project (1967–72) and its Continuation Project, both funded by the Schools Council and aimed at thirteen-to-sixteen-year-old pupils of average and below average ability. The Kent Mathematics Project developed a resource bank of materials for individualized learning in mixed-ability classes covering the nine-to-sixteen age range. However, the majority of schemes suitable for comprehensive schools continued broadly to differentiate on the basis of pupils' examination potential: O-level, CSE or 'non-examination'. (209) Furthermore, the top-down approach to school curriculum reform in mathematics was identified by the Cockcroft Report (1982) as a major trend, with some worrying consequences in the case of mathematics for the multitude:

> We believe . . . that the changes in the examination system and in the organisation of secondary schools which have taken place in recent years have influenced the teaching of mathematics in ways which have been neither intended nor sufficiently realised. At the present time up to 80 per cent of pupils in secondary schools are following courses leading to examinations whose syllabuses are comparable in extent and conceptual difficulty with those which twenty years ago were followed by only about 25 per cent of pupils. Because . . . it is the content of O-level syllabuses which exerts the greatest influence, it is the pupils whose attainment is average or below who have been most greatly disadvantaged. (210)

The work of the MA's Teaching Committee took some account of new developments associated with the comprehensive school movement. In 1964, in conjunction with the ATM, a letter was sent to the fourteen regional CSE examining boards concerning the new arrangements and the Associations' potential role. (211) A full review of all syllabuses was undertaken by the MA and, together with questionnaire data from LEAs and schools, this provided the basis for a pamphlet which was published in 1968. (212) In the previous year a comprehensive schools subcommittee was set up, initially with just one member! A couple of articles resulted but otherwise it appears to have been unproductive. (213)

In 1965 a new subcommittee was established to focus on 'mathematics for children from 11 to 16'. Matthews explained:

> It will examine whether the time is ripe to synthesise the new thinking of the past years and to make recommendations on the subject as a unity, rather than producing further reports on single topics such as 'arithmetic' or 'geometry'. The question also arises as to how far this unity can extend to different types of school . . .

As Matthews pertinently added, 'Clearly this sub-committee has a Herculean task.' (214) The nature of the difficulties were spelt out at the annual meeting of the MA in 1967:

most previous Association reports . . . dealt with subjects already settled and against a fairly static period. [The subcommittee chairman, Alan Barton of Cheltenham College] spoke of the impact of new topics, underlying ideas rather than techniques, new languages, precision of language, vast changes in ideas of methods of learning and the particular role of the teacher in all this development . . .

Mr Barton went on to talk of the effects of the introduction of comprehensive schools, abolition of the 11 plus examination, the LEAs' ability to adjust ages of transfer from primary to secondary education and the present freedom in the primary schools and its possible effects. (215)

The MA was by this time working on its second primary report, which was published in 1970 as a companion to the pioneering report of 1955. (216) But, as Riley pointed out, the first primary report had taken seventeen years to produce and the secondary modern report of 1959 had taken thirteen years. (217) What was now being demanded was a major report representing a consensus on mathematics as a whole for the multitude of secondary pupils. Such a report – *Mathematics Eleven to Sixteen* – was eventually published in 1974. (218) Its 187 pages included chapters on pattern, number, computation, space and representation, together with contributions on teaching methods, resources and assessment. It was the last report to be published by G. Bell and Sons for the MA, but there was no strong sense of mission in relation to the audience for and purpose of such a report at this time. It did, however, lead to an exceptional joint meeting involving HMI, ATM and MA representatives. Some efforts were also made to link the use of the report with a short INSET course for secondary teachers, supported by the DES and followed up through the MA's branches. (219)

The MA's experience of having to respond to such a wide range of new developments concerning mathematics in education during the 1960s raised fundamental questions about its role as a subject teaching association, its policy and its established practices. With the coming of the centenary year, in 1971, the time was ripe for a full evaluation of its position, as a basis for determining future policy. The outcomes of such an evaluation, the new challenges raised for the MA in the 1970s and 1980s, and the extent of its adaptation, will be discussed in the final chapter.

CHAPTER EIGHT

PROFESSIONALISM AND POLITICS IN MATHEMATICS EDUCATION

The Mathematical Association was founded . . . in 1871 . . . It may be that a hundred years is, to quote Humpty Dumpty, 'an uncomfortable sort of age' for a Society. It is not romantically old, nor does it have the shine of newness upon it. It is however an age for taking stock . . . The past hundred years have seen an explosive growth in mathematics, science and technology . . . and I believe that the Mathematical Association can play a vital part in the progress of mathematical teaching at all levels. (1)

(Bertha Jeffreys, MA President, 1969)

Although the Association and our sister association the ATM continue to play vitally important roles it is not always possible to do so explicitly. Politics has become such a dominant feature in education that it is difficult to discuss educational issues calmly . . . It also raises uncomfortable questions about the nature of our Association which exists solely to improve the teaching of mathematics. We are not a trade union: we are ill-constructed for the business of political lobbying. (2)

(Peter Reynolds, Presidential address, 1990)

By way of introduction, a personal aside is necessary in relation to this final chapter. As the opening quotation suggests, the coming of the MA's centenary was a fitting time to take stock and to shape a policy adapted to the changing demands of the 1970s and beyond. Any history of the MA would be incomplete without some consideration of the conclusions of this exercise and the outcomes. In the event, one major recommendation led to the transfer of the MA's offices from London to temporary accommodation in Reading and, in 1975, to a permanent base in Leicester. The achievement of a century and subsequent relocation might be taken as a convenient cut-off point for a history of the MA. It must be admitted that it was this author's original intention to end the story around this point and not to confront the difficulties and complexities of writing very recent history. Some recent studies of post-war developments in school mathematics and science have yielded substantial books in themselves. (3) But there is a gap which needs to be filled: Howson's (1982) history of mathematics education in England sheds little light on post-1960 developments; and Cooper's (1985) treatment of post-war reform terminates around the mid-1970s. (4) Furthermore, the MA itself is entering a new phase of its development in 1993, following a radical shake-up of its constitution.

In contemporary curriculum history the political context begins to loom large from the mid-1970s. Peter Reynolds's remarks at the 1990 Leicester conference of the MA bring into sharp relief the rapidly changing political circumstances, which continue to have profound implications for all individuals and institutions involved in the field of mathematics education in England and Wales. The pace of change has been unprecedented, particularly since Kenneth Baker's Education Reform Act of 1988. Margaret Thatcher had addressed the centenary conference of the MA in 1971, and Baker was the next major politician to follow this precedent, at the Birmingham conference in 1988. Thatcher confined her remarks to the continuing problem of mathematics teacher supply. (5) In sharp contrast, Baker dwelt upon the perceived ills of mathematics education for the multitude in England and Wales, by comparison with other countries, and sketched some of the government's proposed remedies, involving major changes in the structure and management of the school system, the introduction of a National Curriculum, and the development of a system of assessment for all pupils in state schools at the ages of seven, eleven, fourteen and sixteen. (6) It is too early to make an assessment of the effects of these radical measures. But this concluding chapter will provide a personal view of the changing political climate in relation both to the scope and influence of the MA's work and to the state of professionalism in mathematics education. It will be left to readers to draw their own conclusions concerning the implications for professional activity in the context of further political developments.

POLICY COMMITTEE

The MA's Policy Committee of six members was established in 1968 and it represented a range of interests and experience, embracing primary, secondary, technical and university education. It was chaired by John Thurston, from a technical college (who became secretary of the Branches Committee), and its report with recommendations on future policy and methods of working was presented to the Council in 1969. Its deliberations were informed by two kinds of evidence: the results of a questionnaire survey of all members, and oral or written submissions from a number of key individuals. (7) Just under a third of the membership – 1691 members – replied to the questionnaire, 92 per cent of whom worked in education. Significantly, the breakdown by institution is as follows: primary, 1 per cent; secondary grammar or direct grant, 34 per cent; independent, 12 per cent; secondary modern, 4 per cent; secondary technical 1 per cent; comprehensive, 9 per cent; tertiary, 26 per cent; others, 4 per cent. But there was overwhelming support – around 90 per cent – for the MA to have as its primary aim the *teaching* of mathematics at *all* levels. (8) This aim was endorsed by the Policy Committee. Its main tactical proposals were presented by Thurston to the annual meeting in 1970 and summarized in the *Newsletter*:

1. The removal of the Association's office from London to temporary premises in Reading and the establishment of a permanent office.
2. The appointment of a Secretary-General in about 4 or 5 years' time.
3. The publication of a new periodical for the first time in 1971. (9)

The committee also favoured a more active role for the branches in relation to MA policy and report production, and some streamlining of the central committee structure was recommended. Thurston summarized the main strategic thrust of the proposals:

> There is a need to invigorate the Association by attracting more young persons to become members and for more positive encouragement of co-operation with other bodies such as the Institute [of Mathematics and its Applications] and the A.T.M. Our general view was that the level of activity needs stepping up, but this can only be done in the long run with the help of more finance. (10)

Such proposals had implications for subscription rates and raised a need to secure additional finance in other ways. The questionnaire survey had exposed an imbalance in the age distribution of the respondents: only 28 per cent were under thirty-five, with the same proportion in their fifties or older. (11) But at least a clear sense of direction was now generally recognized, at a time when Maxwell judged that the MA was 'climbing out of a bad patch'. (12)

In taking stock, the Policy Committee touched on all the major facets of the MA's internal development including membership, branches, accommodation, administration, finance, constitution and rules, periodicals, the work of the Teaching Committee and the scheme for diplomas. Thus it is fitting in this final chapter to consider each of these facets in turn, reviewing the post-war state of affairs up to around 1970, making links with the detailed work of the Policy Committee and pointing to some of the general trends in subsequent developments.

MEMBERSHIP

The graph of the growth of the membership in the post-war period up to 1970 (Figure 8.1) shows that the major gains were achieved in the ten years from 1955, a time of major activity and report production beginning with the publication of the seminal report on primary mathematics. In the immediate post-war period a membership drive had helped to achieve some early gains. Subscription increases explain the short-term losses after 1950 and 1970. Combridge claimed that a total of 6000 had been reached by 1965 but subsequent figures reported to the Standing Committee of Council are somewhat less than this. (13) The numbers reported by the Council between 1976 and 1981 were stable and around the 5000 mark, including

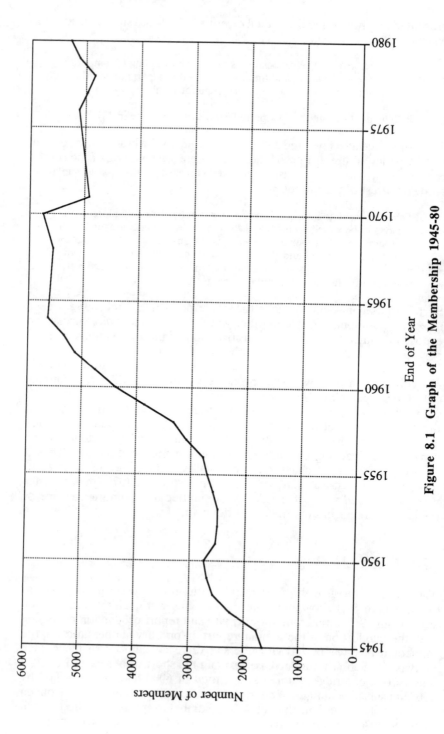

Figure 8.1 Graph of the Membership 1945-80

approximately 500 from abroad. The growth of the ATM from the 1960s drew some of the potential membership away from the MA, though many people did choose to join both Associations. Of the 1691 respondents to the Policy Committee's questionnaire, 39 per cent were also members of the ATM, 20 per cent were IMA members and 13 per cent belonged to other mathematical societies. (14)

In 1982 the Cockcroft Report referred to the scale of the membership of the MA and the ATM in the following terms:

> We understand that the joint membership of the two associations which are most directly concerned with mathematics teaching in schools . . . amounts to some 12,000 but that, if those who belong to both associations are counted only once, the total is nearer to 9000; nor do all of these teach in schools. In comparison with some 30,000 teachers who teach mathematics in secondary schools and the very many who teach mathematics in primary and middle schools, this is a very small number. (15)

By comparison, the total membership of the ASE exceeded 16,000 in 1982, including around 1000 overseas members. (16)

Since 1971 the MA has taken various steps to increase its membership: publicity and membership drives; special concessions for student members and members under twenty-five; differential rates for members based on the periodicals chosen (the new periodical – *Mathematics in School* – started in 1971); and institutional membership from 1987 has helped to draw in primary teachers. The introduction of institutional membership has helped to boost the MA's total membership to over 8000 in 1992. By comparison, this is twice the ATM's total, which includes around 1500 institutional members. But the MA's individual membership has stubbornly refused to grow significantly since the mid-1960s, in spite of all its efforts. (17)

BRANCHES

In 1947, when MA branch activity was largely resumed, there were ten branches in England and two in Wales. Over the next ten years the number did not increase significantly, but, with the establishment of the Oxford and District branch in 1959, there followed a period of notable growth, which coincided with the emergence of the movement to modernize school mathematics. (18) By the end of 1962 there were twenty-five branches in England and Wales and this number had grown to thirty by 1970. (19) By this time there were two established branches in Scotland (Edinburgh and Dundee), six overseas (Malaya, Sierra Leone, Salisbury in Rhodesia, Victoria and Canberra in Australia, and Christchurch in New Zealand), plus six affiliated associations. (20) A new branch was also formed at Glasgow in 1970. (21)

Branch activity was considered by the Policy Committee, which was provided with the results of a questionnaire from the Branches Committee; twenty-seven out of thirty-two branches responded. The survey found approximately 1000 members and 700 associates involved in these branches, but only 100 from the primary sector, where two branches accounted for over half the teachers from this sector. Four branches reported 'losing Primary teachers to A.T.M.'. (22) However, eight branches had held joint meetings with the local ATM branch and five had corresponding links with the IMA. A total of 271 members and associates of the London branch was exceptional; the general range was 40 to 80. But the fact that so few MA members were also involved in the branches was a cause for concern. The Branches Committee reported in 1975:

> the number of Association Members taking part in Branch activities continues to show a steady decline, and is now of the order of some seven hundred. Despite the offer of *Mathematics in School* as an alternative to the *Gazette*, it has not been possible to attract into Association Membership many of the Associates who form a considerable fraction of Branch membership. (23)

There was also provision for the establishment of student and junior branches but the general impact here has been small and these faded in the 1970s, as did the overseas connections through the branches. (24)

The number of branches in England and Wales reached its ceiling in 1970. Subsequent efforts to extend the geographical coverage of the branches yielded only very limited gains; at the same time, some branch activity was in a state of decline. (25) Twenty-nine branches in England and Wales were listed in 1984 but with a qualification in six cases: 'regular activities temporarily suspended'. (26) The principal aim over the last ten years has been to try to maintain the geographical coverage, and the level and range of activity within the branches. But the list of branches in 1992 contained only twenty-three in England and Wales, plus the Scottish trio; and inclusion on the list does not necessarily imply a healthy level of activity. In April 1993 Thurston claimed there were only twenty-one 'active' branches. (27) In the current political and educational climate the role of MA branches as local centres for voluntary professional activity has become problematic, and their future is uncertain.

ACCOMMODATION, ADMINISTRATION AND FINANCE

Kellaway was the first of the leading members of the MA to give evidence to the Policy Committee. He had acted as honorary general secretary for nearly twenty years and was unequivocal about the state of the MA's affairs from a business and management perspective:

> the main failure of the Association had been its financial weakness. It had been run 'on the cheap'. The subscription in recent years had not risen even by an amount commensurate with other increases. It was quite inadequate for a professional organisation, and the consequence was shabby office accommodation and amenities, and the lack of really professional office staff. (28)

Moreover, E.W. Tapper, general secretary of the ASE, gave evidence which underlined the MA's relatively inferior position. The ASE employed the equivalent of about six full-time staff, including a general secretary, and plans were well advanced for a move from office accommodation in Cambridge to new, purpose-built headquarters on the site of Hatfield College of Technology. (29) Prudent financial management and an appeal fund helped to raise the necessary £40,000, and the new headquarters was opened in 1969. (30)

The MA essentially followed the ASE's lead and the Policy Committee's recommendations. In 1970 the MA moved from 22 Bloomsbury Square, London, and a five-year leasehold, into 'comparatively luxurious accommodation', on a five-year lease at 150 Friar Street, Reading. (31) A centenary appeal was launched in 1971, with the aim of obtaining a permanent headquarters near the University of Leicester, a geographically central location where the library was already housed. The plan was to purchase, modify and equip a suitable property, and to appoint a full-time executive secretary, supported by adequate office staffing. (32) In the past, short-term leaseholds and associated costs had proved expensive and had acted as a drain on the MA's limited finances in the post-war period.

Since the Second World War the MA has taken various steps to stabilize its financial position. For tax purposes a trust deed was drawn up in 1945. (33) Morgan's period as honorary treasurer, 1948–59, was one of rapidly rising costs but also of rapidly growing activity, particularly in report production. (34) A system of seven-year covenanting for membership was introduced in 1954 and was followed by appeals for donations or loans. (35) Optimistically, the Council had conceived that 'the financial structure of the Association may gradually become less like a hasty flood defence and more like a planned irrigation system'. (36) The covenanting scheme ran into difficulties with the Inland Revenue, which were not resolved until 1959, but a 'handsome gift' from the Gulbenkian Foundation proved timely. The Council's report for 1959 claimed: 'The financial position can now be regarded as sound, following the difficulties of the past two or three years ...' (37)

But financial difficulties persisted through the 1960s and beyond. In Howson's terms, the MA was 'battling along', and his own life subscription helped to buy some stamps! (38) From the mid-1960s there were three separate accounts – general, industrial and diploma – and professional auditors were employed for the first time in 1968, when Lindsay took over as treasurer, a position he held until 1972. (39) The Council acknowledged:

> his untiring efforts to steer us clear of the 'red' and into the 'black' during what must inevitably come to be known as four of the most difficult years in the financial archives. (40)

Lindsay gave evidence to the Policy Committee which underlined the problematic financial implications of its proposals. The need for a successful appeal on a large scale and subscription rises was now clear. (41)

The 1971 centenary conference provided an ideal opportunity to broadcast the launch of the centenary appeal with a target of £30,000. Following

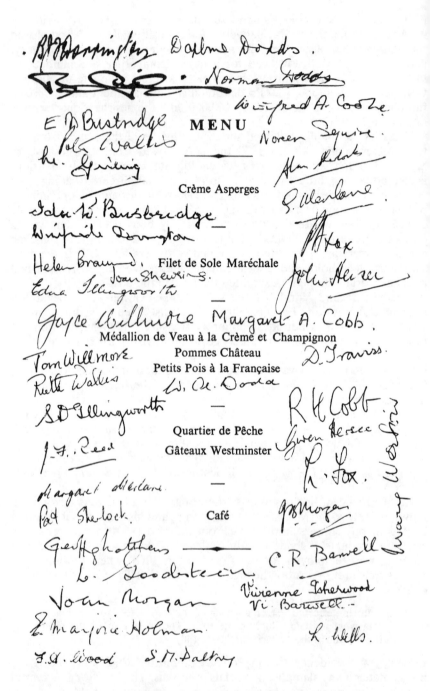

MENU

Crème Asperges

Filet de Sole Maréchale

Médaillon de Veau à la Crème et Champignon
Pommes Château
Petits Pois à la Française

Quartier de Pêche
Gâteaux Westminster

Café

Plate 8.1   Signed Menu from Centenary Dinner 1970

TOASTS

———

Her Most Gracious Majesty

The Queen

The Mathematical Association

Proposed by ... ... W. L. LANGFORD, ESQ., M.Sc.

Response by ... ... PROFESSOR M. J. LIGHTHILL, F.R.S.

Our Host and Our Guests

Proposed by ... ... MRS. E. M. WILLIAMS, C.B.E., M.A.

Response by ... ...IVOR STANFORD, ESQ. M.P., B.Sc. (ECON.)

Margaret Thatcher's supportive opening address, M.J. Lighthill, Lucasian professor of mathematics at Cambridge, delivered the Presidential address in which he underlined the importance of the appeal – directed to members, trusts, industry and other interested organizations – for the future of the Association. (42) Lighthill chaired the centenary appeal committee, which had the potential to attract substantial donations through personal contacts. The organizing committee was chaired by Margaret Rayner, and Winifred Cooke acted as appeal secretary, upon whom much of the ongoing administrative work through the 1970s depended. Seven-year covenanting was again an important option for boosting the value of donations to the MA as a registered charity. (43)

In only two years around £20,000 was raised, with promises of the additional £10,000. The value of miscellaneous donations was matched by seven-year covenants and notably boosted by a single grant of £5000 from the Wolfson Foundation. (44) A further £4000 was raised before the appeal finally ran its course. (45) Professor Goodstein, the MA's Leicester-based librarian and President for 1975–6, was the prime mover in the search for a suitable property, which was secured in 1974 by the freehold purchase of 259 London Road, Leicester, at a cost of £20,000. The new headquarters was officially opened in 1975, and E.A. Buckland, a former accountant, was appointed as the first executive secretary. (46) A headquarters committee was set up in 1975 to manage the transition; this committee and the centenary appeal committee were both disbanded in 1979. The results of their efforts and those of the organizing committee were important not only for the state of the MA's administration and finances but also for its status as a subject teaching association.

Early in 1976, J.A. (Jim) Gray, who had worked in publishing, took over from Buckland as executive secretary and he was, from 1977, initially supported by a staff of two full-timers and three part-timers. (47) F. Alan Wood, who had pursued a teaching career in schools and further education, took over from Gray and served for six years in a full-time appointment until he retired in 1990. His replacement was Heather Whitby, a much younger executive secretary and a former administrative officer for the ATM. (48) It is disturbing to note that the MA is continuing to experience major financial instability into the 1990s. A recent letter of appeal from the President, John Hersee, put the matter starkly:

> we ended last year [1991–2] with an operating deficit of more than £100K. We now know that this was not just an isolated bad year . . . next year is threatened. Our current severe cash flow problems must be solved or there will be no next year at all. We are looking at all possible ways of reshaping the Association so that our income will cover our outgoings. (49)

Thus donations or loans have again become vital to the future of the MA.

CONSTITUTION AND RULES

In the immediate post-war years the MA was governed by a Council of thirty to forty members, consisting of the officers (including a number of Vice-Presidents), the chairman and secretary of the Teaching Committee, representatives of the branches, and a number of other members without office. A Branches Committee had been in existence since 1932. The Teaching Committee's composition had been fundamentally changed in 1937, and it was again modified after the 1944 Education Act, to reflect the new division of schools into primary and secondary, the former linked with the independent preparatory schools and the latter covering the tripartite and independent divisions. (50)

The rules also allowed for the appointment of a standing subcommittee of the Teaching Committee. From 1950 the need for a similar subgroup was also recognized by the Council, which typically met only three times per year, with an attendance of up to around thirty and much routine business to conduct. (51) A Standing Committee of Council acted throughout the 1950s and 1960s, as the external pressures on the MA mounted. It consisted of the President, secretaries, treasurer, and editor of the *Gazette*, with a Vice-President acting as chairman. The librarian and the chairmen of the Teaching and Branches Committees were also involved, by invitation and with voting rights, when the business required such representation. (52)

Throughout the 1960s there was an evident and unresolved tension between the need for the centre of the MA's organization to respond relatively swiftly to external developments and, at the same time, to reflect 'the mind of the Association'. As Cambridge pointed out to the Hertfordshire branch in 1969:

> it is now more than ever necessary that our Association should have a mind of its own, know what it is, and be able to express its views on all matters that concern it – and, equally important, be able to perceive in advance matters that will require action and initiate debate in good time. (53)

The Policy Committee endorsed the need for a more active role from the branches in relation to central activity, but it also raised some questions about the effectiveness of the central management structure itself.

In his evidence to the Policy Committee, Morgan, the Standing Committee's chairman, was unequivocal:

> In recent years [the Standing Committee] had simply not been able to cope with the amount of work both in policy-forming and administration that was now being asked of it. Its function had been conceived before the membership had grown to its present size . . . Standing Committee as at present constituted was too big. (54)

Matthews, chairman of the Teaching Committee, felt that both the Council and its Standing Committee had become unwieldy in size: 'Council was very cumbersome, managed little real discussion, and might even be abolished.' (55) In the event, and following the recommendations of the Policy Committee, the changes in the rules affecting the MA's central organization were modest.

The Council was given the authority to appoint an executive secretary and also a Finance and General Purposes Committee, the composition of the latter being similar to that of the earlier Standing Committee. (56) Since the 1970s the position of the Finance and General Purposes Committee has strengthened. The chairman of the Teaching Committee, the secretary of the Branches Committee, the editor-in-chief (for periodicals) and the President-designate (if any) were all admitted by right to membership. Executive and finance subcommittees were also introduced, and the relationships between these subcommittees and with the executive secretary were clarified. (57) By contrast, the Council continued to be a very large and ineffective body. The membership had grown to seventy by 1970 and was still in the sixties twenty years later, when it included over fifteen Vice-Presidents and very full representation for all sections of the MA's work, both centrally and in the branches. (58)

Since 1990 the role of the Council and its functions in relation to the work of the leaner and fitter Finance and General Purposes Committee have been fundamentally reviewed, and major changes to the rules were finally adopted in April 1993. (59) The membership of the Council has been cut drastically to just twenty-two, a membership which includes a regular chair but excludes all Vice-Presidents, representatives of the branches, editors of periodicals and assistant secretaries. A Standing Committee of just five members is now empowered to act within defined limits, between meetings of the full Council. Concerns for more democracy and greater efficiency and effectiveness underpin the new constitution, at a time when the capacity of all professional associations to respond effectively to rapid and sweeping external developments in education, driven by new ideological and political agendas, has been and is being severely tested. (60) The challenge for the MA's new central organization is a very difficult and pressing one at the present time.

PERIODICALS

The *Gazette*, which was first published in 1894, remained the sole organ of the MA until 1962, when the *Newsletter* was introduced. The *Newsletter* has appeared in various formats ever since and has served a clear purpose: to provide up-to-date news about the MA and related activity in the world of mathematics education. Over nearly a century it is unsurprising that the *Gazette* has not consistently enjoyed such clarity of purpose, through the periods of the Perry movement from 1900, inter-war consolidation, post-war expansion, the growth of modern mathematics, and the rise of the movement towards mathematics for all. As we have seen, the *Gazette* went through a difficult period from the mid-1950s, and its scope and functions were very much under the spotlight when the Policy Committee undertook its wide-ranging investigations.

By the time Maxwell took over as editor of the *Gazette*, in 1963, the circulation had grown to around 6000. The journal had an established international reputation as a minor mathematical serial and its reviews section was widely valued. Its circulation extended well beyond the membership of around 5000 and included many exchanges with foreign journals. A section for 'classroom notes', in addition to the mathematical notes section, had been added in the 1950s and had become a regular feature. Maxwell freely admitted to the Policy Committee that 'much good *highbrow* material was submitted' but that 'good elementary articles were in short supply'. (61) Comments volunteered by respondents to the Policy Committee's questionnaire focused more on the *Gazette*, as 'the mouthpiece of the Association', than on any other aspect of the MA's work and indeed echoed Maxwell's editorial regrets. Thurston summarized the general thrust of these comments:

> Many comments were critical of the *Gazette*, the most frequent being that much of its material was above the level of the reader. There were frequent pleas for help in classroom work – articles on syllabus trends, the problems of teaching the less able or of teaching mathematics to girls. (62)

A few respondents suggested the idea of a second journal and the conclusions of David Fielker of the ATM were also reported to the Policy Committee: 'Judging by the respective journals . . . A.T.M. was providing a far better service to most teachers; possibly two separate magazines would be a good idea for the M.A.' (63) Furthermore, Bryan Thwaites, in his oral evidence, 'expressed concern at the image of the Association created by the *Gazette*. The A.T.M. journal was more vigorous and appealed to the practising teacher.' (64) The clear need for a second periodical was emphasized in the Policy Committee's report and accepted by the Council. The proposal that members be given the option of receiving either or both of these two periodicals was also adopted. (65)

The new periodical was initially referred to as a magazine rather than a journal, to emphasize its complementary function in relation to the *Gazette*. Quadling explained the relationship:

> It is, of course, no part of the plan that the *Gazette* should in future play any less prominent part amongst the Association's publications than it does at present. Indeed, the hope is that, by catering separately for what we may roughly describe as 'professional' and 'academic' interests, the *Gazette* should be able to do its job better than before. (66)

In practice the broad division was initially between 'professional' interests in teaching all pupils, principally over the seven-to-sixteen age range, and 'academic' interests in mathematics at sixth form and undergraduate levels. The intention was that *Mathematics in School*, as the new magazine was entitled, should have wide appeal for both specialist and non-specialist teachers and make a significant impact beyond the MA's membership. (67) To this end a publishing agreement was secured with Longmans, and the magazine started under the editorship of Peter Reynolds, then head of

Plate 8.2 **First** *Mathematics in School* **1971**

mathematics at Doncaster College of Education. Reynolds joined a small editorial board, along with Quadling (*Gazette* assistant editor), W.A. Dodd (*Newsletter* editor), and Howson, who was an MA secretary and became much involved in the difficult business negotiations at a time of financial stringency. (68)

The first issue of *Mathematics in School* appeared in November 1971 and was followed by six issues per year up to 1976, when Reynolds handed over to an editorial team of three and the number of issues was cut to five per year because of rising costs. (69) Reynolds vividly recalls his 'voyage of discovery' in editing the first twenty-eight issues. He was largely given a free hand to shape the new magazine and, in particular, to pursue a less 'authoritative' line than was typified by the *Gazette* and the MA's major reports. Such freedom extended to the use of less polished, more ephemeral and sometimes controversial material. (70)

In 1972 Quadling took over as editor of the *Gazette* and he became editor-in-chief within the editorial board for the MA's periodicals. *Mathematics in School* had made an encouraging start, with 1300 subscriptions from outside the MA in its first year and international publicity through complimentary copies presented to delegates at the 1972 Exeter ICME. (71). Reynolds judged the early supply of material to be adequate in quantity but added: 'there is still a need for more reporting from classroom teachers, who are often too modest to expose their views to public scrutiny'. (72) Under Reynolds's editorship *Mathematics in School* became established alongside the ATM's *Mathematics Teaching*, but, increasingly, the place and functions of the MA's two periodicals have become less clear as mathematics education has developed as a field of international enquiry, with corresponding growth in the number of periodicals and their degree of specialization.

An international comparative study by Kilpatrick (1992) clearly shows the burgeoning of mathematics education as a research field, from the mid-1960s, but with its roots going back to the two decades on either side of the turn of the century. (73) The growth of this field in the 1960s and 1970s was bound up with two major developments: the international curriculum reform movement and its aftermath, spearheaded by science and mathematics, which helped to establish the interdisciplinary field of curriculum studies within education ; and the growth of professionalism in teacher education, at a time of rapid expansion, through the strengthening of its place in, and links with, institutions of university standing. As Kilpatrick and Schubring have shown: 'career patterns like those of the established disciplines began to emerge, the field began to reflect on its own activity, and communication among its members improved'. (74) To borrow Kilpatrick's terminology, an international community of mathematics education 'coalesced' in the 1970s, as new institutions and journals were created. The start of the ICMEs in 1969 was also part of this trend.

In 1968 the international journal *Educational Studies in Mathematics* started under the editorship of Hans Freudenthal, who became director and inspired the creative work of the Dutch Institute for the Development of Mathematics Education (IOWO). (75) Two years later, in the USA, the NCTM launched a new journal, the *Journal for Research in*

Mathematics Education. In Germany the journal *Zentralblatt für Didaktik der Mathematik* was started in 1969 as one service provided by a new centre for mathematical didactics at the University of Karlsruhe. At Bielefeld the Institute für Didaktik der Mathematik (IDM) started in 1973. Other centres were springing up in the USA and in France, and two Shell centres for mathematical education were established in England, at the University of Nottingham and at Chelsea College, University of London. (76)

Reflecting some of these developments in England, an informative survey of articles on mathematics education appearing in a number of periodicals between 1961 and 1974 was produced by Carter and Wain of the Centre for Studies in Science [including mathematics] Education at the University of Leeds. (77) The survey covered the *Gazette, Mathematics Teaching, Mathematics in School,* the *Bulletin* of the IMA, *Mathematical Education for Teaching,* the organ of the Mathematics Section of the ATCDE, a single international journal – the *International Journal of Mathematical Education in Science and Technology* – and a number of periodicals covering aspects of science, including mathematics, education. The reviewers noted the 'considerable growth' in the number of periodicals concerned with mathematics education in England. (78)

The *Gazette* continued under Quadling's editorship until 1980, when he handed over to Victor Bryant, a university mathematician. The MA took over the publication from Bell and Hyman (previously G. Bell and Sons) in 1979. The *Gazette* has continued to place its emphasis on mathematical exposition, diversions and enrichment, at sixth form and undergraduate levels. As Howson has pointed out, articles specifically devoted to research in mathematics education are rare. (79) Furthermore, theorizing and discussions about the place and shape of mathematics in education have declined since the 'golden age' of the *Gazette* before the First World War. By contrast, research and development has been an ongoing aspect of the ATM's work since the 1960s, with related coverage in the pages of *Mathematics Teaching*. (80) To some extent *Mathematics in School* has provided an outlet for both practical contributions about teaching school mathematics and for small-scale studies in mathematics education. But the latter emphasis has to some extent undermined the initial concept of a magazine for classroom teachers that was to include a focus on the primary phase. On the practical side, in the 1980s the MA extended the number and range of periodicals offered to members: *Mathematics Round the Country*, produced for primary teachers by Hereford and Worcestershire LEA under the title *Mathematics Round the County* and edited by Ian Evans, is distributed nationally by the MA; *Struggle*, focused on mathematics for low attainers, has been taken over from the Inner London Education Authority; *Mathematical Pie*, a magazine for teachers and pupils founded by Roland Collins, has been adopted by the MA; and a magazine for higher attaining pupils – *Plus* – has also been started on the MA's initiative. As Reynolds has suggested, the options for members have grown in a rather 'random and eclectic way'. (81)

The *Gazette* and *Mathematics in School* remain the MA's two principal periodicals but they now have to compete for contributions and subscribers not only with the range of periodicals already indicated but also with a small number of new British periodicals specializing in particular aspects of mathematics education. Such periodicals include *Teaching Statistics,* the ATM's *Micromath* and the IMA's *Teaching Mathematics and Its Applications.* A new journal focused on mathematics teacher education – *Mathematics Education Review* – and two very recent magazines for eleven-to-sixteen secondary and sixth form pupils – *Summit* and *Mathematics Review* respectively – have recently been launched. This continuing growth and specialization raises further questions about the place and functions of the MA's own periodicals in the 1990s. As the *Gazette* approaches its first century, the challenge for its current editor Nick MacKinnon, a teacher at Winchester College, is a considerable one.

TEACHING COMMITTEE

The MA's general reports on primary mathematics (1970) and secondary mathematics for all (1974) were to be the last in a long line of painstakingly produced overviews of the content and presentation of school mathematics. Much of the MA's twentieth-century work dealt with selective secondary and sixth form mathematics. Post-war reconstruction and the modernization of school mathematics forced the MA to adopt a less authoritative, less ambitious and more peripheral line in its publications policy. Following the report of the Policy Committee, the 1970s saw further modifications in the work and output of the Teaching Committee.

The Teaching Committee undertook a general review of its operations, and, in 1973, John Hersee became its chairman. In his view the change in the perception of the Teaching Committee's role was a fundamental one:

> Reports were thought of as . . . the definitive word . . . the change recognized that there *were* different approaches . . . that, in a way, it's as important to stimulate discussion and debate as it is to lay down the law, as you might say; and that in itself is a reflection of the way the Association has changed. (82)

The Teaching Committee for 1971–5 included a standing subcommittee and subcommittees for the five-to-thirteen, nine-to-sixteen and fourteen-to-eighteen age ranges, as well as for the further education and teacher training sectors. New terms of reference for subcommittees were introduced in 1971:

1. To keep under continuous review developments in the teaching of mathematics within the field assigned.
2. To submit articles, items of news and other material to the Association's journals.
3. To submit proposals for the preparation of Reports or Pamphlets on matters within their purview and to deal with matters referred to them by the Standing Sub-committee.
4. To contribute to press correspondence or public debate on important issues. (83)

Subcommittees were encouraged to develop links with the branches as well as the editors of the three periodicals: the *Gazette*, the *Newsletter* and *Mathematics in School*. In addition, following the move in 1975 to the new headquarters in Leicester, a pattern was established of speedier, low-cost production of short A5 or A4 pamphlets. The list of such pamphlets up to 1980 also gives a good indication of a shift away from the content of school mathematics and towards strategy and tactics in the curriculum and pedagogy:

1976	*Why, What and How?*
1976	*Calculators Have Come!*
1977	*Notation and Language in School Mathematics*
1977	*The Bunny Book of Numeracy*
1978	*Mathematics in the Proposed Certificate of Extended Education*
1979	*Evaluation: Of What, By Whom, For What Purpose?*
1979	*Tests*
1980	*Pupils' Projects: Their Use in Secondary School Mathematics*

This shift of emphasis is partly associated with the development of mathematics education itself as a field, involving a growing number of MA members with occupational locations in higher education for teaching or LEA advisory work. Previously, when the central focus was on the substance of school mathematics, leading teachers from selective secondary schools plus a small number of university mathematicians had dominated on the MA's subcommittees.

Another development in the 1970s was the growing number of sub-committees charged with specific tasks. Seven subcommittees in 1975 had grown to thirteen by 1978 and to seventeen by 1980, when William Wynne Willson (MA President for 1993–4) took over from Hersee as chairman of a Teaching Committee involving over eighty members. (84) The areas of interest ranged widely: booklists, handbook for probation-ary teachers, calculators, interface (primary and secondary), kernel and core, projects in mathematics lessons, middle years, ICME, industrial and business mathematics, mathematics and science, mathematics and geogra-phy, gifted children (9–13), microprocessors, first year degree teaching, posters, applied mathematics at A-level, mathematics teaching as a career, and 'shadowing' the Cockcroft Committee. Posters provided a new means of communication along with reports, pamphlets and articles.

From 1977 a new constitution and an executive committee encour-aged both greater flexibility in relation to identified needs and more efficiency. (85) Subcommittee activity continued to flourish in the 1980s. The pattern of development since 1970 provides a further indicator of growing specialization and refinement in the field of mathematics educa-tion. Most recently, the growing use of microcomputers for both word processing and desk-top publishing has also promoted greater flexibility, efficiency and economy in relation to publication. The output of the Teaching Committee continues to provide a significant means of support for initial and in-service training. (86) The MA's most recent report, on computers in the mathematics curriculum, is a major contribution to a apidly developing field. The production of this report of 188 pages took eight years and involved around twenty contributors working under the chairmanship of John Higgo of Oakham School. However, the Teaching Committee's major twentieth-century role in the shaping of secondary school mathematics, particularly through its influence on examining bodies and textbook writers, has largely been lost. Its role has become peripheral in relation to the development of mathematics for the multitude in the National Curriculum era. The change has been well highlighted by Reynolds:

> Whereas, at the beginning of my career, the Association was at the forefront of development, the initiative now rests with the government. In earlier times it was common for the author of a text-book to mention indebtedness to the most recent Report of this Association. It made the book respectable; it helped it to sell. To-day's authors must quote the National Curriculum. (87)

EXAMINATIONS AND VALIDATION

As we have seen, the MA took a significant lead in the 1960s by establishing its own diploma examinations in mathematics for secondary teachers and college lecturers. The scheme was phased out in the 1970s, but, by 1975, the possibility of a modified role for the MA had emerged, as an awarding body for a new clientele. In 1975 the MA set up a small working party, including representation from the ATM and other associations, to consider the possibility of devising a course of study and appropriate assessment arrangements to serve the needs of teachers interested in mathematics for the five-to-thirteen age range. (88) The idea took root, and, in the following year, a committee was set up with Quadling as secretary, to prepare detailed proposals for a new diploma course in *mathematical education*. (89) The framework for the new scheme was circulated in a press release in April 1977, the MA's rules were modified to include a new section on the Diploma in Mathematical Education, and the first teachers were registered in January 1978 at Roehampton Institute of Higher Education. (90) The progress of the new Diploma became a notable success story for the MA, and its rapid development owed much to the work of four leading spirits: Quadling, Edwin Kerr, Chief Officer of the CNAA and the MA's President for the year 1976–7, Peter Reynolds, the first chairman of the Diploma Board, and Mike Cornelius, its first secretary. (91)

The new framework was a major departure from that of the older Diploma in Mathematics (Teaching). Kerr persuaded the MA to act as a validating and awarding body, along CNAA lines, as opposed to an examining body. (92) The MA itself provided an outline syllabus, a scheme for assessment, a specimen reading list and specimen papers. Two-year, part-time courses, involving 200 hours contact time, were to be devised, taught and assessed in local colleges, drawing on their experience in initial teacher training and INSET, and arrangements for the establishment and monitoring of standards were placed under the overall control of a Diploma Board. The fifteen, voluntary, Diploma Board members played a key role locally in the licensing of individual courses. They were supported by moderators, appointed to supervise around fifty colleges, which became involved in teaching about 1200 teachers at any one time; national moderators' meetings were also organized by the Board. (93)

The aims of the new Diploma scheme for primary and middle school teachers involved much more than the development of these teachers' mathematical capabilities:

> the health of mathematics in our schools depends in the long term on the presence in every school of at least one teacher who has thought deeply about the aims of mathematics teaching, the ways in which it is learnt and can be taught, and the structure of the subject, and who is sufficiently knowledgeable about mathematics to be able to advise and support colleagues. (94)

The arrangements for assessment embraced these broader aims: the teacher's mathematical competence, assessed mainly by written examination; personal mathematical investigation through coursework assignments; a special study of a child or children learning mathematics; and aspects of mathematical education, assessed through essays, projects or written examination.

As experience developed, it was the assessment of a teacher's mathematical competence, by means of a written paper, which proved to be the most problematic element, but this provision did give some guarantee for the Burnham Committee, which was eventually persuaded to give a merit addition to the salary of diplomates. On the financial side, as Howson has pointed out, the MA's validation fees from colleges provided a much-needed boost: 'it gave a kind of financial stability'. (95) The MA's success as a validating body also encouraged other associations, notably the ASE, to develop their own schemes. (96) The first wave of 400 diplomates qualified in 1980 and registrations subsequently ran to a total of over 6000 teachers. (97)

The Diploma in Mathematical Education clearly served a substantial need amongst primary and middle school teachers for a major award-bearing course focused on mathematics and its teaching. The courses also helped to boost the confidence and expertise of a growing number of mathematics advisory teachers, appointed by LEAs in the 1980s. But, in this same decade, the MA's Diploma had to face growing competition from other major INSET providers: the Open University, which started its own courses in mathematics education in the 1980s; CNAA diplomas offered by colleges and polytechnics; and other award-bearing courses validated by the universities.

A DES-funded evaluation (1980–2) of the MA Diploma's progress was conducted by Jean Melrose, who joined Cornelius on a fellowship at the University of Durham. In this same period the MA also launched its Low Attainers Diploma, which was developed jointly with the National Association for Remedial Education (NARE). Links were developed with a Schools Council project, which shared the same focus on the needs of 'low attainers' and their teachers in mathematics. This Diploma was the brain-child of Reynolds and it posed a fundamental challenge: the bridging of the gap between the two cultures of mathematics and remedial teachers. In Reynolds's judgement, his work here involved 'more "pioneering", in many ways, than anything else with which I have been associated'. (98) Provision for the Lower Attainers Diploma grew to nineteen courses and registrations totalled about 800. (99)

The need for a major course focused on leadership in secondary mathematics was also identified by the MA. A new Heads of Department Diploma started in 1985, but only six courses were approved, involving about 200 teachers. (100) The target group was relatively small, with a need to recruit across LEAs. The heavy demands of a 200-hour course for departmental heads, who were all experiencing the educational pressures of the 1980s, would have been a limiting factor; and the challenges for course providers to plan, recruit for and 'deliver' a high-quality programme were considerable. However, taken as a whole, the diploma validation by the MA in the 1980s was a major contribution to INSET in the form of long, award-bearing courses for non-specialist and specialist teachers of mathematics.

The prospects for the MA as a validating body in the 1990s are uncertain. The three Diploma Boards were first replaced by a Diploma Committee, with a wider brief and a more flexible framework for validation. The work of this Committee has since 1992 been subsumed under that of a new Professional Development Committee. But, increasingly, validation is moving into the hands of course providers themselves: the Open University and other established universities involved in teacher education; the new breed of 'universities' which were formerly polytechnics; and the colleges, which have secured greater autonomy, from the CNAA or neighbouring universities, in course development and monitoring.

Major changes in the funding arrangements for INSET, with devolution of finance to schools and less control exercised by LEAs, have resulted in a shift away from long, award-bearing courses. Substantial investment in the professional development of a relatively small number of teachers has been replaced by wider and often thinner coverage in such forms as training days, school-based INSET conferences, short courses, and schemes involving credit accumulation towards recognized awards. Exceptionally, courses of around twenty days' duration, focused on National Curriculum mathematics for primary teachers, have developed impressively on a national scale since 1990. Higher education institutions have co-operated in various ways with neighbouring LEAs in the development of these courses, working within a framework for course approval laid down by the DES. Accreditation may be available for teachers registered on such DES-designated courses, and the MA has provided the option of a Certificate, based on course attendance, related school-based work and individual projects. But a number of course providers have chosen to offer their own schemes for credit accumulation towards a certificate and with the option of further work towards a diploma.

In connection with awards and examinations, one other service provided by the MA deserves recognition. The target group here is not teachers but able pupils in secondary schools, and the idea of competitions for high attainers spread to Britain from Eastern Europe and the USA in the early 1960s. (101) With sponsorship from the Mathematical Association of America and the Society of Actuaries, a mathematics contest was started in England, in 1961, and it gained considerably in popularity over the next four years, under the organization of F.R. (Joe) Watson of Manchester Grammar School. In 1965, on the initiative of Professor W.K. and Mrs Margaret Hayman (MA President, 1974–5), this contest became the first stage leading to participation in a British Mathematical Olympiad for the fifteen-to-seventeen age range. (102) From 1967 the British Olympiad also provided a springboard for the involvement of a British team in the International Mathematical Olympiad, which was first held in Rumania in 1959. (103)

Financial and administrative support for the National Mathematics Contest (NMC) and British Mathematical Olympiad came initially from the Guinness Awards scheme for science and mathematics teachers. From 1970 the MA became closely involved in both the mathematical overseeing of these contests and their administration. For a five-year period, and still with Guinness sponsorship, the MA's responsibility was exercised through its own Committee for Mathematical Awards. (104) From 1975 the contests were jointly sponsored and organized by the SMP and the MA, acting through a National Committee for Mathematical Contests. (105) Thus following the lead of the Mathematical Association of America, the MA came to play an important part in the development of competitions to stimulate the growth of mathematical talent in Britain. Furthermore, the popularity of the NMC, under the MA's organization, has grown very impressively indeed since 1989, from around 10,000 candidates to 30,000 in 1992. (106)

PROFESSIONAL DEVELOPMENT

In his editorial for the four-hundredth number of the *Gazette* (1973), Quadling was prompted to remind readers that:

> the Mathematical Association – particularly through its *Gazette*, reports, branch meetings and conferences – initiated 'in-service training' for mathematics teachers long before the term itself was coined. (107)

In this chapter we have already surveyed the most recent developments in relation to the MA's periodicals, publications and branch activity, and its validation of diploma and certificate courses.

The annual conference, held at various locations in England since 1949 provides another means of professional invigoration, largely for the benefit of active MA members. A pattern of formal lectures, including the Presidential address, chaired discussions (possibly involving a panel), MA business and committee meetings, exhibitions, and a choice of visits became well established in the post-war period. The conference was first held in Wales, at the Welsh CAT, Cardiff, in 1967, and in Scotland, at

Edinburgh University, in 1972. The first visit to Oxford was in 1965 and to Cambridge in 1969. The MA fittingly returned to London for its centenary conference in 1971. This particular conference did include one new feature: a break-out into smaller discussion groups, following a platform discussion. (108)

John Thurston, who chaired the Policy Committee (1968–9), made a fact-finding visit to the ATM's annual meeting and was struck by the sharp contrast in the degree of informality he found there, an informality foreign to the MA's gatherings. (109) This contrast has diminished considerably over the last twenty years, partly as a consequence of changes in programme structure. The ATM's programmes for its annual meetings aim to involve individual members through working groups, workshops and other activities, with an important element of choice. The MA's programmes have correspondingly changed, since the 1970s, to include more variety and a growing choice of activity, and to cater for differentiated interests in primary, secondary, further, tertiary and teacher education, and in the pursuit of mathematics and its applications.

Responsibility for the detailed organization of the MA's annual conferences rests with the branches. Continuity from year to year was provided by the Programme Committee until 1992; this Committee now forms part of the new Conferences Committee. Exceptionally, for 1992, a one-off organizing committee took the major responsibility for the first joint conference with the ATM, held at the University of Nottingham. This conference offered an unprecedented range of options in the programme, and its coming to fruition is a clear indication of closer links between the two associations. But, to date, there are no plans to repeat this experiment.

In relation to conference organization by the MA, one other development in the 1980s deserves mention. In 1979 a Conference Committee was set up to encourage the development of occasional conferences and weekend seminars devoted to particular topics; in 1993 this Committee became part of the new Conferences Committee. The first weekend conferences were focused on A-level applied mathematics, mathematically gifted children and the uses of microcomputers. Links with the work of subcommittees of the Teaching Committee – a conference or seminar providing a stimulus for new work or a platform for developing existing work – were also encouraged. (110) This link between subcommittee work and weekend conferences became a particularly strong one in the case of further education, a sector of education which has not been neglected by the MA.

In the immediate post-war years, the MA was active in the development of mathematics for technical schools and colleges. Kellaway played a leading part here, and, as in teacher education, the MA has consistently been able to maintain contact through a small number of energetic members with relevant experience. (111) Ever since the Perry movement of the 1900s, the relationship between academic and vocational education in England has been problematic. Looking back on the development of polytechnics in the 1960s, the *Times Educational Supplement* referred in a headline to 'a snobbish obsession with universities'. (112) In the words

of Thurston, a former head of mathematics from a college of furthe
education:

> Quite a lot of people felt that FE was something to do with industry
> rather than real education and university work. There has been a lot
> of prejudice to overcome. (113)

Not surprisingly, given the rise of modern mathematics for schools from
the late-1950s and the plethora of other developments, the MA's attention
to mathematics in vocational education temporarily faded. But, by 1971
the Council was able to report:

> One particularly active sub-committee has been that on Further Educa-
> tion which has been exploring the state of mathematics teaching in a
> rapidly growing sector largely neglected by the Association in recent
> years. (114)

Over twenty years later this subcommittee is still very active, with a
somewhat broader interest in both adult education and school and college
work post-sixteen, and with a matching title since 1990: mathematic
in further, tertiary and continuing education. (115) This is the longest
standing subcommittee of the Teaching Committee. It enjoys the privi
lege of not having to work to a particular brief and has been kept alive
and active through the efforts of leading members such as Thurston and
Tom Appleton, an assistant director of Thames Polytechnic. (116)

The work of the MA in this sector of education has undoubtedly
helped to serve a major professional development need. An impressive
network of contacts has been built up over the years, including the active
involvement of both LEA advisory staff and HMI with responsibilitie
in further education. (117) After Rollett retired, the links between the
MA and HMI for schools faded, but, in the case of further education
HMI have actively supported the work of the MA's subcommittee and
in particular, its weekend conferences, which regularly attract forty to
fifty delegates. There has been a consistently strong demand for place
at these residential conferences. High quality conference accommodation
and facilities are expectations from industry which are shared by delegate
from the vocational sector of education; financial support has not proved
to be a problem.

The further education subcommittee ensures that its particular interest
are regularly accommodated in the programme for the MA's annual confer
ence. Communication is further maintained through circulation of a bulle
tin or newsletter. (118) Thus the MA continues to provide a contribution
to professional development in a relatively neglected sector of education
Developing the relationship between academic and vocational education
post-sixteen, is now a major item on the national education agenda for the
1990s. Clearly the MA's subcommittee has an important and continuing
role to play in working out the implications for mathematics education of
new developments in policy and practice.

As in the cases of the MA's work in further education and teacher
training, the major contribution of a very small number of leading members

is also striking in the case of the MA's relationship with the primary sector. Elizabeth Williams was an important figure in the early-post-war developments leading up to the MA's 1955 report on primary mathematics. Ten years later she was elected MA President, at a time when Matthews, chairman of the Teaching Committee, was also director of the Nuffield Mathematics (5–13) Project. Their influence led to the reconstitution of the primary subcommittee, whose further report was published in 1970. This subcommittee included Hilary Shuard (1928–92) from Homerton College. Williams and Shuard shared common interests in teacher education and collaborated in the 1960s on INSET courses in Essex. (119) Their names became firmly associated from 1970, when the first edition of their encyclopaedic and very successful book was published: *Primary Mathematics Today*. Shuard became President of the MA for the year 1985–6.

Shuard focused on primary developments in her Presidential address to the annual conference at Cambridge in 1986. The programme also included a 'primary school day', intended to attract non-members from primary schools. The accommodation of primary school teachers' interests, and also advisory teachers' needs, whether members or not, has continued as a priority in constructing annual conference programmes. Shuard was also instrumental in the establishment of the Primary Education Initiatives Committee in 1985. This Committee took an initial overview of relevant MA publications such as *Mathematics Round the Country* and the *Prism Packs* of classroom activities. The Committee also proposed the introduction of institutional membership (to include the regular receipt of these primary publications), which since 1987 has helped to extend the MA's influence in primary schools. In 1993 this Committee was wound up and its concerns were subsumed under those of the Teaching Committee, the Conferences Committee and the new Professional Development Committee.

The potential of the MA to attract individual members from primary schools is obviously very limited, given the pressures on all primary teachers to 'deliver' the National Curriculum in the core subjects of English, mathematics and science, plus all the other foundation subjects. But since 1988 the introduction of the National Curriculum, particularly at the primary stage (Key Stages 1 and 2), has motivated closer co-operation among the four core subject teaching associations: MA, ATM, ASE and NATE. A Core Subjects Steering Committee and Core Subjects Development Group have been set up, and three successful publications for primary teachers have resulted: *The National Curriculum: Making It Work for the Primary School, Teacher Assessment: Making It Work for the Primary School* and *The National Curriculum: Making It Work at Key Stage 2*. Unfortunately, efforts to establish a cross-curricular magazine for primary teachers – *Primary Associations* – have floundered. Co-operation has also extended to monitoring the progressive implementation of aspects of the National Curriculum. (120)

In assessing the contribution of the MA to the professional development of teachers, it is important to recognize the growing contribution, from the 1960s, of not only higher education institutions but also the LEAs and their advisory services. The provision of teachers' centres, stimulated by the Nuffield Mathematics Project, provided an alternative to involvement in MA branch activity. (121) The new secondary mathematics projects – notably the SMP, MME and MEI – also provided a stimulus for professional development through the dissemination of teaching materials and the organization of meetings, courses and working groups.

LEA advisory services expanded rapidly through the 1960s, and further stimulus for rationalization and growth came from the reorganization of local government in 1974, when the number of LEAs in England and Wales was reduced from 146 to 104. (122) The National Association of Inspectors and Educational Advisers acted as the mouthpiece of the LEA inspection and advisory services, and growing specialization within this service is exemplified by the establishment, in 1974, of the National Association of Mathematics Advisers (NAMA). (123) Although a relatively small group numerically, mathematics advisers may also be supported by mathematics advisory teachers, whose number was boosted in the 1980s, following the Cockcroft Report. NAMA became a member of the JMC, along with the MA, ATM, NATFHE Mathematics Section and UDEMSG: altogether five associations with a particular concern for school mathematics.

As the concern for standards in school mathematics grew in the 1970s, and mathematics education became increasingly a political issue, so the associations within the JMC with major interests in school mathematics and teacher education moved a little closer together through the establishment of their own umbrella organization: the Standing Conference of Associations concerned with Mathematics Education in Schools (SCAMES). (124) It was felt that the voice of these associations was being muted by the dominant interests within the JMC itself, which were perceived to focus on university mathematics and the production of future mathematicians. (125) SCAMES makes its own formal recommendations and representations in addition to acting informally through the JMC. However, SCAMES has done little to bring the associations closer together, and in 1993 its separate existence is coming into question.

The 'Great Debate' on education was officially launched in 1976, by James Callaghan in his speech at Ruskin College, Oxford. In the same year the Mathematical Instruction Subcommittee of the Royal Society published its own report: *The Training and Professional Life of Teachers of Mathematics*. This publication was intended as a contribution to the Karlsruhe ICME, as well as to policy making in England and Wales where the supply of suitably qualified mathematics teachers was still a major concern. (126) But, by this time, the vision for developing initial and in-service teacher education, which had been broadcast in the James Report of 1972 – *Teacher Education and Training* – had been overtaken by political and economic events. A mood of optimism and the prospect of a further period of expansion – heralded by the 1972 White Paper, *Education: A Framework for Expansion* – were both overturned by industrial strife, the oil price crisis, radical public expenditure cuts and demographic contraction. In the words of Brian Simon it was 'downhill all the way' in the 1970s. (127)

As Edwin Kerr emphasized in his MA Presidential address of 1977, the colleges of education were affected by the new climate in a dramatic vay. The rapid expansion of the system in the 1960s was followed in the 970s by major cuts, both in annual intakes for initial training and in n-service provision. The consequences were institutional closure, or the merger of a college of education with a polytechnic, a further education college or, in a few cases, a university. (128) In addition to the effects of demographic factors and institutional developments, Kerr also identified two other important sources of pressure on teachers: proposals for major examination reform and public criticisms. Such pressures were investigated by the Cockcroft Committee of Inquiry, which was set up in 1978 as a political response to a range of concerns which were summarized in a report (1977) by a subcommittee of the Parliamentary Expenditure Committee:

> the apparent lack of basic computation skills in many children, the increasing mathematical demands made on adults, the lack of qualified maths teachers, the multiplicity of syllabuses for old, new and mixed maths, the lack of communication between further and higher education, employers and schools about each group's needs and viewpoints, the inadequacy of information on job content or test results over a period of time, and the responsibility of teachers of mathematics and other subjects to equip children with the skills of numeracy. (129)

COCKCROFT REPORT

The Cockcroft Committee started work in September 1978 with the following terms of reference:

> To consider the teaching of mathematics in primary and secondary schools in England and Wales, with particular regard to the mathematics required in further and higher education, employment and adult life generally, and to make recommendations. (130)

The Committee's membership covered a wide range of perspectives on school mathematics: primary, secondary, further and higher education, teacher training, LEA administration and advisory services, the DES and HMI, curriculum development projects, employers and trade unions. A very large number of organizations, including the MA, exerted their influence on the Committee's thinking through written submissions backed up, in some cases, by oral evidence. On an individual basis the MA was also informally linked with the Cockcroft Committee through four of the twenty-four members: Professor M.F. Atiyah FRS, MA President 1981–2, John Hersee, executive director of the SMP and chairman of the Schools Council Mathematics Committee, Peter Reynolds, a mathematics adviser, and Hilary Shuard, deputy principal of Homerton College, Cambridge. The secretary of the Committee was W.J.A. (Freddy) Mann HMI, and its report was published in 1982. (131)

The Cockcroft Report traced the origin of employers' concerns about school leavers' attainments back to 1973. Early criticisms focused on pupils entering apprenticeships, and the modernization of school mathematics was identified as a factor contributing to the alleged decline in school leavers'

performance on 'the basics'. (132) Both comprehensive reorganization an
the raising of the school leaving age were major advances towards the ide:
of equality of opportunity but the new curricular opportunities followed
top-down pattern, from O-level through CSE to non-examination course:
with more or less 'modern' mathematical content filtering down to th
majority. The lack of curricular differentiation, in this sense, was identifie
as a major problem by Margaret Hayman, in her 1975 MA Presidenti.
address, which was reported in *The Times*. (133) Hayman made a stron
case for differentiation on the basis of both vocational need and researc
evidence. The latter was beginning to expose the intrinsic difficulty of mar
O-level mathematics topics, notwithstanding their modified presentatio
for the majority.

The Cockcroft Committee received some two hundred written submi:
sions expressing employers' views and also considered the findings of tw
research studies from the Universities of Bath and Nottingham, whic
identified the actual mathematical needs of various types of employmen
The Committee came to a striking conclusion:

> The overall picture which has emerged is much more encouraging than
> the earlier complaints had led us to expect. We have found little real
> dissatisfaction amongst employers with the mathematical capabilities
> of those whom they recruit from schools except in respect of entrants
> to the retail trade and to engineering apprenticeships . . . We have also
> found little evidence that employers find difficulty in recruiting young
> people whose mathematical capabilities are adequate. (134)

The Committee also firmly rejected the 'back to basics' movement, wher
this implied a concentration of effort on the practising of arithmetical skil
divorced from relevant contexts. In the short term both these conclusior
helped to clear the ground for further curriculum and professional deve
opment in school mathematics.

The list of organizations which made submissions to the Committe
provides a good measure of the state of professional organization i
both mathematics and the more recently developing field of mathematic
education. (135) On the mathematical side the list includes the Roy:
Society, the LMS, the IMA, the Royal Statistical Society and the Institut
of Statisticians, plus groups of professors of statistics and applied mathema
ics, heads of mathematics departments in polytechnics and colleges, and
special interest group which was formed in 1971: the British Society fc
the History of Mathematics. This last group also has a significant stak
in the mathematics education field; its membership, like the MA, include
mathematicians, teacher educators and schoolteachers, and has grown fror
around 80 to 350 in twenty years. (136)

The five constituent members of SCAMES each made separate submi:
sions, along with two more recently formed special interest groups i
mathematics education: the British Society for the Psychology of Learnin
Mathematics (1978) and the Committee for Girls and Mathematics (1981
The former grew out of international activity, which started at the fir:
ICME in 1969 and led to the establishment of the International Group fc
the Psychology of Mathematics Education at the 1976 ICME in Karlsruhe

The Group held its first meeting in 1977 and the British subgroup (BSPLM) first met in the following year at the Centre for Science Education, Chelsea College. (137)

The interest in gender in relation to mathematics education was boosted through international activity. The Cockcroft Report drew heavily on the proceedings of the fourth ICME, held at Berkeley in 1980, and on the personal contribution of Shuard, who provided a substantial appendix on the subject, drawing on historical evidence and international research (mainly from the USA). (138) Apart from the Committee for Girls and Mathematics, the Cockcroft Committee itself received surprisingly little evidence on a subject which has attracted growing attention in Britain over the past decade and continues to be a central concern for what is now the Gender and Mathematics Association (GAMMA).

Submissions were also forthcoming from a number of mathematics curriculum development projects, including the SMP and fixed-term projects funded by the Schools Council, which also made its own submission. The MA's Diploma Board and Schools and Industry Committee made separate submissions. The SCAMES five, the IMA, SMP and Schools Council were all called to give oral evidence. The JMC is also included in the list of submissions, along with the Council of Subject Teaching Associations (COSTA), which was formed in 1971 on the initiative of Brian Atwood of the ASE. (139) COSTA involved some twenty subject teaching associations at the outset, with the aim of improving co-ordination and communication. It did achieve some success in persuading the Schools Council to include representatives of subject teaching associations on its subject committees but, like the JMC, it was a second-tier organization lacking a stable body of individual members and a secure financial and administrative base to match its aspirations.

It is significant that both the Royal Society and the IMA, which were already linked through their own Joint Committee for Mathematical Education, withdrew from the JMC in 1979 and effectively undermined this Council's ambition to speak for the collective world of mathematics and mathematics education. (140) In any case, the need for a united front was not a problem in connection with the Cockcroft Inquiry. The Committee itself included representatives from all the major constituencies with a stake in school mathematics including, perhaps surprisingly, just one professor of mathematics (Atiyah) and one former professor (Cockcroft himself). A time-scale of three years allowed the Committee to consider 930 written submissions (with discussions in 73 cases) from individuals and bodies of many kinds representing very many shades of opinion, to study relevant publications and statistics, to commission and utilize research studies, and to make site visits.

The final report provided an unprecedented survey of all aspects of school mathematics in England and Wales together with a vision for its foreseeable future. It was warmly welcomed by Sir Keith Joseph, the Secretary of State for Education and Science:

> Few subjects in the school curriculum are as important to the future
> of the nation as mathematics; and few have been the subject of

more comment and criticism in recent years. This report tackles the criticism head on. It offers constructive and original proposals for change. (141)

The principle that a wide range of teaching styles should be employed at all levels – paragraph 243 – was bold and striking but not original. Indeed the ATM could claim to have championed such a cause for many years. But the official support of the Cockcroft Report, and follow-up work by HMI and LEA advisory services, provided a major stimulus for the widespread development of teaching methods, to include more practical work, discussion, problem solving and investigations, for all ages and abilities. The recommendations concerning secondary syllabuses were fundamental in relation to subsequent developments and certainly tackled 'head on' the growing reaction against the top-down pattern of reform, exemplified by Margaret Hayman's critique, with which the Committee concurred.

The Committee boldly advocated the inversion of the top-down pattern:

> We believe that this is a wrong approach and that development should be 'from the bottom upwards' by considering the range of work which is appropriate for lower-attaining pupils and extending this range as the level of attainment of pupils increases. (142)

The Committee's aim was to reverse the historical trend:

> We have . . . moved from a situation in which, twenty years ago, there was in our view too great a difference between the mathematics syllabuses followed by those who attempted O-level and those who did not to one in which, at the present time, there is far too little difference in the mathematics syllabuses which are followed by pupils of different levels of attainment. (143)

Examination statistics and the findings of two research studies – from the Concepts in Secondary Mathematics and Science (CSMS) Project and the Assessment of Performance Unit (APU) – were used to support the argument. Essentially, to borrow Cooper's fitting interpretation, 'reconstructing differentiation' was the Committee's aim and it subsequently became the major trend in the 1980s, involving examination reform followed closely by the introduction of the National Curriculum. (144)

The Committee also made a clear start on defining differentiation by presenting a 'foundation list' of mathematical topics, intended as a minimal syllabus for all pupils and 'by far the greater part of the syllabus of those pupils for whom CSE is not intended, that is those pupils in about the lowest 40 per cent of the range of attainment in mathematics'. (145) The possibility of using graduated testing across the full foundation list was also suggested for lower-attaining pupils. Working out the details of differentiation for the full ability range was to become a major task for the examination boards. The Committee welcomed the Government's decision to introduce a single sixteen-plus examination system, which provided an ideal opportunity to implement two fundamental principles:

The first is that the examination papers and other methods of assessment which are used should be such that they enable candidates to demonstrate what they do know rather than what they do not know. The second is that the examinations should not undermine the confidence of those who attempt them. (146)

Given the need for a differentiated curriculum, the need for differentiated examination papers was one obvious corollary.

Along with the examination boards, the Cockcroft Report identified five other major agencies for implementing its vision: the teachers themselves; LEAs, through their in-service provision and support for curriculum leaders in schools; central government, particularly in connection with teacher supply and recruitment; initial teacher training institutions; and curriculum development and research agencies, and funding bodies. The need for widespread public support was also recognized. This view of 'the way ahead' has since been fundamentally affected by the introduction of the National Curriculum and other measures relating to the 1988 Education Reform Act and subsequent legislation.

The influence of LEAs on curriculum policy and practice, which initially grew through the work of mathematics advisers and advisory teachers (Joseph's Cockcroft missionaries), has already been severely reduced through the devolution of funding to schools. But the introduction of the General Certificate of Secondary Education (GCSE) gave timely support to the Cockcroft Report's vision for mathematics in the last two years of compulsory schooling.

TOWARDS CENTRAL CONTROL

In his MA Presidential address of 1981 Quadling welcomed the fresh opportunity to reshape the secondary mathematics curriculum through the GCSE examinations. He added: 'We had a chance two decades ago with the CSE examination, but it ran on the rocks because its syllabuses were overshadowed by the spectre of O level, and the need to compete with that at the upper grades.' (147) From the outset the dual system of CSE and O-level examinations had posed curricular and administrative problems for heads and teachers in the growing number of comprehensive schools. By 1970 the Schools Council had started to investigate the possibility of a common examination system at sixteen-plus. (148) Over the next five years the school leaving age was raised to sixteen and in England the proportion of pupils in comprehensive schools grew rapidly from around one-third to over two-thirds. Pressure from the teaching profession for reform was mounting, and the Schools Council conducted feasibility trials with CSE and GCE boards.

In 1976 a formal proposal for a common system was made by the Schools Council to Shirley Williams, Labour's Secretary of State. But ten more years were to elapse, bringing with them a change of government in 1979 and two more Secretaries of State – Mark Carlisle and Keith Joseph – before pupils could start on the new GCSE courses and sit the first examinations in 1988. We need not dwell here on the lack of political will in this matter: 'the long saga of resistance and prevarication' has been charted by Simon and other historians of education. (149). Suffice it to say that there were powerful and persistent forces at work to preserve the 'gold standard' of O-level, in spite of the development of the comprehensive system. Such forces have also successfully resisted the reform of A-level, which continues to exert a dominant influence on the post-sixteen curriculum.

The detailed development of the GCSE examination system took place largely under Keith Joseph's control, before he was replaced in 1986 by Kenneth Baker. The new single-subject examinations in England and Wales are administered by just five regional consortia of the former GCE/CSE boards: a much more manageable number for the purpose of unifying standards. The idea of differentiated papers or questions was generally adopted, to cover seven grades of performance, the top three corresponding to the pass grades of O-level and the remaining four spanning the CSE range of ability. The arrangements made for the syllabuses clearly expose a growing centralist tendency, initially towards control of the secondary school curriculum.

GCSE syllabuses are governed by national criteria approved by the Secretaries of State. In both science and history, Joseph became publicly involved in defining aspects of the national criteria. (150) In 1982 Joseph announced the planned abolition of the Schools Council, a body with strong representation for both LEAs' and teachers' unions. Such professional interests were to become increasingly eroded in the 1980s. The Schools Council was replaced during 1983–4 by two bodies: the School Curriculum Development Committee (SCDC) and the Secondary Examinations Council (SEC); the membership of both new bodies was by nomination of the Secretary of State. (151) The SEC was responsible for enforcing the compliance of syllabuses with the national criteria; and subject working parties of the SEC were involved with the development of grade-related criteria. These various GCSE developments have prompted Simon to conclude: 'It was now becoming abundantly clear that the stage was being set for a government (or central) take over both of examinations (and assessment) and of the curriculum.' (152)

Evaluation of the impact and consequences for 'standards' of the GCSE is a complex and value-laden matter, where politicians and educational activists do not fear to tread. Arguably both the 'bottom-up' approach to syllabus development, in differentiated bands, and the use of coursework elements for assessment have helped to realize two Cockcroft principles: better matched courses for a wider range of ability and the adoption of a broader range of teaching styles. Teachers point to improved pupil (and teacher) motivation but to greater work-loads for teachers (and pupils). What is particularly remarkable is that the examinations were first sat in 1988, around twenty years after the proposal for a common system first surfaced. In sharp contrast, Baker's Education Reform Act of 1988 brought rapid and sweeping change on a number of major fronts. A minimum of time was allowed for consultation and response 'in spite of the opposition of teachers, parents and LEAs, and of objections from former ministers' (including Joseph). (153) As the educational historian Aldridge has argued,

,oth Carlisle and Joseph proceeded relatively cautiously as Secretaries of
State between 1979 and 1986. Their successor – Baker – was a man in a
iurry and the pace of educational change has been maintained under a
uccession of Conservative Secretaries of State: Baker, John MacGregor,
Xenneth Clarke and John Patten (at the newly named Department for
Education).

Although the build-up to the 1988 Act was very rapid from the time
Baker took over at the DES in May 1986, it is important to recognize that
:he gestation period for the political and educational thinking underpinning
:he introduction of the National Curriculum arrangements stretches back
at least ten years, to the Labour Prime Minister Callaghan's Ruskin
speech and the 'Great Debate' initiated by Shirley Williams. As the
educational historian Brooks has demonstrated, Callaghan's speech ranged
widely to capture a number of major strands in thinking which relate to
subsequent developments. (154) In particular, the possibility for more
central government involvement in the curriculum was entertained, and
the idea of teacher autonomy in relation to the 'secret garden' was seriously
questioned.

The curriculum was already under scrutiny in the 1970s from a number of
different angles: widespread concerns about the standards of basic literacy
and numeracy of school leavers; the need to raise the status of technical
and vocational elements in the curriculum, to strengthen the links between
education and industry and provide a better preparation for the world
of work; the attacks of *Black Paper* authors on 'progressive education',
particularly as manifested in primary schools imbued with the child-centred
and activity doctrines of the 1967 Plowden Report; and the need to match
the system of examinations at both sixteen- and eighteen-plus to a wider
range of pupils, in terms both of ability and aspiration. Callaghan pointed
to the need for teachers and schools to be more accountable to parents and
employers and he supported greater parental involvement in education. He
also advocated a drive towards greater efficiency in the use of necessarily
limited educational resources, together with the development of suitable
ways to monitor 'value for money'.

The 'Great Debate' of 1976–7 concentrated on four areas: the five-to-
sixteen curriculum; the assessment of standards; the education and training of teachers; and school and working life. A growing centralist tendency,
with increasing powers for the Secretary of State, became the dominant
feature of subsequent developments in relation to the first three of these
four major areas. (155) As with the Cockcroft Inquiry which followed it,
industrialists, employers, and other interest groups, including parents,
were invited to contribute to the 'Great Debate', along with various
educational organizations, including the MA. There was little time for
initial consultation – a now familiar pattern – and a series of one-day
regional conferences culminated in the production of the Green Paper
(1977) *Education in Schools: A Consultative Document.* (156) Through
its FGPC the MA expressed its views in two letters to the Secretary of
State; a weekend seminar was held to explore the areas for debate; and the
MA was also invited to discuss a related HMI paper: *Mathematics, Science
and Modern Languages in Maintained Schools in England* (1977). (157) But

the MA was now only one among a growing number of bodies involved in educational 'consultations' and representations. In the light of subsequent developments, the tentative view of Chitty seems a very reasonable one:

> It could be argued that the Great Debate began the process which ended with the national curriculum proposals of 1987. 'Teacher power', if it ever existed, was to be first eroded, then destroyed – at least in theory. (158)

Following the 1977 Green Paper, there was a steady stream of publications concerning the curriculum from the DES and HMI; and LEAs were required to develop and clarify their own curricular policies. (159) The Assessment of Performance Unit (APU), which was established as early as 1974, issued its first survey reports in 1980, on assessments in mathematics at eleven- and fifteen-plus. The evidence in APU reports focused on pupil performance in written and practical tests; earlier HMI national survey reports were based on 'eyes and ears' data from school inspections. From 1985 the introduction of education support grants to LEAs for specific purposes also contributed to central control in determining educational priorities, including in-service training. Initial teacher training had already been brought under much tighter control, following the White Paper (1983) *Teaching Quality* and the establishment in 1984 of the Council for the Accreditation of Teacher Education (CATE). (160)

The 1988 Act has been described as 'a watershed in educational policy in England' and a 'massive measure' which will probably prove to be 'the most significant single piece of educational legislation in the country's history'. (161) A major ground for such a claim is the clear intention of the Act to reverse the course of history in relation to the relative powers of the central and local authorities. The Acts of 1870, 1902 and 1944 cumulatively extended the powers of local government in the educational field and firmly established the principle of partnership between the central and local authorities. In a number of its provisions the 1988 Act seeks drastically to reduce the powers of LEAs: the principle of open enrolment giving parents the freedom to choose schools; the introduction of local management of schools (LMS), with increased powers for school governing bodies in the areas of finance and staffing; the possibility for schools to opt out of LEA control and become grant-maintained, with direct financing from central government; the establishment of special trust-funded city technology colleges; the abolition of the Inner London Education Authority; and the removal of colleges and polytechnics from LEA control. (162)

A general aim underpinning much of this legislation is to develop the educational system as a whole along freely competitive lines, with more diversity of provision and greater choice for the consumers: parents and students. We need not speculate upon the extent of the influence of the 'new right' in promoting the free-market ideology in education through the 1988 Act and related legislation. By contrast, in the case of the five-to-sixteen curriculum, as some critics have been quick to point out, there is now an unprecedented lack of freedom in English education, at least in the maintained sector. (163) A subject-based, statutory National

Curriculum has been introduced, with English, mathematics and science at its core. National testing at the ages of seven, eleven, fourteen and sixteen is also being phased in, under the direction of the School Examinations and Assessment Council (SEAC), a body appointed by the Secretary of State, with wider powers than its predecessor the SEC. At the same time the SCDC has been replaced by the National Curriculum Council (NCC), whose chair and members are also appointed by the Secretary of State. These two Councils are in 1993 being merged, to form the School Curriculum and Assessment Authority (SCAA) under Sir Ron Dearing, the chairman of both NCC and SEAC.

Through the specification of statutory attainment targets and programmes of study, and the arrangements for national assessment and testing, the central authority now has unprecedented powers; by comparison, the influence of teachers, professional organizations and the LEAs has been drastically reduced. Through the reporting of test and examination results the system also provides a means of monitoring school performance and informing consumer choice in the new market place. As Margaret Brown has fittingly put it, teachers operating within such a system may be simply regarded as 'workers' whose job it is to 'deliver' someone else's 'intended' curriculum and to be subjected to the monitoring of their 'implemented' curriculum through the assessment of the 'attained' curriculum of the learners. (164) In his 1989 Presidential address to the MA, Howson drew some striking comparisons with the nineteenth-century system of payment by results, based on HMI assessments of pupil performance on the seven standards in the 3Rs, laid down by the Education Department. Howson also commented on the wider political context of these changes:

> We are having to adjust to the imposition of a National Curriculum and testing procedures which, in their extent, not only have no parallel in English educational history, but, so far as their structure is concerned, in no other country. Moreover, it is an imposition marked by a frenetic timetable, insufficient thought and consultation, and the setting aside of much of the advice offered. (165)

At an early stage Howson produced a personal critique of the Task Group on Assessment and Testing's (TGAT) model for the National Curriculum. He has since produced a valuable comparative study for the MA which clearly shows the uniqueness of the English approach. (166) In the graduated scheme at ten levels there is a common progression in subject matter from level to level for all pupils; differentiation is restricted to the rate of progress up the levels and the levels actually attained. In other countries differentiation is achieved by means of different courses or a core with options.

A Mathematics Working Group was appointed by the Secretary of State to produce a detailed specification across what became in the 'first iteration' (Baker's metaphor) fourteen attainment targets for mathematics. In her 1991 MA Presidential address, Margaret Brown, a member of the Working Group, presented a strong critique of the circumstances surrounding the first iteration. In particular, she reinforced some of the earlier criticisms of Howson:

> the haste with which the subject groups (especially those in mathematics and science) had to report, and the management structure chosen, prevented any serious collection or discussion of essential information, such as comparative information from other countries, proper theoretical underpinnings of a curriculum framework, or research results;
> consultation was not taken seriously, either in the way it was conducted or in the regard for the results;
> essential trialling and piloting of the attainment targets and programmes of study did not take place, and the trialling of the assessment was disrupted by policy changes;
> the implementation in schools was premature, before teachers had had sufficient information, teaching resources, specialised inservice input, or planning time. (167)

Further policy changes continue to be introduced in great haste and in a manner that is open to similar criticisms: the reduction of the number of attainment targets in mathematics to five and a first revision of the specification (undertaken by DES officials and HMI); a shift away from broadly conceived standard assessment tasks (SATs) to 'pencil and paper tests'; revision of the national criteria for GCSE to bring them into line with the National Curriculum model; and the restriction of the coursework element in the GCSE to a maximum of 20 per cent of the assessment.

Howson was quick to point to the dramatic changes in the political context of English education and the implications for professional organization and influence:

> It really is essential for the well-being both of our subject and of our country, that we as educators begin to express ourselves with greater clarity, unanimity and force. (168)

In Howson's view the MA now had a dual responsibility: to help teachers to work with the policies and rapid changes being implemented, and 'to fight at a national level for improvements in mathematics education, in a manner which is essentially independent of the government policies of the day'. (169) The MA had started life essentially as a curriculum pressure group seeking to influence a large number of examining bodies, the majority of which were independent of the state. This responsibility has now returned with a vengeance but there is now just one major and all-powerful curriculum change agent, the Department for Education. For the AIGT in the 1870s the examination system was a complex target but institutional relationships were relatively simple: the British Association and the Headmasters' Conference were the AIGT's only allies. A major development since the 1960s has been the growing complexity of institutional interests and relationships in mathematics education. Howson's observations are again pertinent:

> it must be admitted that the mathematics community is at present a much divided one. We cannot expect our message to be clearly heard

when it is presented as a piece for several solo voices, not always in harmony. (170)

Howson also pointed to the need to do more than respond and recommend:

> More important though is the need to develop channels of communication with those who make policy-decisions. What is the use of framing policies, of making proposals, if one cannot effectively communicate these to the decision makers; if one cannot make them aware of the true context in which their decisions are being made. (171)

Thus the present climate raises fundamental questions about the state of professional organization and the place and functions of the MA and related bodies.

PROFESSIONAL ORGANIZATION AND THE FUTURE OF THE MA

The Presidents of the MA since 1989 – Peter Reynolds, Margaret Brown, Alan Bishop, John Hersee and William Wynne Willson – have each contributed to the debate and developments concerning the new 'pressures and priorities', a topic which Quadling had also chosen to address as President at the time of the Cockcroft Report. The last six MA Presidents have all pursued careers in mathematics education as opposed to mathematical scholarship; and they have also made their own professional impact as individuals operating in a period of growing centralization. Hersee was a member of the Cockcroft Inquiry, as was Reynolds, who also served on the National Curriculum Mathematics Working Group, along with Brown. (172) Since the Cockcroft Inquiry the whole business of 'consultation' in English education has changed its character. In any case, as Combridge is quoted as saying, an organization like the MA is essentially 'a body without a mind'. (173) Increasingly, individual thought and action have come to play a more prominent role, albeit within very tight political constraints. Here individuals may obtain material or human support through their professional associations, whose formal representations may have been ignored. Furthermore, through individual action there still remains the possibility of some professional subversion of political ends, in the detailed shaping of the curriculum and assessment instruments. (174) Professionals may also speak out and gain media coverage which exposes some of the effects of recent policy in practice, as the last five MA Presidents have done. Professor Paul Black, former chairman of TGAT, and Professor Eric Bolton, a former Senior Chief Inspector, are two very recent and notable examples: 'prophets with honour', in the words of the editor of the *Times Educational Supplement*. Duncan Graham, a former NCC chairman, has been another outspoken critic. (175)

The reduced potential for exerting influence through professional associations notwithstanding, it has to be said that the state of professional organization continues to limit still further the potential of such action. However, the SCAMES five became a four in 1990, with the merger of the Mathematics Section of NATFHE and AUMET, to form the Association of Mathematics Education Teachers (AMET), thereby sinking differences based on the binary divide in further and higher education. Given the likely demise of SCAMES, the coexistence of the MA and ATM is now a major focus of concern. The functions of these two mathematics teaching associations – both professionally and politically – have largely converged over the last fifteen to twenty years. Since the 'Great Debate' both associations have been drawn into the business of political lobbying, with reluctance on both sides and particularly from the ATM. (176) Furthermore, their professional services are now very similar.

The ATAM started in the 1950s with a sense of mission, new priorities and innovative modes of working, and the two associations largely went their separate ways during the development of modern mathematics in the 1960s. In the 1950s and 1960s professional freedom in relation to the curriculum was taken for granted. But as early as 1970 the problem of coexistence was raised by Arthur Dodd in the MA *Newsletter*, soon after the Policy Committee reported:

> For the young schoolteacher, the problem of membership is compli-
> cated by the difficulty of having to choose which organization to join.
> Not only is the Association encouraging him to become a member but
> so also is the ATM. The latter, having grown rapidly and vigorously,
> seems to appeal to younger members of the profession. How is one
> to decide which is the 'better buy'? . . . In order to get the best
> of both worlds is it necessary to join both? . . . Is it possible that
> some kind of joint membership scheme could be devised that would
> have the additional advantage of drawing in those who belong to no
> organisation at all? (177)

The age distribution and institutional location of members were major differences which gradually declined with the development of comprehensive education. Dodd also pointed to differences of style and outlook: 'There is a greater emphasis on informality both in the organization of the ATM and in its view of what should go on in the classroom.' (178) Trevor Fletcher, amongst others, has amusingly characterized the differences in terms of dress. The occasion was an exceptional conference in the mid-1970s, which brought representatives of both associations together to discuss the MA's report *Mathematics Eleven to Sixteen* (1974). Fletcher was staff inspector for mathematics at the time and recalls: 'Throughout this conference the MA all wore jackets and the ATM all wore jerseys, to a man. I wore a knitted cardigan which saved me.' (179) But, undoubtedly, the changing political climate since the 'Great Debate' has brought the issue to the fore.

In 1979 a special three-day conference was held at Loughborough, involving HMI, Cockcroft and other members of his Committee, and representatives of both associations. A number of areas of agreement were identified and subsequently reported by Tammadge, MA President 1978–9, including the following, which have since lost little of their relevance:

teachers need protection from uninformed criticism;
Understanding and activity are the keys to mathematical education;
Continuing career-long teacher training is crucial;
The morale of the profession needs to be bolstered . . . ;
Teachers need time to think;
There is a danger that 'political' pressure is pushing for Arithmetic (by ancient methods) rather than Mathematics and that the motives are not strictly educational;
There is dissatisfaction with 'A' level for 'new' sixth-formers and many 'old' sixth-formers too . . . (180)

But two major 'divergences' now appear out of place in the context of the National Curriculum:

The ATM veers towards what it calls an 'arbitrary curriculum', i.e. mathematics is an activity and so curriculum is not of primary importance . . .
The autonomy of the teacher in his/her classroom was an ATM article of faith not shared by MA representatives . . . (181)

Since Baker took over as Education Secretary, closer co-operation has been evident, not only between the MA and ATM but also with the ASE and NATE. These four associations cover the three core subjects of the National Curriculum. 'Driven together by government initiatives' (to quote an ATM view), they have developed a number of co-operative strategies: joint statements for the media; joint responses to government and links through NCC and SEAC; the organization of joint conferences; monitoring of the implementation of the National Curriculum; the production of in-service materials for primary teachers; and the formation of a new company – Primary Associations Ltd (1991) – to handle joint publications. (182)

Individually the ASE is 'the largest, most active, most influential, and most professionally organized of all the subject associations'. (183) The ASE provides a potentially strong, solo voice and an umbrella organization for professional interests in science education. It was formed in 1963 as 'an arranged but very successful marriage' between the Association of Women Science Teachers and the Science Masters' Association. (184) The younger of the English associations, NATE, was formed as recently as 1963 and coexists with the much older English Association, founded in 1906. (185) But the latter continues to have a strong base in English scholarship, and the interests and activities of the two associations have not converged in relation to the teaching of English in schools.

In the case of foreign languages teaching, a new association was again formed in the 1960s: the Audio-Visual Language Association (1961), founded nearly seventy years after the Modern Language Association (MLA) started (1892). The younger association became the British Association for Language Teaching (BALT). There are obvious parallels here with the establishment of the ATAM in the 1950s, which started with a focus on teaching aids and broadened its range to become the ATM in the 1960s. But the language teaching associations – MLA, BALT and a number of other more specialist associations – have progressively moved closer together. The Joint Council of Language Associations was founded in 1964, as a second-tier organization, like the JMC, but co-operation has been taken much further. In 1990 a single professional association to unite language teachers was established: the Association for Language Learning (ALL). The aim is 'to speak with a stronger voice and safeguard the interests of languages in all sectors'. (186)

Debate about the coexistence of the MA and ATM was stimulated in 1988, when an informal survey of small samples of opinion was conducted at both annual conferences and the results published. (187) At this time less than a third of the ATM conference respondents favoured merger, by comparison with more than half at the MA conference. Further debate about the MA/ATM relationship was revived from 1990 by a strong case made for the SCAMES four to form a federation with a view to subsequent merger. (188) Alan Bishop's argument was published in *Mathematics Teaching* and it opened up a wide range of views within the ATM. Bishop's case rested on four grounds: the ideal of a united mathematics education community involving all sectional interests; the need for one voice in changed and rapidly changing political circumstances; the problem of duplication of voluntary human effort particularly in stressful times; and financial and administrative considerations.

The MA responded very positively by electing Bishop, a former chair of the ATM, as its President for the year 1991–2. This provided a platform for making his views more widely known within the MA and through his Presidential address at the first ever joint conference of the two associations, held at the University of Nottingham. (189) At Nottingham, Jeremy Kilpatrick of the USA also provided a valuable comparative perspective on professional associations in mathematics education in a lecture significantly entitled 'Ties that Bind'. (190) In other subject areas the English 'ties that bind' are clearly stronger than in mathematics. Furthermore, across the Atlantic the NCTM provides a strong voice which is being heard at national government level.

In the USA a national curriculum consensus has essentially been achieved over the past five years through the NCTM's own development of a vision for school mathematics in terms of a set of wide-ranging and carefully drafted 'standards' involving very wide consultation. The term 'standard' is in tune with the political agenda for education in the USA but the vision is a broad and influential one which owes a clear debt to the Cockcroft Report. The question of assessment in relation to the 'standards' is now a major concern for both the NCTM and the Mathematical Sciences Education Board (MSEB). The latter represents a wide range of professional constituencies in mathematics, education and administration, as well as parents and school board members. As Kilpatrick has put it : 'Assessment has proven to be the magic charm that has opened the door [for the NCTM and MSEB] to the halls of policy and power in Washington.' (191) Professional influence on the content of the National Curriculum in the UK has also been strong, particularly through the large measure of consensus achieved by the Cockcroft Committee and the Mathematics Working Group. But issues associated with assessment have become increasingly politically charged.

The political and professional contexts within which mathematics educa-

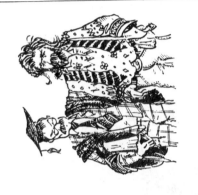

FROM THE ORIGINAL QUESTIONNAIRE

Do write in and air your views — Eds.

TOWARDS MATRIMONY????

......to everybody attending......

....the ATM Course/Winchester/5-8 April 1988
....or the MA Conference/Birmingham/6-9 April 1988

MUCH AMUSEMENT has been derived over the years from the stereotypical images of the members of the ATM ('muesli and sandals') and the MA ('pipe tobacco and elbow patches'). But rumour has it that muesli eating is now commonplace amongst MA members, and elbow patches de rigeur with the more fashion-conscious ATM members!

SERIOUSLY THOUGH, does continued separate existence of the two organisations make any sense? Discussion of this seems to have been non-existent since Mike Price raised it some years ago (see MT107 p5 and MiS March 1985 p40). Since then it seems that we've all been in a flat spin responding to seemingly endless government innovations and initiatives, but perhaps in such circumstances we'd have been better off responding with a single voice...and there'd have been less duplication of effort?

Plate 8.3   Questionnaire on Merger of MA and ATM 1988

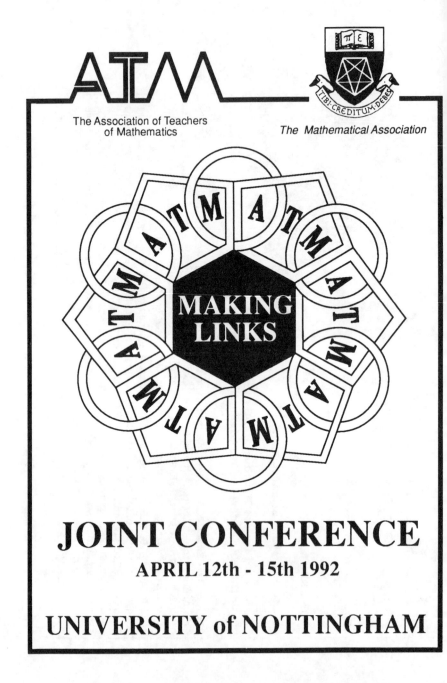

The Association of Teachers
of Mathematics

The Mathematical Association

MAKING
LINKS

JOINT CONFERENCE
APRIL 12th - 15th 1992

UNIVERSITY of NOTTINGHAM

Plate 8.4   First Joint Conference of MA and ATM 1992

tion is located in the USA and UK are very different, and strategies for influencing the curriculum and its assessment cannot be simply transferred. The need for a united voice like the NCTM's or the ASE's is still pressing but seems a long way from being satisfied. The crux is the coexistence of the MA and ATM; both AMET and NAMA represent more specific constituencies which might be incorporated within an umbrella organization. Obviously there are practical difficulties in merger, but oral evidence suggests that differences in ideology and style, whether perceived or real, continue to act as a barrier to progress, particularly on the ATM side. (192)

We have dwelt at some length on the declining external influence of the MA on the school curriculum and its assessment, an inevitable consequence of national developments in education since the 1970s. At the start of that decade the MA celebrated its centenary, and, in the light of the Policy Committee's report, a period of internal development was under way. The various lines of development were detailed earlier in this chapter and we have already seen how external developments have limited the capacity of the MA to grow in size and influence through its membership, branches, periodicals and publications, diplomas and certificates, and conferences. The nature of the MA's central organization and its limited finances have also restricted its capacity to adapt. During his period as President of the MA (1989–90), Reynolds defined a wide-ranging agenda for another review of the MA's policy and influence, in educational circumstances which were very different from those at the time of the Policy Committee's work some twenty years earlier. (193)

One short-term outcome of Reynolds's review was the appointment of three one-year, part-time, INSET field officers, as a response to the rapidly declining advisory services provided by LEAs coupled with continuing INSET needs for schools under local management and their teachers. But this initiative raises the general question of priorities in relation to the MA's provision of services and the uses made of very limited funds. In Hersee's view such priorities should be judged against the interests of the members themselves: 'the Association is its members basically'. (194) In addition, the MA is a voluntary organization which relies heavily on the efforts of a small number of members to sustain its activity. As Kilpatrick has aptly put it, such associations are 'callow, fragile things' and the following generalization is also fitting: 'Through most of their lives, our professional associations have truly struggled to keep alive.' (195) But, notwithstanding these limitations, through its publications and professional awards the influence of the MA continues to extend well beyond the membership.

With the concept of professionalism under attack and teachers increasingly being treated as 'workers', in the sense of Brown, it could be argued that the need for an organization such as the MA to support teachers as 'learners', again in Brown's sense, is itself in decline. Bishop, however, has argued to the contrary that subject associations are vital to the maintenance of a professional base for mathematics education. In addition, in Bishop's view, the changed political climate has brought new responsibilities which extend well beyond the self-interests of the membership:

> The more strongly centralised and controlled our system becomes, the
> greater is the need for us to hold on to independence wherever it exists
> . . . Professional associations are now expected to play a much greater
> role in maintaining and promoting the health of their subject. (196)

From this standpoint the MA's independence is one of its great strengths
The current 'health' of the subject depends upon policy making in a number
of major areas:

> over the recent issues of the mathematics curriculum, coursework,
> Key Stage assessments, resources, inservice education, initial train-
> ing and international comparisons, I believe we do have legitimate
> concerns. (197)

The battle over such concerns continues to engage the MA, ATM, AMET
and NAMA in separate and joint lobbying, albeit against the odds in
terms of influencing political decision making at the present time. (198)
Bishop's view again provides one driving force for continuing such action
'Mathematics education is far too important to be controlled by the
bureaucrats.' (199) It seems appropriate to conclude on an optimistic
note by quoting the relatively detached view of Asa Briggs, an eminent
social historian:

> In education, the ultimate success of any policy depends on the
> co-operation of the teachers. It is such a long process, and there
> are so many opportunities for subverting reforms at any level, that
> unless you have the teachers with you there is no point in talking
> about educational change at all. (200)

NOTES AND REFERENCES

Notes and References – Chapter One

1. For obituary tributes to Greenstreet see *MG*, 40 (1930), 181–6.
2. The inscription from Horace came from an Oxford don through Ida Busbridge (1908–88), in her Presidential year, 1964–5. I am grateful to Walter Langford for the details concerning the coat of arms and to Ian Cook for tracking down the Horace Ode: III 5, 6. The background is also detailed in MA, *Newsletter*, 7 (Feb. 1965), p.1.
3. Historical Association, *The Historical Association 1906–56* (George Philip and Son, 1955), p.52.
4. Howson, A.G., 'New challenges', *MG*, 73 (1989), 175–86.
5. Ibid., p.175.
6. Howson, A.G., *A History of Mathematics Education in England* (Cambridge University Press, 1982).
7. For a critical essay-review of Howson's history through biographies see Price, M.H., 'Utility or mental discipline in mathematics education?', *Studies in Science Education*, 11 (1984), 102–8.
8. Op.cit. (3).
9. Layton, D., *Interpreters of Science: A History of the Association for Science Education* (John Murray, 1984). This book is organized in three complementary parts to cover the constitutional, social and political dimensions of the ASE's history, which goes back to 1901.
10. The last issue of the Modern Language Association's journal contains a substantial historical feature: 'Souvenir section', *Modern Languages*, 70 (1989), 237–47.
11. For example, the first volume of the *Gazette* (in six numbers) contains such articles as: Mackay, J.S., 'Greek geometers before Euclid', *MG*, Quarto 1 (1894), 3–4, 19, (1895), 56–7; and Greenstreet, W.J., 'Herbart's view of the place of mathematics in education', *MG*, Quarto 1 (1894), 9–11. Note that the first octavo volume of the *Gazette* (1896–1900) was also numbered volume 1.
12. Loria, G., 'A.I.G.T.', *AIGT Report*, 19 (1893), 46–8.
13. See number 103 – the hundredth number was missed – *MG*, 7 (1913), 25–48; number 200, *MG*, 14 (1929), 377–436; number 300, *MG*, 32 (1948), 97–224; number 400 was beaten by the centenary issue, number 392: *MG*, 55 (1971), 121–248.
14. Hayward, R.B., in *AIGT Report*, 7 (1881), 12–17. For a tribute to Hayward see *MG*, 34 (1950), 81, with photograph facing.
15. Wilson, J.M., 'The early history of the Association', *MG*, 10 (1921), 239–44. For a biography of Wilson see Howson, op.cit. (6), pp.123–40.
16. Siddons, A.W., 'Progress', *MG*, 20 (1936), 7–26. For an obituary see Snell, K.S., *MG*, 44 (1960), 35–6.
17. The address of another schoolmaster President, some ten years later, is just as illuminating and more wide-ranging: Bushell, W.F., 'A century of school mathematics', *MG*, 31 (1947), 69–89. For an obituary see Combridge, J.T., *MG*, 59 (1975), 109–10.
18. Neville, E.H., 'The food of the gods', reprinted in *MG*, 55 (1971), pp.166–79. For obituary tributes to Neville see *MG*, 47 (1964), 131–9.
19. Quadling, D.A., 'Pressures and priorities', *MG*, 65 (1981), 157–66; Howson, op.cit. (4); Reynolds, P., 'Full circle', *MG*, 74 (1990), 211–23.
20. See the Presidential address op.cit. (16) and, subsequently: 'The A.I.G.T. and the M.A.', *MG*, 32 (1948), 160–2; 'The first twenty years of the Teaching Committee', *MG*, 36 (1952), 153–7; 'Fifty years of change', *MG*, 40 (1956), 161–9.
21. Combridge, J.T., 'The Mathematical Association: A centenary', *Bulletin of the Institute of Mathematics and its Applications*, 7 (1971), 130–2; 'The rise of the Mathematical Association 1871–1897', *Mathematics in School*, 1 (1) (1971), 3–5; 'The Mathematical Association reaches its first century', *Mathematics in School*, 1 (2) (1972), 6–8. For obituary tributes to Combridge see Kilmister, C.W., *Bulletin of the London*

Mathematical Society, 20 (1988), 156–8 and Kellaway, F.W., 'Winifred and Theodore Combridge', *MG,* 71 (1987), 307–9. His wife, who was also a long-standing and loyal servant of the MA, predeceased him by a few months.

22. Combridge, J.T., 'Among the archives: a centenary echo', in MA, *Newsletter,* 47 (Dec. 1979 – Jan. 1980), p.3. Mrs Thatcher even took the trouble to query Combridge's spelling at one point: 'I had written of a Board being "busy getting under weigh". The "weigh" attracted an exceptionally thick and wavy underline from the blue pencil.' (p.4.) I am grateful to Ruth Tobias for sending me an earlier draft of Combridge's lecture.

23. Combridge, op.cit. (21), 'The rise of the MA', p.3. For an interesting Russian view of the MA's history, which has recently been translated by Eric Barton, see Gaiduk, Y.M., 'On the past and present of the English Mathematical Association and the *Mathematical Gazette', Matematicheskoe Prosveshchenie,* 1 (1957), 87–105. I am grateful to Eric Barton for drawing my attention to this surprising secondary source and for undertaking the labours of translation.

24. For a view of the MA's library, past and present, see Price, M.H. and Dampier, M.D., *An Introduction to the Mathematical Association's Library* (MA, 1990).

25. The Joan Marshall Room was named after a member who died in 1976 and left a legacy which contributed to the cost of conversion.

26. MA, *Index to the Mathematical Gazette Volumes 1–15* (G. Bell and Sons, 1933). Combridge's notes on records and sources are deposited in the archives. I also corresponded with Combridge in 1979 and valued his perspective and personal encouragement at that time.

27. There were no reports of the AIGT in 1876, 1879 and 1880.

28. For a number of years the first minute book of the Teaching Committee, 1902–12, was also missing from the archives, but then it appeared through my letter-box in 1987, having been rediscovered by a former chairman of the Teaching Committee, C.A.R. Bailey, to whom I am grateful for plugging this gap.

29. Cooper, B., *Renegotiating Secondary School Mathematics: A Study of Curriculum Change and Stability* (Falmer Press, 1985). For a thought-provoking response to Cooper's work see Brookes, B., 'Personal enquiry as objective', *Mathematics Teaching,* 114 (1986), 52–5.

30. Carr-Saunders, A.M. and Wilson, P.A., *The Professions* (Frank Cass and Co., 1933; Oxford University Press, reprint 1964).

31. The Institute of Mathematics and its Applications was not founded until as late as 1964.

32. Webb, S., 'English teachers and their professional organisation', *New Statesman,* 5 (Sept. 1915), 1–22 (additional pp.); 5 (Oct. 1915), 1–24 (additional pp.).

33. Ibid., (Oct.), p.14.

34. Ibid., (Oct.), p.14.

35. Broadbent, T.A.A., 'Institute; Joint Council; Association', *MG,* 49 (1965), 262–5, p.262. Broadbent was editor of the *Gazette,* 1931–55, and was also actively involved with the London Mathematical Society. For an obituary see Maxwell, E.A., *MG,* 57 (1973), 195–7.

36. See Howson, op.cit. (4), pp.176–8, for some sobering comparisons between the system of payment by results and the contemporary National Curriculum arrangements.

37. Archibald, R.C., 'Notes on some minor English mathematical serials', *MG,* 14 (1929), 379–400, pp.396–8.

38. The *Gazette* itself is also included in Archibald's survey.

39. In the USA organized activity in mathematics education on a *local* basis developed from the turn of the century. In the Chicago area a Central Association of Science and Mathematics Teachers became well established, with its own organ: *School Science and Mathematics.* See National Council of Teachers of Mathematics, *A History of Mathematics Education in the United States and Canada,* 32nd yearbook (NCTM, 1970).

40. Whitby, H., 'Management in voluntary organisations' (Diploma dissertation, Nottingham Polytechnic, 1988).

41. I am particularly grateful to Brian Atwood, former general secretary of the ASE, for giving up the time to provide me with a management perspective on the ASE.

Notes and References – Chapter Two

1. Broadbent, T.A.A., 'The Mathematical Gazette : Our history and aims', *MG*, 30 (1946), 186–94, p.186.
2. Ibid., quoted in footnote, p.185.
3. For a recent view of the evolution of examinations based on the models developed in the early nineteenth century at the Universities of Oxford and Cambridge, see Rayner, M., 'On examinations', *MG*, 72 (1988), 173–84. Rayner draws heavily on Roach, J.P.C., *Public Examinations in England 1850–1900* (Cambridge University Press, 1971). For a comprehensive general survey of the growth of English examinations as 'administrative devices' see Montgomery, R.J., *Examinations* (Longmans, 1965).
4. Berry, A., 'Recent changes in the Mathematical Tripos at Cambridge', in Board of Education, *Special Reports on Educational Subjects*, 27 (HMSO, 1912), 183–95, pp.184–5. For further details on the history of the mathematical tripos and its influence see Rayner, op.cit. (3), pp.175–8, and Rouse Ball, W.W., *A History of the Study of Mathematics at Cambridge* (Cambridge University Press, 1889); also Rouse Ball, W.W., 'The Cambridge School of Mathematics', *MG*, 6 (1912), 311–23. Other retrospective and more anecdotal views have been provided by Forsyth, A.R., 'Old Tripos Days at Cambridge', *MG*, 19 (1935), 162–79, and Bushell, W.F., 'The Cambridge Mathematical Tripos', *MG*, 44 (1960), 172–9.
5. The University of London's matriculation examination was instituted as early as 1838 and it subsequently became important as a terminal leaving certificate for some middle class schools, as well as a university qualifying examination.
6. A rich and wide-ranging survey of the English secondary-school examination system and its history is also provided in Board of Education, *Report of the Consultative Committee on Examinations in Secondary Schools* (HMSO, 1911). By contrast, the Scottish Education Department was responsible for inspecting and examining for secondary certificates, and, in Prussia, secondary curricula were powerfully influenced by the centralized *Arbiturienten Examen*. As Roach, op.cit. (3), p.256, has pointed out, England was 'unique among European countries'.
7. For a good analysis of the 'instrumentary education' see Selleck, R.J.W., *The New Education 1870–1914* (Pitman, 1968), pp.24–45. For details of the administrative developments see Birchenough, C., *History of Elementary Education in England and Wales from 1800 to the Present Day* (University Tutorial Press, 1914; 2nd edn 1930).
8. Board of Education, *Reports on Elementary Schools 1852–1882 by Matthew Arnold* (new edn, HMSO, 1908), p.128.
9. Ibid., p.128.
10. Schools Inquiry [Taunton] Commission, *Reports of Assistant Commissioners*, 6 (HMSO, 1868), p.506. The Commission reported in twenty-one volumes, which gives some indication of the scale and complexity of its inquiry.
11. Commissions also investigated the affairs of the two ancient universities over the period 1850–2 and one consequence was the passing of Acts affecting Oxford (1854) and Cambridge (1856), which served to reduce religious restrictions and to promote open competition through entrance scholarship examinations.
12. Howson, A.G., 'Mathematics – the fight for recognition', *Mathematics in School*, 3 (6) (1974), 7–9, and Siddons, A.W., 'Progress', *MG*, 20 (1936), 7–26, pp.7–10.
13. Public Schools [Clarendon] Commission, Report of the Commissioners, 1 (HMSO, 1864), p.15. The Commission reported in four volumes.
14. Siddons, op.cit. (12), p.12.
15. Public Schools Commission, op.cit. (13), p.23.
16. Popular editions of Euclid were those of Potts, Colenso and Todhunter, building on the eighteenth-century edition of Simson. The coverage of other topics in Euclid is as follows: Book 3, circles; Book 4, polygons and constructions; Books 7–9, number theory; Book 10, irrationals; Books 11–13, solid geometry.
17. Bushell, W.F., 'A century of school mathematics', *MG*, 31 (1947), 69–89, p.81.
18. Quoted ibid., p.79.
19. Schools Inquiry [Taunton] Commission, *Report of the Commissioners*, 1 (HMSO, 1868), pp.29–30.

20. Ibid., p.30.
21. Schools Inquiry Commission, op.cit. (10), pp.506–7.
22. Brock, W.H., 'Geometry and the universities: Euclid and his modern rivals 1860–1901', *History of Education*, 4 (2) (1975), 21–35, pp.23–5.
23. Schools Inquiry Commission, op.cit. (19), p.30.
24. Ibid., p.30. Brock, op.cit. (22), pp.24–5, has drawn attention to the links between Key and Hirst, who was the first President of the AIGT and taught at University College School, when Key was headmaster.
25. Temple's links were significantly with Oxford University, where mathematics, including Euclid, was held in much less high esteem than at Cambridge. He had been involved in the pioneering work of the Oxford local examinations in the 1850s shortly before Cambridge entered this field. Like Arnold, he had experience of elementary schools and training colleges through his work for the Education Department as an examiner and inspector.
26. Wilson, J.M., 'The early history of the Association', *MG*, 10 (1921), 239–44, p.241.
27. Quoted in Howson, A.G., 'Euclid: "a very English subject" ', *Sciences et Techniques en Perspective*, 5 (Nantes University, 1984), 60–102.
28. Ibid., p.60. Simson's edition formed the basis for very many subsequent editions of Euclid. At Cambridge there developed a 'special devotion' to the Simson-Todhunter presentation: see Forsyth, op.cit., (4), p.170.
29. Howson, op.cit. (27), pp.61–4, has sketched the historical development of geometrical textbooks and identified a trend in which the gulf between the 'liberal' and 'vocational' elements gradually widened to form two separate streams in geometrical education. The Science and Art Department began examining in science subjects only in the 1860s. Euclid was part of the pure mathematics syllabus and practical geometry was a separate subject within the examinations schedule.
30. Broadbent, op.cit. (1), p.186.
31. Brock, op.cit. (22), pp.24–5. On Wormell see Brock, W.H., 'Richard Wormell, Teacher', in Brock, W.H. (ed.), *Science for All* (forthcoming); and his obituary in *Educational Times*, 67 (634) (1914), 66–7.
32. Wilson, J.M., in *Educational Times*, 21 (87) (1868), 60.
33. Wilson, J.M., *Elementary Geometry Part 1* (Macmillan, 1868). At Rugby, 'It was studied by the boys with extreme care, because I offered sixpence for every mistake and misprint, however trifling.' (Wilson, op.cit. (26), p.241). Hirst again provided some scholarly support for Wilson's efforts. The French stimulus also came directly through the comparative work of Demogeot and Montucci, which included a visit by Demogeot himself to Rugby School (p.240).
34. Ibid., p.241.
35. Wilson, op.cit. (33), p.v.
36. 'Thomas Archer Hirst', *MG*, 30 (1946), 249.
37. Davenport, H., 'Looking back', *Journal of the LMS*, 41 (1966) 1–10, p.2; and see Collingwood, E.F., 'A century of the London Mathematical Society', *Journal of the LMS*, 41 (1966), 577–94.
38. Wilson, J.M., 'Euclid as a text-book of elementary geometry', *Educational Times*, 21 (90) (1868), 125–8, p.126.
39. Wilson, op.cit., (26), p.241.
40. Richards, J.L., *Mathematical Visions : The Pursuit of Geometry in Victorian England* (Academic Press, 1988), p.165.
41. Sylvester, J.J., in BAAS, *Report of the Thirty-Ninth Meeting ... Exeter 1869* (John Murray, 1870), 1–9, p.6.
42. Ibid., p.8.
43. BAAS, op.cit. (41), p.lxxvii.
44. Mathematical and pedagogical refinements in the debates about elementary geometry and its teaching are well explored in Richards, op.cit.(40), pp.161–85. Kelland chaired a meeting in Edinburgh in 1870 at which Wilson spoke, and he was, in Wilson's view, op.cit. (26), p.242, 'wholly and openly opposed to the change'.
45. BAAS, *Report of the Forty-Third Meeting ... Bradford 1873* (John Murray, 1874), pp.459–60.
46. Wilson, op.cit. (26), p.242.

47. On the role of *Nature* in the AIGT's formation see *Nature*, 106 (2672) (1921), 638–9.
48. For obituaries of Levett see Mayo, C.H.P. and Godfrey, C., 'A great schoolmaster', *MG*, 11 (1923), 325–9, with photograph facing p.325.
49. Brock, op.cit. (22), pp.26–7.
50. Levett, R., in *AIGT Report*, 1 (1871), p.13. The first conference announcement, with the signatures of Levett, MacCarthy, Tucker and Wilson, was also published in *Nature* in December 1870, and the circular is reproduced in *MG*, 55 (1971), pp.123–4.
51. Association for the Reform of Geometrical Teaching, *List of Members – October, 1870*, MA archives.
52. Roche, J.W., 'The first half-century of the Headmasters' Conference, 1869–1919' (PhD thesis, University of Sheffield, 1972), p.450. On the history of the HMC see also Percival, A.C., *The Origins of the Headmasters' Conference*, (John Murray, 1969).
53. *AIGT Report*, 1 (1871), pp.5–8. Apart from Hirst, a Fellow of the Royal Society, the other non-school representatives at the first conference were C.W. Merrifield FRS, W. Spottiswoode FRS, who was also a member of the BAAS committee on geometry teaching, and J.F. Iselin, an inspector for the Science and Art Department and the sole representative of practical and vocational interests in geometry teaching.
54. Smith, H.J.S., in BAAS, op.cit. (45), p.5.
55. Wilson, J.M., 'On two fragments of geometrical treatises found in Worcester Cathedral', *MG*, 6 (1911), 19–27, p.19.
56. Hirst, T.A., in *AIGT Report*, 2 (1872), p.24, and BAAS, op.cit. (45). Brock, op.cit. (22), p.27, has drawn attention to the significance of some overlap in the membership of the BAAS committee and the AIGT for the tactics adopted by the latter.
57. BAAS, op.cit. (45), p.460.
58. BAAS, *Report of the Forty-Sixth Meeting ... Glasgow 1876* (John Murray, 1877), p.9.
59. *AIGT Report of Committee* (Jan. 1877), pp.13–17.
60. *AIGT Report*, 6 (1878), p.18.
61. *AIGT Report*, op.cit. (59), p.12.
62. *AIGT Report*, 6 (1878), p.19.
63. 'The Mathematical Association', *School World*, 6 (62) (1904), 56–8.
64. Howson, op.cit. (27).
65. Hayward, R.B., in *AIGT Report*, 10 (1884), p.23.
66. Todhunter, I., *The Conflict of Studies and Other Essays on Subjects Connected with Education* (Macmillan, 1873), pp.136–92.
67. Todhunter, I., to Tucker, R., 6 March 1871, photocopy in MA archives. I am grateful to J.M. Rollett for this source.
68. Dodgson, C.L., *Euclid and his Modern Rivals*, (2nd edn, Macmillan, 1885; reprint Dover, 1973). On Dodgson see Eperson, D.B., 'Lewis Carroll – mathematician', *MG*, 17 (1933), 92–100.
69. Langley, E.M., in *AIGT Report*, 15 (1889), p.21. For tributes to Langley see *MG*, 17 (1933), 225–9.
70. Bushell, op.cit. (17), p.84. A useful distinction between 'practical', 'power' and 'value' barriers to curriculum reform is elaborated in Howson, A.G., Keitel, C. and Kilpatrick, J., *Curriculum Development in Mathematics* (Cambridge University Press, 1981).
71. AIGT, *The Elements of Plane Geometry Parts 1 and 2* (Swan Sonnenschein, 1884, 1886).
72. *School World*, op.cit. (63), p.57.
73. Ibid., p.57.
74. *AIGT Report*, 15 (1889), p.18. Miss Beale was the first woman to join the AIGT, in 1874.
75. *AIGT Report*, 10 (1884), p.25.
76. Godfrey, op.cit. (48), p.328.
77. The AIGT's failure and comparisons with the Perry movement's early success are discussed in Price, M.H., 'Mathematics in English education 1860–1914: Some questions and explanations in curriculum history', *History of Education*, 12 (4) (1983), 271–84.
78. Richards, op.cit. (40), pp.170–9, emphasizes Hirst's and the AIGT's geometrical

conservatism.
79. *AIGT Report,* 1 (1871), p.3. Jones was Wilson's former headmaster at King William' College, Isle of Man.
80. Ibid., pp.14–15.
81. *AIGT Report,* 6 (1878), p.3.
82. *AIGT Report,* 8 (1882), pp.32–5.
83. Ibid., pp.5–6.
84. *AIGT Report,* 10 (1884), pp.5–9.
85. Ibid., p.3.
86. Hayward, R.B., in *AIGT Report,* 12 (1886), p.23.
87. Ibid., p.4.
88. Lists of members were published in the *AIGT Reports.*
89. For some discussion of the development of secondary education for girls, and university and professional training for women, see Howson, A.G., *A History of Mathematic Education in England* (Cambridge University Press, 1982), pp.172–81. On Philippa Fawcett and her educational circumstances see Siklos, S., *Philippa Fawcett and th Mathematical Tripos* (Newnham College, 1990). I am grateful to Trevor Fletcher fo drawing my attention to Siklos's work.
90. Rayner, op.cit. (3), pp.174–5, has drawn attention to the links between Miss Beale an St Hilda's College, Oxford. On Misses Buss and Beale see Kamm, J., *How Differen from Us* (Bodley Head, 1958), and Dyhouse, C., 'Miss Buss and Miss Beale: Gende and authority in the history of education', in Hunt, F. (ed.), *Lessons for Life: Th Schooling of Girls and Women, 1850–1950* (Basil Blackwell, 1987), 22–38. Mrs Bryan distinguished herself as a mathematician and was the first woman in England to receiv an academic doctorate. She was largely educated by her father and never attended an school. (Dyhouse, C., *Girls Growing Up in Late Victorian and Edwardian Englan* (Routledge and Kegan Paul, 1981), p.45.)
91. MA, *Council and Roll of Members* (Jan. 1900).
92. Hayward, R.B., in *AIGT Report,* 7 (1881), p.14.
93. Ibid., p.15.
94. Ibid., p.16.
95. Wormell, R., in *AIGT Report,* 19 (1893), p.14.
96. Hayward, R.B., in *AIGT Report,* 15 (1889), pp.19–20.
97. AIGT, *Presidential Addresses to Section A of the British Association by Professo Henrici (1883), and Professor Chrystal (1885)* (reprint, W.J. Robinson, 1887). Henrici a professor at the City and Guilds of London Institute, supported Sylvester's 1869 ple for a complete overhaul of geometry in education, to incorporate recent development in geometrical knowledge, and was critical of the AIGT's conservatism: 'There is ver little of the influence of modern ideas to be found in the different syllabuses whic have been published.' (p.7).
98. Hayward, op.cit. (96), p.20. For a history of algebra teaching see Price, M.H., 'Th history of school algebra in mathematical education in England and Wales' (M E dissertation, University of London, 1974).
99. *AIGT Report,* 19 (1893), p.11. The size of Mrs Bryant's class was not specified. Th attendance list included five female and six male 'visitors' who had presumably com to see the demonstration.
100. Langley, E.M., 'The early history of the *Mathematical Gazette*', *MG,* 7 (1913), 134–6 p.135.
101. See *MG,* 7 (1913), p.25, and a biographical note on Langley, p.28, with photograph facing. A comparable French journal, *L'Enseignement Mathématique,* was started ir 1893.
102. Price, M.H. and Dampier, M.D., *An Introduction to the Mathematical Association' Library* (MA, 1990), pp.1–2.
103. Layton, D., *Interpreters of Science* (John Murray, 1984), pp.9–10, points to the MA' lead in relation to the development of the Association of Public School Science Masters from 1901.

Notes and References – Chapter Three

1. Godfrey, C., 'The passing of Euclid', *Cornhill Magazine*, new series 21 (July 1906), 72–7, p.76.
2. Godfrey, C., 'Geometry teaching: the next step', *MG*, 10 (1920), 20–4, p.20.
3. MA, *Council and Roll of Members* (Jan. 1900). The AIGT's membership in 1871 was limited to England, plus two members from Scotland. By 1900 the Scottish contribution had grown to nine, including the President of the Edinburgh Mathematical Society, R.F. Muirhead, plus three honorary members: Professors Chrystal and Tait of Edinburgh University and Lord Kelvin, formerly of Glasgow University.
4. MA, Minute Book of Council, 19 Jan. 1901, MA archives.
5. For a detailed assessment of the Perry movement see Price, M.H., 'The Perry movement in school mathematics', in Price, M.H. (ed.), *The Development of the Secondary Curriculum* (Croom Helm, 1986), 103–55. The conclusions in much of the present chapter are based principally on this work.
6. Lawson, J. and Silver, H., *A Social History of Education in England* (Methuen, 1973), pp.356–7.
7. Birchenough, C., *History of Elementary Education in England and Wales from 1800 to the Present Day* (University Tutorial Press, 1914; 2nd edn 1930), pp.150–5, 384–5; Selleck, R.J.W., *The New Education 1870–1930* (Pitman, 1968), pp.45–69. For the changing role of HMI see also Board of Education, *Report of the Board of Education 1922–23* (HMSO, 1924), pp.9–45.
8. Public or HMC schools were listed in the *Schoolmasters Yearbook* from 1889 and their number had increased to around 150 by 1925.
9. Baron, G., 'The origins and early history of the Headmasters' Conference, 1869–1914', *Educational Review*, 7 (1955), 223–34; and Layton, D., *Interpreters of Science* (John Murray, 1984), pp.1–3.
10. Smith, R.H., 'Reform in mathematical education', *Engineer*, 93 (1902), 129–30, p.129.
11. Layton, op.cit. (9), p.2.
12. Selleck, op.cit. (7), pp.78–101. The term 'declinism' is taken from Brock W.H., 'The knowledge that is most worth', *Studies in Science Education*, 7 (1980), 171–7, p.172.
13. Butterworth, H., 'The Science and Art Department examinations: origins and achievements', in Macloed, R. (ed.), *Days of Judgement* (Nafferton Books, 1982), 27–44.
14. Board of Education, *Report of the Consultative Committee on Secondary Education with Special Reference to Grammar Schools and Technical High Schools* (HMSO, 1938), pp.52–62.
15. Royal [Bryce] Commission on Secondary Education, *Report of the Commissioners*, 1 (HMSO, 1895), p.73.
16. Henrici, O., *Elementary Geometry: Congruent Figures* (Longmans, Green and Co., 1879), p.ix.
17. Royal [Bryce] Commission on Secondary Education, *Appendix: Statistical Tables*, 9 (HMSO, 1895), which includes a collection of specimen timetables, pp.404–23.
18. Bushell, W.F., 'A century of school mathematics', *MG*, 31 (1947), 69–89, p.69.
19. Millis, C.T., *Technical Education: Its Development and Aims* (Arnold, 1925), pp.89–92.
20. For the historical background to the creation of the Board of Education see Bishop, A.S., *The Rise of a Central Authority for English Education* (Cambridge University Press, 1971). For a general history of educational administration see Gosden, P.H.J.H., *The Development of Educational Administration in England and Wales* (Basil Blackwell, 1966).
21. Layton, op.cit. (9), p.3; and see Cane, B.S., 'Scientific and technical subjects in the curriculum of English secondary schools at the turn of the century', *British Journal of Educational Studies*, 8 (1959), 52–64.
22. Board of Education, *Report of the Consultative Committee on Examinations in Secondary Schools* (HMSO, 1911), particularly ch.1.
23. Board of Education, *Report of the Consultative Committee on the Education of the Adolescent* (HMSO, 1926) particularly pp.26–31.

24. Perry, J., *England's Neglect of Science* (Fisher Unwin, 1900), pp.102–3. On the significance of squared paper and graphical methods generally, see Brock, W.H and Price, M.H., 'Squared paper in the nineteenth century: instrument of science and engineering and symbol of reform in mathematical education', *Educational Studies in Mathematics*, 11 (1980), 365–81.

25. Brock, W.H., 'An experiment in technical education', *New Scientist*, 84 (1182) (1979) 622–3.

26. Selleck, op.cit. (7), p.203; and see pp.102–51 on the practical educationists.

27. Wormell, R., 'Mathematics', in Barnett, P.A. (ed.), *Teaching and Organisation with Special Reference to Secondary Schools* (Longmans, Green and Co., 1897), 78–97 pp.82–3.

28. Ibid., p.83.

29. Wormell, R., in *AIGT Report*, 19 (1893), p.13.

30. Selleck, op.cit. (7).

31. Findlay, J.J., 'The teaching of elementary mathematics: impending reforms', *Educational Times*, 55 (492) (1902), 184–7, p.185. This article was based on a lecture to the College of Preceptors from a notable educationist who, in 1903, became the first professor of education at the University of Manchester.

32. Brock, W.H., 'From Liebig to Nuffield: a bibliography of the history of science education, 1839–1974', *Studies in Science Education*, 2 (1975), 67–99, p.75.

33. Wormell, R., 'Unstable questions of method in the teaching of elementary science' *Educational Times*, 53 (470) (1900), 240–3, p.241.

34. Layton, op.cit. (9), ch.1. The APSSM became the Science Masters' Association in 1919 and combined with the Association of Women Science Teachers to become the ASE in 1963.

35. Eggar, W.D., *Practical Exercises in Geometry* (Macmillan, 1903), p.v.

36. Findlay, op.cit. (31), p.185.

37. Jenkins, E.W., *From Armstrong to Nuffield: Studies in Twentieth-Century Science Education in England and Wales* (John Murray, 1979), pp.252–5.

38. Eggar, W.D., 'The co-ordination of the teaching of elementary mathematics and physics', *School World*, 3 (34) (1901), 361–3; and Layton, op.cit. (9) pp.15–16.

39. Bryan, G.H., 'The British Association discussion on the teaching of mathematics' *School World*, 4 (39) (1902), 88–91, p.90. No obituary of Bryan was published in the *Gazette* but he was a Cambridge wrangler (fifth) and Smith's prizeman see Venn, J.A., *Alumni Cantabrigienses*, 6 vols. (Cambridge University Press 1940–54).

40. Anon., 'The teaching of elementary geometry', *Educational Times*, 56 (511) (1903) 465–7, p.465.

41. The elementary stage of the new syllabus in practical mathematics is reproduced in Howson, A.G., *A History of Mathematics Education in England* (Cambridge University Press, 1982), pp.222–4.

42. Perry, J. (ed.), *British Association Meeting at Glasgow, 1901: Discussion on the Teaching of Mathematics* (Macmillan, 1901), p.25; Price, op.cit. (5), pp.129–30.

43. DSA, *Practical Mathematics: Summary of Six Lectures Delivered to Working Men by Professor John Perry* (HMSO, 1899).

44. Perry, J., 'Practical mathematics', *Nature*, 90 (2237) (1912), 34–5, p.35.

45. Perry, J., 'The teaching of mathematics', *Nature*, 62 (1605) (1900), 317–20.

46. Price, op.cit. (5), pp.105–7.

47. On the new practical mathematics textbooks see Boyt, J.E., 'Reviews: practical (or experimental) mathematics', *MG*, 3 (1906), 294–300.

48. Abbott, P., 'The preliminary mathematical training of technical students', in Board of Education, *Special Reports on Educational Subjects*, 27 (HMSO, 1912), 10–26 p.10.

49. Correspondent, 'The reform in mathematical education', *Engineering* (19 June 1903) 803–5, p.803.

50. Price, op.cit. (5), pp.114–15.

51. Findlay, op.cit. (31), p.184.

52. Muirhead, R.F., 'The teaching of mathematics', *MG*, 2 (1901), 81–3, p.81.

53. Perry, op.cit. (42).

54. On Forsyth see Piaggio, H.T.H., 'Three Sadleirian professors: A.R. Forsyth, E.W. Hobson and G.H. Hardy', *MG*, 15 (1931), 461–5, pp.461–3; and his obituary by Siddons, A.W., in *MG*, 26 (1942), 117–18.
55. Perry, J., 'Reform of mathematical education', *Engineer*, 93 (1902), 203.
56. Perry, op.cit. (24), p.49.
57. Muirhead, op.cit. (52), p.82.
58. Love, A.E.H., Review of Perry, op.cit. (42), in *Nature*, 65 (1690) (1902), 457–8, p.458.
59. Perry, op.cit. (42), p.ix.
60. Price, op.cit. (5), pp.118–19.
61. MA, op.cit. (4), 3 Oct. 1901. For a tribute to Lodge, who moved to Charterhouse in 1904, see Tuckey, C.O., *MG*, 22 (1938), 3–4.
62. Muirhead, op.cit. (52), and see *MG*, 2 (1901), 105–11. For a biography of Godfrey see Howson, op.cit. (41), pp.141–68.
63. Godfrey C., in *MG*, 2 (1901), p.106.
64. The circumstances surrounding the letter are fully detailed in Price, M.H., 'The reform of English mathematical education in the late nineteenth and early twentieth centuries' (PhD thesis, University of Leicester, 1981), pp.109–10.
65. See 'The public schools and the question', *MG*, 2 (1902), 143–6. Only eight signatories of the letter were also members of the MA at the time and only twenty-two names were listed in published versions. S.T.H. Saunders of Merchant Taylors' was the twenty-third, along with three other masters at the same school. Winchester contributed five names and Charterhouse six, including C.O. Tuckey (1875–1967) who became a remarkably long-serving member of the MA's Teaching Committee from 1902 and was rewarded by being granted honorary membership of the MA sixty years later. For an obituary of Tuckey see Bushell, W.F., *MG*, 52 (1968), 281–5. I am grateful to J.M. Rollett for passing on copies of some correspondence involving his father, A.P. Rollett HMI, concerning the schoolmasters' letter. This material has been deposited in the MA archives.
66. Russell, B., 'The teaching of Euclid', *MG*, 2 (1902), 165–7, p.165.
67. Richards, J.L., *Mathematical Visions* (Academic Press, 1988), p.161. This work also details the development of Russell's thinking in relation to the Cambridge tradition (ch.5) and the demise of the unified view of geometry in England (ch.6).
68. MA, 'Discussion on reform in the teaching of mathematics', *MG*, 2 (1902), 129–43, p.132.
69. MA, op.cit. (4), 18 Jan. 1902.
70. MA, Minute Book of Teaching Committee, list of members up to the fifth meeting of 1902, MA archives.
71. Siddons, A.W., 'Charles Godfrey, M.V.O., M.A.', *MG*, 12 (1924), 137–8, p.137.
72. MA, *The Teaching of Elementary Geometry* (George Bell and Sons, 1902), and *MG*, 2 (1902), 168–72.
73. Godfrey, C., 'Report on the teaching of geometry', *Nature*, 66 (1704) (1902), 201–2, p.202.
74. Godfrey, op.cit. (2), p.20.
75. *MG*, 2 (1902), 181–3.
76. MA, *The Teaching of Elementary Mathematics* (George Bell and Sons, 1902).
77. *MG*, 2 (1902), 197–201. The report was also published in other educational and scientific periodicals before it appeared in the annual report of the BAAS in 1903.
78. The detailed evidence concerning examination reform is provided in Price, op.cit. (64), pp.62–7, 103–4 and 115–20. The monthly *School World* proved to be a particularly valuable source for this detail.
79. MA, op.cit. (70), 22 March 1902. The change was reported to the fourth meeting of the MA's Teaching Committee, while its members were still working on the first geometry report.
80. Godfrey, op.cit. (1), p.76.
81. Godfrey, C., 'Methods of intuition and experiment in secondary schools', in Board of Education, *Special Reports on Educational Subjects*, 26 (HMSO, 1912), 429–38, p.431.
82. Langley, E.M., in Perry, op.cit. (42), p.44.

83. MA, op.cit. (70), 15 March 1902.
84. 'Mathematical reform at Cambridge', *Nature*, 68 (1756) (1903), 178–9, p.178.
85. 'The Mathematical Association', *School World*, 6 (62) (1904), 56–8, p.58.
86. Ibid., p.58.
87. *Nature*, op.cit. (84), p.179.
88. Perry, J., 'Mathematics in the Cambridge locals', *Nature*, 67 (1726) (1902), 81–2, p.82.
89. *Nature*, op.cit. (84), p.179.
90. Godfrey, op.cit. (2), p.20.
91. Price, op.cit. (64), pp.120–1, where the analysis is based on the indexes and catalogue of the British Museum, a copyright deposit library.
92. For a complete list of books reviewed in the *Gazette* up to the fifteenth volume (1930–1) see MA, *Index to the Mathematical Gazette Volumes 1–15* (G. Bell and Sons, 1933) pp.106–60.
93. Price, op.cit. (5), pp.125–30.
94. French, C.H., 'New London matriculation syllabus in mathematics', *School World*, (46) (1902), 363–6, p.365.
95. For the published output in 'graphical algebra' see the indexes and catalogues of the British Museum.
96. Godfrey, C., 'The teaching of mathematics at preparatory schools', *School World*, (44) (1902), 288–91, p.289.
97. Hall, H.S., 'The use and abuse of graphs', *School World*, 7 (76) (1905), 158–9, p.159.
98. Turner, H.H., 'John Perry – 1850–1920', *Proceedings of the Royal Society*, series A, 111 (1926), i-vii, p.v.
99. S.C., 'Euclid's Elements. By an ancient geometer', *Journal of Education*, 450 (Jan 1907), 32. The 'famous *pons*' is a reference to the *pons asinorum* or bridge of asses which became a common name for the fifth proposition in Euclid Book 1: the base angles of an isosceles triangle are equal. Without using a hypothetical construction e.g. bisecting the angle at the apex, the argument in Euclid was notoriously difficult for the tyro. The new freedom to use hypothetical constructions removed this particular difficulty.
100. Membership numbers are taken from the annual reports of Council, published in the *Gazette* from 1903, and the MA's lists – *Council and Roll of Members* – published biennially from 1898. The membership total for 1905 was 402, so there was actually a slight drop in the subsequent year.
101. 'Introduction', *MG*, 7 (1913), 25–7, p.27.
102. MA, 'Report of the Council for 1905', *MG*, 3 (1906), 281–2, p.281.
103. Greenstreet, W.J., 'An appeal', *MG*, 3 (1906), 282–4, p.283.
104. MA, op.cit. (70), 18 June 1904 and 16 Feb. 1907.
105. A more detailed content analysis up to 1930 is provided in Price, op.cit. (64) pp.141–4.
106. Archibald, R.C., 'Notes on some minor English mathematical serials', *MG*, 14 (1929) 379–400.
107. There were only three issues annually of the *Gazette* up to 1899, then normally six from 1900, with additional numbers published in 1907, 1908, 1910 and 1913.
108. Archibald, op.cit. (106), pp.396–8.
109. Hurst, G.H.J., 'Mathematics and physics in public schools', *Nature*, 63 (1633) (1901) 370–1, p.371.
110. Bryan, op.cit. (39), p.89.
111. For obituary tributes to Fletcher see Siddons, A.W., in *MG*, 43 (1959), 85–7 and Strachan, J., p.87, reprinted from *The Times*.
112. Price, op.cit. (5), pp.124–33.
113. Bayliss, R.H., 'Practical mathematics', *School World*, 7 (78) (1905), 214–16, p.214.
114. Greenstreet, op.cit. (103).
115. For an obituary of Mathews see Gray, A., in *MG*, 11 (1922), 133–5.
116. MA, op.cit. (92), pp.8–10.
117. Bryan, G.H., 'The neglected British teacher: a plea for organisation in mathematics' *MG*, 4 (1907), 28–33, p.28.

18. Ibid., p.30.
19. Blomfield, C.H., of Bradford Grammar School, in Bryan, G.H., 'The future of the Mathematical Association', *MG*, 4 (1907), 74–7, p.75.
20. Ibid., p.76.
21. Combridge, J.T., *The Mathematical Association: Records and Sources*, MA archives, undated, pp.18–19.
22. Bryan, op.cit. (117), p.30.
23. MA, op.cit. (4), 10 April 1907.
24. Bryan, op.cit. (117), p.31.
25. 'The first local branch of the Mathematical Association', *MG*, 4 (1908), 201.
26. Bryan, G.H., 'The address of the retiring President', *MG*, 5 (1909), 44–51, pp.44–5.
27. MA, 'Meeting of the Council of the Mathematical Association', *MG*, 5 (1909), 121–2; MA, 'Southampton and District Mathematical Society', *MG*, 5 (1909), 122–3.
28. Bryan, op.cit. (117), pp.32–3.
29. In 1905 the Council agreed to pay Greenstreet £25, in addition to £5 expenses, for his 'very valuable services'. The honorarium was increased to £100 in 1911: see MA, op.cit. (4), 28 Jan. 1905 and 11 Jan. 1911.
30. Bryan, op.cit. (117), p.31. He also reiterated these unfavourable comparisons with Germany and America, and also France, in his 1908 Presidential address: Bryan, G.H., 'The uses of mathematics and the training of the mathematical teacher', *MG*, 4 (1908), 221–8, p.223.
31. Bryan, op.cit. (117), p.32.
32. Ibid., p.33.
33. MA, *Reports on the Teaching of Elementary Mathematics 1902–8* (George Bell and Sons, 1908), p.3.
34. MA, op.cit. (92), pp.8–10.
35. In geometry, the popular textbook writers for Macmillan, Hall and Stevens, followed the MA's recommendations, but Godfrey and Siddons in constructing their *Elementary Geometry. Practical and Theoretical* (Cambridge University Press, 1903) had been advised by Forsyth to ignore the restriction of Euclid's order.
36. MA, op.cit. (70), 3 Oct. 1903.
37. MA, op.cit. (133), pp.14–16.
38. Perry, J. (ed.), *British Association Meeting in South Africa, 1905. Discussion at Johannesburg on the Teaching of Elementary Mechanics* (Macmillan, 1906).
39. MA, *The Teaching of Algebra and Trigonometry* (G. Bell and Sons, 1910), list inside front cover.
40. MA, 'Committee on the teaching of elementary mathematics', *MG*, 2 (1903), 349–51, p.349.
41. Ibid., pp.350–1.
42. Godfrey, op.cit. (1), p.77.
43. MA, op.cit. (133), 20–9, p.20.
44. Ibid., 17–18.
45. Ibid., 18–19.
46. MA, op.cit. (4), 26 Jan. 1907.
47. For obituary tributes to Hardy see *MG*, 32 (1948), 49–51; see also Piaggio, op.cit. (54), pp.464–5.
48. Richards, op.cit. (67), p.202.
49. Hardy, G.H., 'The case against the mathematical tripos', reprinted in *MG*, 32 (1948), 134–45, p.138. This outspoken Presidential address was first published in 1926.
50. Ibid., p.137.
51. Forsyth, A.R., in Perry, op.cit. (138), pp.28–9.
52. This conclusion is based on a scrutiny of the large collection of school textbooks in the MA's library.
53. Berry, A., 'Recent changes in the mathematical tripos at Cambridge', in Board of Education, *Special Reports on Educational Subjects*, 27 (HMSO, 1912), 183–95, pp.190–1.
54. Some valuable statistics and discussion concerning the numbers of honours graduates from British universities, up to 1940, are presented in Chapman, S., 'University training of mathematicians', *MG*, 30 (1946), 61–70. Chapman's graphs are reproduced

in Howson, op.cit. (41), p.145.
155. On Hobson see Piaggio, op.cit. (54), pp.463–4.
156. The progress of the campaign to reform the Cambridge mathematical tripos is detaile
in Hassé, H.R., 'My fifty years of mathematics', *MG*, 35 (1951), 153–64, pp.155–7.
157. Dixon, A.L., 'Mathematical examinations at Oxford', in Board of Education, op.ci
(153), 68–182.
158. MA, op.cit. (133), pp.18–19. Hardy was invited to join the subcommittee o
mathematical scholarships but did not reply: see MA, op.cit. (70), 28 Sept. 1907.
159. Richards, op.cit. (67), p.232.

Notes and References – Chapter Four

1. Hobson, E.W., 'The democratization of mathematical education', *MG*, 6 (1912
234–43, p.235.
2. MA, 'Report of the Mathematical Association Committee on the teaching (
mathematics in public and secondary schools', *MG*, 9 (1919), 393–421, p.411.
3. Hobson, op.cit. (1), p.235.
4. Godfrey, C., 'Mathematics in English schools', *Science Progress*, 6 (1912), 161–8(
p.161.
5. Hobson, op.cit. (1), p.236.
6. Wolff, G., *Der Mathematische Unterricht der Höheren Knabenschulen Englan*
(Teubner, 1915), pp.119–21. For a tribute to Wolff see Fletcher, T.J., in *MG*, 6
(1978), 114–16.
7. Perry, J., in BAAS, *Report of the Seventy-Second Meeting . . . Belfast 1902* (Joh
Murray, 1903), 711–29, p.719.
8. Young, J.W.A., *The Teaching of Mathematics in the Elementary and Secondary Scho*
(Longmans, Green and Co., 1907; 2nd edn 1914), p.105.
9. Ibid., pp.87–121.
10. Layton, D., *Interpreters of Science* (John Murray, 1984), pp.9–10.
11. Siddons, A.W., 'A short memoir', in Carrington, C.E. (ed.), *Godfrey and Siddo*
(Cambridge University Press, 1952), 2–15, p.3.
12. Layton, op.cit. (10), pp.25–6. Eton and Harrow between them provided almost
quarter of the man-years of service to the committee of the APSSM between 190
and 1918. The APSSM became the Science Masters' Association in 1919.
13. A.T.S., 'London Conference of Science Teachers', *Nature*, 67 (1733) (1903), 259–60.
14. *Schoolmasters Yearbook and Directory* (Swan Sonnenschein, 1905), p.223.
15. Jackson, C.S., 'The teaching of mathematics and physics', *MG*, 3 (1904), 75–8.
16. MA, Minute Book of Teaching Committee, 3 Oct. 1903, MA archives.
17. *MG*, 9 (1917), 45–9, p.47. See also Jackson, C.S., 'The slide rule and its use in teachir
logarithms', *MG*, 2 (1903), 330–7.
18. BAAS, *Report of the Seventy-Third Meeting . . . Southport 1903* (John Murray, 1904
p.cii.
19. Perry, op.cit. (7), p.719.
20. Perry, J. (ed.), *British Association Meeting in South Africa, 1905. Discussion*
Johannesburg on the Teaching of Elementary Mechanics (Macmillan, 1906). Per
distributed his address widely but received only eleven replies.
21. Ashford, C.E., 'Mathematics at Osborne and Dartmouth', in Board of Educatio
Special Reports on Educational Subjects, 26 (HMSO, 1912), 183–8.
22. Perry, op.cit. (20), pp.33–4.
23. Perry, op.cit. (20), pp.65–6.
24. Ibid., p.66.
25. Besant, W.H., 'The teaching of elementary mechanics', *AIGT Report*, 9 (1883), 33–4'
p.33.
26. Ibid., p.34.
27. Ibid., p.34.
28. Quoted in Jackson, op.cit. (15), pp.76–7. Todhunter's position reflected Whewell
views on a liberal education. Mechanical truth was akin to geometrical truth and shou
be developed in the manner of Euclid. From this standpoint, experimental verificatic

was irrelevant; see Howson, A.G., 'Applications in the history of mathematics teaching', *Llull*, 12 (1989), 365–95, pp.382–5.

29. Siddons, A.W., 'Fifty years of change', *MG*, 40 (1956), 161–9, p.168.
30. Godfrey, C., 'The teaching of experimental arithmetic', *School World*, 8 (90) (1906), 201–2, p.201.
31. BAAS, *Report of the Seventy-Seventh Meeting . . . Leicester 1907* (John Murray, 1908), p.97.
32. Siddons, A.W., 'Practical mathematics at Harrow School', in Board of Education, *Special Reports on Educational Subjects*, 26 (HMSO, 1912), 403–9, p.404.
33. Lodge, A., 'Mathematics in the army entrance examinations', *School World*, 6 (72) (1904), 452–4.
34. Siddons, op.cit. (32), p.407.
35. Godfrey, C. and Bell, G.M., *Note-Book of Experimental Mathematics* (Edward Arnold, 1905).
36. Boyt, J.E., 'Reviews: practical (or experimental) mathematics', *MG*, 3 (1906), 294–300, pp.294–5.
37. Godfrey, op.cit. (30), p.202.
38. Ibid., p.202.
39. Siddons, op.cit. (32), and see Bell, G.M., pp.427–8, on Winchester; Fawdry, R.C., pp.400–2, on Clifton; and Sanderson, F.W., pp.410–26, on Oundle.
40. MA, 'Report of the Council for 1908', *MG*, 5 (1909), 41–4, pp.42–3.
41. Mair was an influential figure, particularly through his work for the Civil Service Commission from 1896. His obituary in *The Times* (23 July 1942) judged that 'his forceful and original mind soon showed itself in modifications and improvements of the examinations which had a far-reaching effect on the subjects both in schools and in the universities'.
42. MA, Minute Book of Council, 31 March 1908, MA archives.
43. MA, op.cit. (40), p.43.
44. MA, op.cit. (42), 28 Jan. 1905.
45. Ibid., 28 Nov. 1908.
46. MA, 'The correlation of the teaching of mathematics and science', *MG*, 5 (1909), 1–40.
47. MA and APSSM, *The Correlation of Mathematical and Science Teaching* (George Bell and Sons, 1909).
48. Ibid., p.10.
49. Siddons, A.W. and Vassall, A., *Practical Measurements* (Cambridge University Press, 1910).
50. MA and APSSM, op.cit. (47), p.12.
51. Ibid., p.5.
52. Turner, H.H., in *MG*, 5 (1910), 220–30, p.229.
53. Ibid., p.230, and see Turner, H.H., 'Practical mathematics at public schools', in Board of Education, *Special Reports on Educational Subjects*, 26 (HMSO, 1912), 393–9.
54. Godfrey, op.cit. (4), p.176. A number of Cambridge graduates subsequently rubbished the character of their own education in applied mathematics with reference to the infamous elephant problem. To quote Arthur Berry, a don at King's College, 'The typical Mathematical Tripos question on mechanics is supposed to begin: "An elephant whose mass may be neglected . . . " A more serious illustration is that a mathematician frequently has difficulty in remembering whether the enormous factor $v=3\times10^{10}$ should be put into the numerator or denominator of a formula.' See Berry, A., 'Recent changes in the mathematical tripos at Cambridge', in Board of Education, *Special Reports on Educational Subjects*, 27 (HMSO, 1912), 183–95, p.188. Bushell, W.F., in 'A century of school mathematics', *MG*, 31 (1947), 69–89, p.70, referred to the elephant problem as 'the most famous one' whilst attacking his own 'unreal and distorted' education in mechanics, hydrostatics, optics and electricity.
55. MA, op.cit. (42), 2 Oct. 1909.
56. *MG*, 5 (1910), 244–71, and *School World*, 12 (134) (1910), 66–9.
57. Ibid., pp.66–7.

58. For obituary tributes to Nunn see *MG*, 29 (1945), 1–3.
59. Nunn, T.P., *William Ellis Endowed School. A Syllabus of the Courses in Mathematics and Science Followed in the Upper School* (Educational Supply Association, 1903).
60. Nunn, T.P., 'Science in correlation with geography and mathematics', *Educational Times*, 61 (564) (1908), 175–80.
61. MA, op.cit. (42), 4 Nov. 1916.
62. MA, 'Report on the teaching of mechanics', *MG*, 9 (1918), 265–92, p.291.
63. Eggar, W.D., 'The teaching of elementary mechanics', in Board of Education, *Special Reports on Educational Subjects*, 26 (HMSO, 1912), 338–50, p.341.
64. Fletcher, W.C., 'The position of mathematics in secondary schools in England', in Board of Education, *Special Reports on Educational Subjects*, 26 (HMSO, 1912), 90–103.
65. Fletcher, W.C., 'Introductory work in mechanics', *School World*, 6 (65) (1904), 170–2.
66. Fletcher, op.cit. (64), p.103.
67. Wolff, op.cit. (6), p.172.
68. [Thomson] Committee, *Report of the Committee Appointed by the Prime Minister to Enquire into the Position of Natural Science in the Educational System of Great Britain* (HMSO, 1918), p.22. For a belated very brief review of this report see Jeffreys, B., in *MG*, 55 (1971), 248.
69. Ibid., pp.31–3.
70. Filon, L.N.G., 'The relations of mathematics and physics', in *Special Reports on Educational Subjects*, 27 (HMSO, 1912), 282–90.
71. Perry, J., 'The correlation of the teaching of mathematics and science', *School World*, 10 (120) (1908), 459–64, p.461; and see MA, op.cit. (46).
72. Ibid., p.463.
73. Godfrey, C., 'The teaching of mathematics in English public schools for boys', *MG*, 4 (1908), 250–9, pp.255–6.
74. Ibid., p.257.
75. Perry, op.cit. (71), p.463.
76. MA, op.cit. (46), p.22.
77. Ibid., p.13.
78. Perry, op.cit. (71), p.464.
79. Fletcher, op.cit. (64), p.95.
80. Ibid., p.94.
81. Strachan, J., 'Mathematics', in Adams, J. (ed.), *The New Teaching* (Hodder and Stoughton, 1918), 195–229, p.197.
82. Robinson, F.E., 'Mathematics for army candidates', *MG*, 3 (1906), 336–8, p.336.
83. Ibid., p.338.
84. Jones, A.C., 'Practical mathematical exercises and graphs', *School World*, 7 (80) (1905), 287–90, p.288.
85. Godfrey, op.cit. (73), pp.255–6.
86. Ibid., p.257.
87. Hobson, E.W., in BAAS, *Report of the Eightieth Meeting . . . Sheffield 1910* (John Murray, 1911), 509–22, pp.521–2.
88. Hobson, op.cit. (1), pp.238–9.
89. Steggall, J.E.A., 'On practical mathematics in schools', *MG*, 7 (1914), 287–94, p.294.
90. Mayo, C.H.P., *Reminiscences of a Harrow Master* (Rivingtons, 1928), pp.132–7.
91. Beard, W.F., 'The reform of mathematical teaching', *Nature*, 62 (1611) (1900), 466.
92. Wolff, op.cit. (6), pp.67–84.
93. Hobson, op.cit. (1), p.239.
94. Ibid., p.243.
95. Bryan, G.H., 'Professor Perry's Practical Mathematics', *Nature*, 91 (2283) (1913), 551–3, p.551.
96. Price, M.H., 'The Perry movement in school mathematics', in Price, M.H. (ed.), *The Development of the Secondary Curriculum* (Croom Helm, 1986), 103–55, pp.134–7.
97. Holmes, H.T., 'Elementary mathematics in evening schools', *MG*, 5 (1910), 200–2, p.200.

98. Benny, L.B., 'The teaching of mathematics to technical students', *MG*, 12 (1924), 59–60, p.59.

99. Piaggio, H.T.H., 'Mathematics for evening technical students', *MG*, 12 (1924), 161–3.

00. MA, *The Teaching of Mathematics to Evening Technical Students* (G. Bell and Sons, 1926).

01. Ibid., p.9.

02. Piaggio, op.cit. (99), p.161.

03. Ibid., p.162.

04. MA, op.cit. (100), p.12.

05. Siddons, A.W., 'The first twenty years of the Teaching Committee', *MG*, 36 (1952), 153–7, p.156.

06. Heywood, H.B., 'The reform of university mathematics', *MG*, 12 (1925), 322–30, p.324. The writer worked for the Civil Service Commission, which was an influential examining body.

07. Forsyth, A.R., in *MG*, 3 (1905), 145–53, p.152.

08. Godfrey, C., 'The passing of Euclid', *Cornhill Magazine*, new series 21 (July 1906), 72–7, p.76.

09. MA, op.cit. (42), 26 Jan. 1907.

10. MA, op.cit. (16), 1 July 1911.

11. Board of Education, *Report of the Consultative Committee on Examinations in Secondary Schools* (HMSO 1911).

12. MA, op.cit. (16), 1 July 1911.

13. Aleph, 'Examinations correspondence', *MG*, 5 (1910), 280.

14. Godfrey, C., 'Geometry teaching: the next step', *MG*, 10 (1920), 20–4, p.20.

15. Board of Education, *Teaching of Geometry and Graphic Algebra in Schools*, circular 711 (HMSO, 1909).

16. Godfrey, C., 'The question of sequence in geometry', *School World*, 14 (165) (1912), 357.

17. 'Local branches', *MG*, 5 (1910), 289–99.

18. Anon., 'University and educational intelligence', *Nature*, 93 (2339) (1914), 685–6, p.686.

19. Siddons, A.W., 'Obituary: W.C. Fletcher', *MG*, 43 (1959), 85–7, p.86.

20. MA, op.cit. (16), 22 Feb. 1913.

21. Godfrey, C., 'The teaching of algebra: what is educational and what is technical?', *MG*, 5 (1910), 230–44.

22. Ibid., p.233.

23. Nunn, T.P., 'The aim and methods of school algebra', *MG*, 6 (1911), 167–72, and *MG*, 6 (1912), 214–9. See also his visionary book: Nunn, T.P., *The Teaching of Algebra (including Trigonometry)* (Longmans, Green and Co., 1914). As Tuckey pointed out after Nunn's death in 1944: 'This was extraordinary as a one-man piece of work. At the time that it was published, 1914, its novelty was much more striking than it would be now, for writers of mathematical textbooks have been cribbing its ideas and suggestions steadily ever since . . .' (see *MG*, op.cit. (58), p.1).

124. MA, *The Teaching of Elementary Algebra and Numerical Trigonometry* (G. Bell and Sons, 1911), p.1.

125. Ibid., p.8.

126. King, H.F., to Howson, A.G., personal correspondence, 6 Feb. 1981.

127. MA, op.cit. (16), 4 May 1912.

128. Ibid., 20 July 1912.

129. Ibid., 30 Nov. 1912.

130. MA, 'Report of the General Teaching Committee', *MG*, 7 (1914), 227–8, p.228.

131. MA, 'Discussion on the syllabus', *MG*, 7 (1914), 259–65, p.264.

132. MA, 'Report of the Council for the year 1917', *MG*, 9 (1918), 185–7, p.187.

133. *MG*, 8 (1915), 1–5; and MA, 'Report of the Council for the year 1919', *MG*, 10 (1920), 17–19, p.18.

134. Kitchener, E., 'Mathematics in the preparatory school', in Board of Education, *Special Reports on Educational Subjects*, 26 (HMSO, 1912), 104–18.

135. MA, *A General Mathematical Syllabus for Non-Specialists in Public Schools*, (G. Bell and Sons, 1913).
136. Siddons, op.cit. (105), p.157.
137. For an obituary of Durell, by Maxwell, see *MG*, 53 (1969), 312–3, and for a survey of his outstanding set of textbooks up to the mid-1930s see *Modern Mathematical Textbooks: C.V. Durell* (G. Bell and Sons, 1934). He also formed a very productive partnership with Alan Robson of Marlborough, through which the range of his textbooks was extended well beyond the three elementary branches.
138. Durell, C.V., 'The arithmetic syllabus in secondary schools', *MG*, 6 (1911), 28–42.
139. MA, 'Report on the teaching of the multiplication and division of decimals', *MG*, 8 (1915), 165–8; and MA, 'The report of the committee on the teaching of arithmetic in public schools', *MG*, 8 (1916), 233–44. The report on the teaching of mechanics – MA, op.cit. (62) – was also published in the *Gazette* but not separately.
140. MA, 'Mathematics in secondary schools', *MG*, 7 (1914), 231–2. This report was also published in the *School World*. There is no minute book of the 'Other Secondary Schools' Special Committee in the MA archives.
141. Howson, A.G., *A History of Mathematics Education in England* (Cambridge University Press, 1982), p.159. Howson also reports that Elizabeth Williams as part of her professional training saw Dobbs teach a demonstration lesson and was 'almost scandalised' because 'there was none of the usual verbal argument' (p.181). See Dobbs, W.J., *A School Course in Geometry* (Longmans, Green and Co., 1913).
142. Quoted in Rollett, A.P., 'Class consciousness', *MG*, 52 (1968), 219–41, pp.233–4. Hope-Jones was elected President of the MA for the year 1938–9 and his atypical and sparkling Presidential address on 'Simplicity and truthfulness in arithmetic' was reprinted in the centenary number of the *Gazette*, 55 (1971), 180–200. For obituary tributes see *MG*, 49 (1965), 258–62.
143. Story, L., 'The organisation of the teaching of mathematics in public secondary schools for girls', in Board of Education, *Special Reports on Educational Subjects*, 26 (HMSO, 1912), 543–59, p.544. For an outline of the early growth of secondary and higher educational opportunities for girls and women see Howson, op.cit. (141), pp.172–7. Women at Cambridge received only special certificates up to 1920, when titular degrees were offered; full BA degrees were not awarded until 1948.
144. Story, op.cit. (143), p.545.
145. Layton, op.cit. (10), pp.33–6; and see Jenkins, E.W., *From Armstrong to Nuffield* (John Murray, 1979), pp.170–214 on the twentieth-century scientific education of girls.
146. Burstall, S.A., 'The place of mathematics in the education of girls and women', in Board of Education, *Special Reports on Educational Subjects*, 26 (HMSO, 1912), 575–81, p.576.
147. MA, *Rules of the Mathematical Association* (Jan. 1908), p.4.
148. Siddons, A.W., 'The A.I.G.T. and the M.A.', *MG*, 32 (1948), 160–2.
149. MA, op.cit. (124), p.1.
150. MA, op.cit. (16), 1 July 1911.
151. For a short tribute to Miss Punnett see *MG*, 30 (1946), p.121. She produced an early 'methods' book, *The Groundwork of Arithmetic* (1914): 'a sane and inspiring course for young children, of great benefit to the novice-teacher'.
152. For obituary tributes to Pendlebury see *MG*, 26 (1942), 1–4. Nunn's comparison of Pendlebury with Todhunter was intended as a compliment. Pendlebury brought mathematical respectability to the teaching of arithmetic through his hugely successful textbooks on this branch from the 1880s. Todhunter's textbooks were authoritative and ranged widely, with the notable exception of arithmetic.
153. MA, Minute Book of the Girls' Schools Committee, 4 May 1912, MA archives.
154. MA, *Council and List of Members and Associates* (Feb. 1914).
155. Burstall, S.A., 'The place of mathematics in girls' education', *MG*, 6 (1912), 203–13.
156. MA, *Index to the Mathematical Gazette Volumes 1–15* (G. Bell and Sons, 1933).
157. Durell, op.cit. (138), p.40.
158. MA, 'A discussion on the report of the committee on the teaching of algebra and trigonometry', *MG*, 6 (1911), 42–56, pp.54–5.
159. Story, op.cit. (143); Burstall, op.cit. (146); Gwatkin, E.R., 'The value of the study

of mathematics in public secondary schools for girls', and Sidgwick, E.M., 'Higher mathematics for women', in Board of Education, *Special Reports on Educational Subjects*, 26 (HMSO, 1912), 560–74 and 582–8. Aspects of the debate at this time are discussed in Howson, op.cit. (141), pp.173–5, and Clements, M.A., 'Sex differences in mathematical performance: an historical perspective', *Educational Studies in Mathematics*, 10 (1979), 305–22.

160. Burstall, op.cit. (155), p.207.
161. Ibid., p.211.
162. Story, op.cit. (143), p.551.
163. Layton, op.cit. (10), p.39. Sophie Bryant, an early AIGT member, was the first honorary member of the Association of Science Teachers and President in 1920. As Layton points out, she 'symbolised what an able woman could achieve in the educational world' (p.43).
164. MA, *Elementary Mathematics in Girls' Schools* (G. Bell and Sons, 1916).
165. MA, op.cit. (154).
166. Price, M.H., 'The first ATM', *Mathematics Teaching*, 108 (1984), 40–1.
167. Carson, G.St L., 'Editorial', *Journal of the Association of Teachers of Mathematics for the South-Eastern Part of England*, 1 (1911), 1. A complete set of eight issues of the *Journal* is held in the library of the MA.
168. Whitehead, A.N., 'The place of elementary mathematics in a liberal education', *Journal of the Association of Teachers of Mathematics for the South-Eastern Part of England*, 1 (1911), 2–12; Whitehead, A.N., 'The place of mathematics in education', *MG*, 7 (1913), 87–94; Whitehead, A.N., 'The aims of education – a plea for reform', *MG*, 8 (1916), 191–203; and Whitehead, A.N., 'Technical education and its relation to science and literature', *MG*, 9 (1917), 20–33.
169. Godfrey, C., 'The teaching of mathematics in English public schools for boys', and Smith, D.E., 'The teaching of mathematics in the secondary schools of the United States', in *Proceedings of the Fourth ICM, Rome 1908*, 3 (Lincei, 1909), 449–64 and 465–77. Godfrey's paper was also published in the *Gazette*, op.cit. (73). The work of the ICMI from 1908 is also detailed in Howson, A.G., 'Seventy five years of the International Commission on Mathematical Instruction', *Educational Studies in Mathematics*, 15 (1984) 75–93.
170. Archibald, R.C., *The Training of Teachers of Mathematics for the Secondary Schools* (Government Printing Office, Washington DC, 1918), p.3.
171. Board of Education, *Special Reports on Educational Subjects*, 26 and 27 (HMSO, 1912).
172. Godfrey, C., 'On the work of the International Commission on Mathematical Teaching', *MG*, 6 (1912), 243–6.
173. Godfrey, C., 'The algebra syllabus in the secondary school', in Board of Education, op.cit. (171), 26, 280–311, p.292.
174. Smith, D.E. and Goldziher, C., *Bibliography of the Teaching of Mathematics 1900–1912*, (Government Printing Office, Washington DC, 1912).
175. MA, 'Report of the Council for 1912', *MG*, 7 (1913), 56–7.
176. Jackson, C.S., 'The International Commission on the Teaching of Mathematics', *MG*, 6 (1912), 384–5, p.385. The library of the MA contains a rare complete set of the reports prepared for the ICMI.
177. Smith, D.E., 'Intuition and experiment in mathematical teaching in the secondary schools', in *Proceedings of the Fifth ICM, Cambridge 1912*, 2 (Cambridge University Press, 1913), 611–32.
178. Godfrey, C., 'Methods of intuition and experiment in secondary schools', in Board of Education, op.cit. (171), 26, 429–438, p.437.
179. Wolff, op.cit. (6).
180. MA, 'International conference on mathematical teaching. Paris, April 1–4, 1914', *MG*, 7 (1914), 221.
181. Godfrey, C., 'The teaching of calculus in public and secondary schools in the United Kingdom', *MG*, 7 (1914), 235–40.
182. Board of Education, op.cit. (171), 26, p.iv.
183. Broadbent, T.A.A., '*The Mathematical Gazette*: our history and aims', *MG*, 30 (1946), 186–94, p.188.

184. MA, op.cit. (156).
185. Broadbent, op.cit. (183), p.188.
186. Howson, op.cit. (141), discusses the early efforts to 'found a discipline of mathematics education' with particular reference to the activities and thinking of Branford, Carson, Nunn, Godfrey and Whitehead (pp.155–9 and 178). See also Howson, A.G., 'Research in mathematics education', *MG*, 72 (1988), 265–71.
187. The thinking of Godfrey and Carson is discussed and exemplified in Price, M.H., 'Understanding mathematics: a perennial problem?', part 3, *Mathematics in School*, 5 (2) (1976), 18–20; and Nunn is considered in part 4, *Mathematics in School*, 5 (3) (1976), 30–1.
188. MA, op.cit. (16), 9 Jan. 1918.
189. Mair had produced an exceptional very early unified mathematics textbook – *A School Course of Mathematics* (1907) – drawing inspiration from Branford in particular.
190. MA, op.cit. (2), p.395. The report was also published separately.

Notes and References – Chapter Five

1. Langford, W.J., 'Secondary school mathematics: an international survey', *MG*, 42 (1958), 177–93, p.191.
2. Ministry of Education, *Teaching Mathematics in Secondary Schools* (HMSO, 1958), p.21.
3. Rollett became an HMI in 1945 and was staff inspector for mathematics from 1951 until his retirement in 1963. For obituary tributes to Rollett see *MG*, 53 (1969), 69–72. The book he produced with Martyn Cundy – *Mathematical Models* – was judged by a former HMI-colleague, R.C. Lyness, to be a 'classic' by 1968 (p.70) and its success has continued into the 1990s.
4. Former-HMI Presidents were Fletcher, for the year 1939–40, and Miss L.D. Adams, for the year 1959–60. The first woman President was Dame Mary Cartwright, 1951–2.
5. Incorporated Association of Assistant Masters in Secondary Schools, *The Teaching of Mathematics* (Cambridge University Press, 1957).
6. In his Presidential address – 'Difficulties – a voice from the past', *MG*, 57 (1973), 153–60 – Daltry acknowledged that Nunn was 'a man to whom I owe everything' (p.155). Daltry took a one-year, postgraduate training course under Nunn and was introduced to the MA through Nunn's involvement in a London branch meeting in 1927. For an obituary of Daltry see *MG*, 65 (1981), 275–6.
7. IAAM, op.cit. (5), p.1.
8. MA, *Report of the Mathematical Association Committee on the Teaching of Mathematics in Public and Secondary Schools* (G. Bell and Sons, 1919; 2nd edn 1928). Two recommendations from the report of 1919 – one on the time allocated for mathematics lessons and the other on the need for both mathematical and professional training for teachers – were omitted in the second edition. Presumably there was no longer a need to press these particular points.
9. Board of Education, *[Spens] Report of the Consultative Committee on Secondary Education* (HMSO, 1938), pp.81–2.
10. MA, Minute Book of Teaching Committee, 4 Nov. 1916, MA archives.
11. *MG*, 9 (1917), 14.
12. Ibid.
13. Board of Education, *Curricula of Secondary Schools in England*, circular 1294 (HMSO, 1922).
14. Quoted in a special supplement (1985) to celebrate three quarters of a century of *The Times Educational Supplement*, first published 6 September 1910.
15. Board of Education, *Report of the Consultative Committee on Examinations in Secondary Schools* (HMSO, 1911).
16. Roach, J.P.C., 'Examinations and the secondary schools 1900–1945', *History of Education*, 8 (1) (1979), 45–58, p.52.
17. Board of Education, op.cit. (9), pp.80–1.
18. Ibid., p.99.
19. Ibid., p.80.

20. Board of Education, *The School Certificate Examination* (HMSO, 1932), p.114.
21. Board of Education, op.cit. (9), p.99.
22. Brereton, J.L., *The Case for Examinations* (Cambridge University Press, 1944), p.96.
23. Cook, H.M., 'The position of common logarithms in mathematical training', *MG*, 10 (1920), 27–9.
24. Ibid., p.28.
25. MA, 'Mathematics in the First School Certificate: a discussion at the London branch', *MG*, 15 (1930), 145–55.
26. MA, 'Report of the Council and committees for the year 1921', *MG*, 11 (1922), 33–6, p.35.
27. MA, op.cit. (25), p.154.
28. MA, 'Report of the Council for the year 1930', *MG*, 15 (1931), 314–15, p.314; MA, 'Report of the Council for the year 1931', *MG*, 16 (1932), 2–4, p.2.
29. Carson, G.St L., 'England', in National Council of Teachers of Mathematics, *Significant Changes and Trends in the Teaching of Mathematics throughout the World since 1910*, 4th yearbook (Columbia University, 1929), 21–31, pp.26–7.
30. Godfrey, C., 'Mathematics in English Schools', *Science Progress*, 6 (1912), 161–80, pp.170 and 173.
31. MA, Minute Book of Council, 29 Oct. 1932, MA archives.
32. Combridge, J.T., to Price, M.H., personal correspondence, 12 Feb. 1979.
33. Siddons, A.W., 'The best method of examining school mathematics, with special reference to the school certificate examination of the Oxford and Cambridge Schools Examination Board', *MG*, 14 (1928), 65–75; Gwatkin, E.R., in *MG*, 14 (1929), 332–44; MA, op.cit. (25); and MA, 'Calculus and co-ordinate geometry at the school certificate stage', *MG*, 16 (1932), 96–110.
34. MA, *The Teaching of Mechanics in Girls' Schools* (G. Bell and Sons, 1923).
35. Board of Education, *Report of the Consultative Committee on the Differentiation of the Curriculum for Boys and Girls Respectively in Secondary Schools* (HMSO, 1923).
36. Board of Education, *Curricula of Secondary Schools*, circular 826 (HMSO, 1913), pp.29–31.
37. Fletcher, W.C., 'The position of mathematics in secondary schools in England', in Board of Education, *Special Reports on Educational Subjects*, 26 (HMSO, 1912), 90–103, p.98.
38. Ibid., p.99.
39. Board of Education, op.cit. (35), p.46.
40. Ibid., p.124.
41. Ibid., pp.103–4.
42. Ibid., p.104.
43. MA, 'Mathematics for girls', *MG*, 13 (1926), 13–15.
44. Ibid., p.13.
45. Ibid., p.14.
46. Ibid., p.15.
47. Gwatkin, op.cit. (33).
48. Jenkins, E.W., *From Armstrong to Nuffield* (John Murray, 1979), pp.178–80.
49. Board of Education, *Curriculum and Examinations in Secondary Schools* (HMSO, 1943), p.104.
50. MA, *Elementary Mathematics in Girls' Schools* (G. Bell and Sons, 1929).
51. MA, Minute Book of the Girls' Schools Committee, MA archives.
52. MA, Minute Book of Council, 2 Jan. 1936, MA archives.
53. MA, op.cit. (31), 30 Oct. 1920.
54. MA, Minute Book of Teaching Committee, list of members of the new Teaching Committee, 1923, MA archives.
55. Ibid., lists in 1926, 1930 and 1934.
56. MA, Minute Book of Boys' Schools Committee, list of members, 1926, MA archives. The names of Godfrey and Durell are conspicuous by their absence. Godfrey died in 1924 and his premature death was a serious blow for the leadership of the MA between the wars. Durell played no active part in the committee work of the MA after the First World War. But no doubt he kept in close touch through the involvement

of his colleagues at Winchester and particularly R.M. Wright, the second master and one of Durell's textbook-writing partners.

57. MA, 'Report on mathematics in entrance scholarships to public schools', *MG*, 11 (1922), 178.
58. MA, *Mathematics in Entrance Scholarship Examinations at Public Schools* (G. Bell and Sons, 1926).
59. Ibid., p.6.
60. MA, *The Teaching of Mathematics in Preparatory Schools* (G. Bell and Sons, 1924).
61. Ibid., p.4.
62. Ibid., p.4.
63. Board of Education, *Geometry*, circular 851 (HMSO, 1914).
64. MA, *The Teaching of Geometry in Schools* (G. Bell and Sons, 1923).
65. IAAM, *The Teaching of Elementary Geometry* (Oxford University Press, 1923).
66. Ibid., p.5.
67. Godfrey, C., 'Geometry teaching: the next step', *MG*, 10 (1920), 20–4.
68. MA, op.cit. (10), 8 April 1922.
69. Ibid., and Nunn, T.P., 'The sequence of theorems in school geometry', *MG*, 11 (1922), 65–72.
70. Langford, W.J., 'Professor Eric Harold Neville', *MG*, 47 (1964), 131–6; see also Broadbent, T.A.A., ibid., 136–9, on Neville's work for the Teaching Committee. Broadbent's suggestion that 'it was natural that he [Nunn] should seek to enlist the most brilliant of his former pupils under the reformers' banner' (p.136) needs to be treated with some caution. There is no mention of Nunn in the Teaching Committee minutes between July 1919 and April 1922 though he is mentioned in a minute of May 1923 as a member of the geometry subcommittee, with co-option to the Teaching Committee. Neville was first elected to the Teaching Committee in 1920.
71. *Nature*, 113 (2833) (1924), 230–2, p.230.
72. MA, op.cit. (64), p.21.
73. Ibid., p.14.
74. Ibid., p.16.
75. Ibid., p.16.
76. Durell, C.V., '*The Teaching of Geometry in Schools*. A report prepared for the Mathematical Association', *MG*, 12 (1925),274–6, p.274.
77. Ibid., p.274.
78. MA, *The Teaching of Geometry in Schools* (G. Bell and Sons, 2nd edn 1925), p.5. At an Oxford summer school, in 1924, Professor Neville drew attention to the importance of not confusing 'what the teacher should know with what he should endeavour to transmit': see Neville, E.H., 'Congruence and parallelism', *MG*, 18 (1934), 23–9, p.24. The first part of Neville's address was also published ten years later, at a time when a revision of the report of 1923 was in prospect: see Neville, E.H., 'The teaching of geometry', *MG*, 17 (1933), 307–12.
79. Neville, op.cit. (78), p.312.
80. Tuckey, C.O., in *MG*, 29 (1945), p.2.
81. Broadbent, op.cit. (70), p.137.
82. Tuckey, op.cit. (80), p.2., and see Tuckey, C.O., 'The geometry reports', *MG*, 35 (1951), 236–8, p.236. A treatment of geometry based on the principles of congruence and similarity – twin foundation stones in the MA's report – was worked through into textbook form by Nunn and a collaborator but was never published. See Nunn, T.P., 'Similarity; or line upon line, principal upon principle', *MG*, 12 (1924), 18–20. Nunn reiterated his views in the *Gazette* fourteen years later when a second MA report on the teaching of geometry was also published. See Nunn, T.P., 'Notes on the place of similarity in school geometry', *MG*, 22 (1938), 234–49.
83. *Nature*, op.cit. (71), p.231.
84. Broadbent, op.cit. (70), p.137.
85. Durell, op.cit. (76), p.274.
86. MA, op.cit. (10), 26 May 1923 and 3 Nov. 1923.
87. Godfrey, op.cit. (67).
88. Ibid., p.24.
89. Howson, A.G., 'Milestone or millstone?', *MG*, 57 (1973), 258–66, p.265.

90. IAAM, op.cit. (5), p.91.
91. Strachan, J., 'Mathematics', in Adams, J. (ed.), *The New Teaching* (Hodder and Stoughton, 1918; popular edn 1922), 195–229, p.208.
92. Carson, op.cit. (29), p.26.
93. See IAAM, op.cit. (5), pp.92–3, and the prefaces of textbooks such as those by Hall and Stevens (1924), Durell (1925) and Siddons and Hughes (1926), which all acknowledged the early influence of the IAAM's report of 1923.
94. Tuckey, op.cit. (82), p.236. As late as 1957, by which time the school certificate had been replaced by single-subject GCE examinations, a Ministry of Education report (op.cit. (2), p.72) drew attention to the fact that six examining bodies still offered a traditional syllabus in geometry and a small residue of prescribed proofs of fundamental propositions still existed. Exceptionally, one body – no doubt the London board – still demanded forty-two theorems, not counting converses!
95. Tuckey, op.cit. (82), p.237.
96. MA, *A Second Report on the Teaching of Geometry in Schools* (G. Bell and Sons, 1938).
97. Fletcher, W.C., in 'The second report on the teaching of geometry', *MG*, 23 (1939), 169–84, p.183. Fletcher was appointed President of the MA for the year 1939–40 and he was succeeded by Tuckey after the war.
98. Ibid., p.183.
99. Kenneth Snell joined Siddons at Harrow in 1929 and acted as honorary treasurer of the MA during a difficult period, 1936–47. He was President of the MA for the year 1952–3. For an obituary tribute to Snell ('an example of all a schoolmaster should be') see J.B. Morgan, in *MG*, 57 (1973), 193–5. Alan Robson was secretary of the Teaching Committee, 1927–37, and chairman 1938–46. He was President of the MA for the year 1949–50 and was paid the following tribute in the report of the MA's Council for the year 1956: 'Always zealous for mathematical integrity, Mr. Robson was a major contributor to almost all the Association's reports from the *Arithmetic Report* [1932] onwards . . . ' (*MG*, 41 (1957), i–iii, p.ii). Geoffrey Matthews was a pupil of Robson at Marlborough and reckoned him to have been 'the best teacher of mathematics of all time': see *Mainly on the Bright Side* (Jumpix Books, 1989), p.20. For an obituary of Robson see C.V. Durell, in *MG*, 42 (1958), 203–4. Durell judged Robson's contribution to teaching method to be comparable with that of Nunn and also complementary given Robson's particular interest in post-school-certificate mathematics in the light of the renaissance of mathematics at Cambridge, inspired by Hardy, Hobson and others, and following the reform of the mathematical tripos examination. G.L. Parsons succeeded Pendlebury as honorary secretary of the MA, 1936–1949, and was President for the year 1955–6.
100. MA, op.cit. (96), p.188.
101. Tuckey, op.cit. (82), p.237.
102. Hooke, M.A., in op.cit. (97), p.172.
103. Beardwood, H., in op.cit. (97), p.174.
104. Inman, S., in op.cit. (97), pp.178–9.
105. Sheppard, in op.cit. (97), p.180.
106. Snell, K.S., in op.cit. (97), pp.181–2.
107. MA, *The Teaching of Mechanics in Schools* (G. Bell and Sons, 1930).
108. Fletcher, W.C., in 'The report on the teaching of mechanics', *MG*, 15 (1931), 339–46, p.343.
109. Ibid., p.343.
110. MA, *The Teaching of Arithmetic in Schools* (G. Bell and Sons, 1932), p.75.
111. Hope-Jones, W., 'A plea for teaching probability in schools', *MG*, 12 (1924), 139–57; MA, 'The study of statistics in a school course', in *MG*, 17 (1933), 158–76.
112. MA, *The Teaching of Algebra in Schools* (G. Bell and Sons, 1934).
113. Board of Education, op.cit. (20), p.114.
114. MA, op.cit. (112), p.9. It can also be argued that the permeation throughout elementary mathematics of numerical and graphical methods – in the broad sense – as a consequence of the Perry movement was an essential part of the tendency towards fusion. Perry's practical mathematics was in fact a unified course in mathematics for engineers.

115. Morgan, J.B., 'The thirteenth grade', *MG*, 48 (1964), 253–67, p.255.
116. MA, *The Teaching of Trigonometry in School* (G. Bell and Sons, 1950).
117. Ibid., p.3.
118. Maclean, J., 'Why teach mathematics?', *MG*, 38 (1954), 96–110, p.100.
119. MA, op.cit. (116), p.3.
120. Membership numbers are taken from the annual reports of the Council, which were published in the *Gazette*.
121. MA, op.cit. (52), 3 Nov. 1934, 7 Jan. 1935 and 23 May 1936. Neville's appeal was circulated to public, secondary and central schools, and helped to recruit 191 new members during 1934, an unusually high figure.
122. MA, 'Report of the Council for the year 1938', *MG*, 23 (1939), 2–5, pp.4–5.
123. MA, op.cit. (52), 15 Oct. 1939.
124. Siddons, A.W., 'The A.I.G.T. and the M.A.', *MG*, 32 (1948), 160–2, p.161.
125. MA, 'Report of the Council for the year 1936', *MG*, 21 (1937), 3–6, p.4.
126. Siddons, op.cit. (124), and for details of branch activity up to 1930 see MA, *Index to the Mathematical Gazette Volumes 1–15* (G. Bell and Sons, 1933), pp.11–13.
127. MA, 'The Yorkshire branch', *MG*, 10 (1920), 47.
128. *MG*, 10 (1920), 81–118.
129. Fawdry, R.C., 'The Leeds meeting', *MG*, 10 (1920), 81–2, p.82. The attendance over the two days averaged a hundred and there were difficulties in accommodating guests for an overnight stay.
130. Milne, W.P., 'The training of the mathematical teacher', *MG*, 10 (1920), 83–5.
131. Nunn, T.P., 'The training of the teacher', in MA, op.cit. (8), 27–9; and Nunn, T.P., 'The training of teachers of mathematics', in Board of Education, *Special Reports on Educational Subjects*, 27 (HMSO, 1912), 291–307. Nunn's paper of 1919 was reprinted by the MA over thirty years later, which is one measure of the longevity of his influence on mathematics teacher education.
132. Westcott, G.B.J., 'The Durham summer course in mathematics for teachers in secondary schools', *MG*, 10 (1920), 161–9. The first Board of Education courses for secondary mathematics teachers were held in 1918 at the London Day Training College and at Manchester Grammar School. In the 1920s courses were also held at Oxford and Cambridge, as well as Durham. The details are provided in the annual reports of the Board of Education.
133. Milne, W.P., 'The uses and functions of a school mathematical library', *MG*, 9 (1918), 209–12.
134. MA, 'Report of the Council for the year 1918', *MG*, 9 (1919), 308–11, pp.310–11.
135. MA, *A List of Books Suitable for School Libraries* (G. Bell and Sons, 1926).
136. MA, op.cit. (31), 4 Jan. 1921 and 29 Oct. 1921.
137. MA (Yorkshire Branch), 'Two-hundredth anniversary of the death of Sir Isaac Newton', undated publicity sheet, MA archives.
138. MA, 'The Yorkshire branch', in *Newsletter*, 40 (1978), 1–2. This sketch of the branch's history includes a couple of errors in the list of distinguished visitors to Grantham in 1927.
139. Greenstreet, W.J. (ed.), *Isaac Newton 1642–1727* (G. Bell and Sons, 1927). The tercentenary of Newton's *Principia* was also commemorated by the MA, in 1987, by the issue of a first day cover. This idea was brought to fruition through the efforts of John Thurston, the current honorary secretary of the Branches Committee.
140. North-Eastern Branch of the MA, Minute Book, 1928–46, 12 May 1928. All the minute books of this branch are held by the branch and I am grateful to Peter Ransom for drawing my attention to their existence and location. There are no branch minute books held in the archives of the MA, but short records of branch meetings were published in the *Gazette* or included as insets. In the case of the London branch, some Presidential addresses and discussions were also published in the *Gazette*: see MA, op.cit. (126).
141. North-Eastern Branch of the MA, Minute Book, 1928–46, 26 Oct. 1928.
142. MA, op.cit. (31), insert.
143. Ibid., 9 Nov. 1929, 6 Jan. 1930 and 1 Feb. 1930.
144. MA, *Draft Report of the Council on the Relation of the Branches to the Association* (1930). The annual subscription remained at 15s until 1950 when it was raised to 21s.

45. Ibid.
46. MA, op.cit. (31), 29 Oct. 1932.
47. MA, 'Report of the Council for the year 1931', *MG*, 16 (1932), 2–4, pp.2–3; MA, 'Report of the Council for the year 1939', *MG*, 23 (1939), 2–5, pp.2–3.
48. MA, op.cit. (31), 23 June 1923.
49. Ibid., 1 Nov. 1924 and 31 Oct. 1925.
50. Ibid., 31 Oct. 1925.
51. MA, op.cit. (56), 2 Oct. 1926.
52. MA, op.cit. (126), pp.8–10, lists all the discussions which were published in the *Gazette* between 1902 and 1931. The MA archives hold a complete set of programmes for the annual meeting from 1933, plus a small number of earlier programmes.
153. Siddons, op.cit. (124), p.162.
154. MA, op.cit. (31), 6 Nov. 1915. It appears that the arrangement for securing clerical assistance subsequently lapsed. In 1929 Pendlebury again pressed for such assistance and an appointment was made at a salary of £40 per annum: see minutes dated 7 Jan. 1929 and 9 Nov. 1929.
155. Punnett, M., 'Charles Pendlebury, 1854–1941', *MG*, 26 (1942), 3–4, p.4.
156. Combridge, J.T., 'The Mathematical Association: records and sources', undated, MA archives, p.11.
157. *MG*, 32 (1948), p.97.
158. Combridge, op.cit. (156), p.12. The financial year returned to the calendar year from 1973. Individual members of the MA audited the accounts and Combridge has recorded the details. A firm of accountants was not brought in until 1968.
159. MA, op.cit. (52), 7 March 1936.
160. Ibid., 23 May 1936.
161. Ibid., 15 Oct. 1939, 16 Sept. 1943 and 9 Dec. 1944.
162. MA, op.cit. (31), 19 Jan. 1901.
163. Ibid., 27 May 1911.
164. Ibid., 29 Oct. 1921, 2 Jan. 1922 and 28 Oct. 1922.
165. Broadbent, T.A.A. and Goodstein, R.L., 'Professor Eric Harold Neville', *MG*, 47 (1964), 136–9, pp.138–9.
166. Ibid., Broadbent, p.138; Langford, W.J, interview 10 Dec. 1987.
167. MA, *A First [Second, Third and Fourth] List of Books and Pamphlets in the Library of the Mathematical Association* (G. Bell and Sons, 1926 [1929, 1930 and 1936]). Langford went up to Reading as a student of Neville in 1923, and helped in checking the catalogue. He recalls that Neville was 'such a stickler for accuracy that we spent many afternoons at his house' (interview 10 Dec. 1987). For a personal tribute to Neville from a former student see Langford, op.cit. (70). In portraying a 'brilliant mathematician', Langford revealingly remarked: 'As a teacher he was an inspiring guide (though sometimes so far ahead as to be almost out of sight) . . . ' (p.134). A bound copy of a lecture on Neville, given by Langford at Reading University in 1973, is deposited in the MA archives.
168. MA, 'The library', *MG*, 25 (1941), 129; MA, 'Report of the Council for the year 1947', *MG*, 32 (1948), 2–5, p.3.
169. MA, 'The Godfrey memorial', *MG*, 12 (1924), 227–32.
170. Neville, E.H., 'Greenstreet and the library', *MG*, 15 (1930), 185–6, p.185.
171. MA, *Catalogue of Current Mathematical Journals, etc.* (G. Bell and Sons, 1913), p.3.
172. MA, 'Report of the Council for the year 1952', *MG*, 37 (1953), 82–4, p.83; MA, 'Report of the Council for the year 1953', *MG*, 38 (1954), 2–4, pp.2–3.
173. MA, *Books and Periodicals in the Library of the Mathematical Association* (MA, 1962). The collection of periodicals continues to grow through exchanges for the *Gazette*. Serial publications from America, France, Germany and Russia are strongly represented, along with journals from more remote parts of the world.
174. For an obituary of Goodstein see Rose, H.E., in *Bulletin of the London Mathematical Society*, 20 (1988), 159–66. The list of Goodstein's 121 published papers and notes, from 1938, includes 68 references to the *Gazette*. He was elected President of the MA for the year 1975–6. Professor R.O. Davies replaced Goodstein as the MA's Leicester-based librarian from 1977. Goodstein's personal library of mathematical

works, with particular strength in the fields of logic and the foundations of mathematics, has recently been donated to the MA's library.

175. Neville, E.H., 'W.J. Greenstreet', *MG*, 15 (1930), 183–4, p.183.
176. Broadbent, op.cit. (165), p.138.
177. Gaiduk, Y.M., 'On the past and present of the English Mathematical Association and the *Mathematical Gazette*', *Matematicheskoe Prosveshchenie*, 1 (1957), 87–105, p.97.
178. MA, op.cit. (31), 5 Jan. 1931 and 31 Oct. 1931.
179. Broadbent, op.cit. (165), p.138.
180. MA, 'Report of the Council for the year 1928', *MG*, 14 (1929), 318–19, p.318.
181. Garreau, G A., 'The problem bureau and some of its problems', *MG*, 51 (1967), 1–4, p.1.
182. MA, 'Report of the Council for the year 1935', *MG*, 20 (1936), 4–6, p.5.
183. MA, *The Report of Council – 1969* (MA, 1970).
184. Siddons, A.W., 'Progress', *MG*, 20 (1936), 7–26, p.25.
185. Ibid., p.26.
186. Broadbent, T.A.A., '*The Mathematical Gazette*: our history and aims', *MG*, 30 (1946) 186–94, p.191.
187. Ibid., p.191.
188. Gaiduk, op.cit. (177), p.104.
189. MA, op.cit. (52), 2 Jan. 1936 and 23 May 1936.
190. MA, 'The new Teaching Committee', *MG*, 22 (1938), 148.
191. MA, 'Report of the Council for the year 1938', *MG*, 23 (1939), 2–5, p.3. 'Teaching the complete duffer' was a topic for discussion at the annual meeting in 1938: see *MG* 22 (1938), 164–79.
192. MA, 'Report of the Council for the year 1939', *MG*, 24 (1940), 1–4, pp.2–3.
193. *MG*, 32 (1948), p.97. For a biography of Mrs Williams see Howson, A.G., *A History of Mathematics Education in England* (Cambridge University Press, 1982), pp.169–204 and see Howson's obituary tribute in *MG*, 70 (1986), 307–9.
194. MA, 'Joint report of the Council and the Executive Committee for the period 1939–1944', *MG*, 28 (1944), 86–9.

Notes and References – Chapter Six

1. Combridge, J.T., in MA, *Newsletter*, 1 (1962), p.3.
2. Combridge, J.T., 'Mathematics – slave, servant or sovereign?', *MG*, 46 (1962), 179–96 p.180.
3. Raison, T., quoted in Chitty, C., 'Central control of the school curriculum, 1944–87' *History of Education*, 17 (4) (1988), 321–34, p.321.
4. Ministry of Education, *Education 1900–1950* (HMSO, 1951), p.1, quoted in Chitty op.cit. (3), p.325.
5. Board of Education, *[Hadow] Report of the Consultative Committee on the Education o the Adolescent* (HMSO, 1926); Board of Education, *[Spens] Report of the Consultative Committee on Secondary Education* (HMSO, 1938).
6. Board of Education, *[Norwood] Report of the Committee of the Secondary School Examinations Council on Curriculum and Examinations in Secondary Schools* (HMSO 1943).
7. Ibid., p.14.
8. Quoted in a special supplement to celebrate three quarters of a century of *The Time. Educational Supplement*, first published 6 September 1910 (1985), p.38.
9. Gordon, P., Aldrich, R. and Dean, D., *Education and Policy in England in the Twentieth Century* (The Woburn Press, 1991), p.182. This book sketches a wide range of twentieth-century developments in English education and includes many reference to more specialist literature.
10. Central Statistical Office, *Social Trends*, 4 (HMSO, 1973), p.146. In 1961, direct gran schools were taking 3 per cent of pupils and independent schools (the public school and other private schools) 7 per cent. The Newsom Report of the Central Advisory Council, on the education of average and below average pupils between the ages o thirteen and sixteen, was entitled *Half our Future* (HMSO, 1963).

1. Lawton, D., quoted in Chitty, op.cit. (3), p.324.
2. The 'secret garden of the curriculum' is a phrase attributed to Sir David Eccles (Conservative Minister of Education 1959–62): see Chitty, op.cit. (3), p.326.
3. Board of Education *[Hadow]*, op.cit. (5), p.189.
4. MA, Minute Book of Teaching Committee, 3 Oct. 1925, MA archives.
5. Layton, D., *Interpreters of Science* (John Murray/ASE, 1984), pp.202–3.
6. Board of Education *[Spens]*, op.cit. (5), p.xv.
7. Ibid., pp.235–42.
8. MA, 'The Spens Report', *MG*, 23 (1939), 201.
9. Board of Education, *[Hadow] Report of the Consultative Committee on the Primary School* (HMSO, 1931); Board of Education, *[Hadow] Report of the Consultative Committee on Infant and Nursery Schools* (HMSO, 1933).
10. Dent, H.C., *The Educational System of England and Wales* (University of London Press, 1961; 3rd edn 1965), p.99.
11. Board of Education (1931), op.cit. (19), pp.139–45.
12. Dent, op.cit. (20), p.99
13. Board of Education *[Norwood]*, op.cit. (6), p.140.
14. Ibid., p.105.
15. Ibid., pp.106–7.
16. In the USA the branches were treated in sequence, rather than in parallel, with a very gradual movement towards 'fusion' into 'unified mathematics' courses, which were initially associated with 'vocational mathematics': see National Council of Teachers of Mathematics, *A History of Mathematics Education in the United States and Canada*, 32nd yearbook (NCTM, 1970), pp.46–53, 173–9, 185. For the progress of the general science movement in England see Jenkins, E.W., *From Armstrong to Nuffield* (John Murray, 1979), pp.70–106. The NCTM (p.422) quote one Canadian teacher, opposed to unification in mathematics: 'We might just as well bind together Physics and Biology and call it "popular science" . . . or put all the subjects in one book and label it "Hash".'
17. Price, M.H., 'The reform of English mathematical education in the late nineteenth and early twentieth centuries' (PhD thesis, University of Leicester, 1981), pp.271–5, 281–5.
18. Tuckey, C.O., 'Sir Percy Nunn, 1870–1944', *MG*, 29 (1945), 1–2.
19. Mair, D.B., *A School Course of Mathematics* (Oxford University Press, 1907). Mair acknowledged a debt to Branford's idealism. The Civil Service Commission's syllabuses and papers in mathematics were strongly progressive, particularly in relation to the treatment of elementary plane and solid geometry: see IAAM, *The Teaching of Mathematics* (Cambridge University Press, 1957), pp.93 and 110. The maverick W.J. Dobbs, with some inspiration again coming from Branford, produced a parallel text to Nunn's in algebra: *A School Course in Geometry* (Longmans, Green and Co., 1913). This textbook adopted transformations in geometry and ranged widely to include parts of trigonometry, mensuration, co-ordinate geometry and calculus. Like Nunn's textbooks, it was a commercial failure.
20. Howson, A.G., *A History of Mathematics Education in England* (Cambridge University Press, 1982), p.163.
21. Siddons, A.W., 'The best method of examining school mathematics, with special reference to the school certificate examination of the Oxford and Cambridge Schools Examination Board', *MG*, 14 (1928), 65–75; Board of Education, *The School Certificate Examination* (HMSO, 1932), pp.116–17.
22. MA, 'Mathematics in the first school certificate: a discussion at the London branch', *MG*, 15 (1930), 145–55, p.148. Durham's algebra syllabus was concentrated on the concept of functionality and the overall breadth extended to some trigonometry, solid geometry and numerical integration.
23. Daltry, C.T., in MA, 'Possible changes in the mathematical syllabus for the school certificate examination', *MG*, 28 (1944), 125–43, pp.125–6.
24. Daltry, C.T., (Correspondence) 'School certificate mathematics', *MG*, 27 (1943), 130–1, p.130.
25. Brereton, J.L., (Correspondence) 'School certificate mathematics', *MG*, 27 (1943), 80. For a personal view of the educational value of examinations as a 'unifying influence'

see Brereton, J.L., *The Case for Examinations* (Cambridge University Press, 1944).

36. Ibid.

37. MA, 'The Teaching Committee', *MG*, 27 (1943), 158.

38. Cambridge Local Examinations Syndicate, *School Certificate Mathematics. [Jeffery Report of a Conference of Representatives of Examining Bodies and Teachers Associations, with a Suggested Alternative Syllabus and Specimen Papers* (MA reprint 1944), p.i.

39. MA, *List of Members* (1948); MA, 'The Teaching Committee', *MG*, 23 (1939), 6.

40. MA, op.cit. (33), p.142.

41. There is also evidence of direct MA involvement in the development of higher schoc certificate and scholarship examination syllabuses for Oxbridge, in the period 1940–5 See, in particular, Robson, A., 'Entrance scholarship examinations', *MG*, 26 (1942) 192; MA, 'Joint report of the Council and Executive Committee', *MG*, 29 (1945) 46–8, p.47; and MA, 'Syllabuses for examinations taken by sixth-form pupils', *MG* 29 (1945), 161–77. The Cambridge Syndicate and Brereton were again instrumenta in developments leading to the establishment of a representative Cambridge advisor committee, but examining bodies outside Cambridge were not directly involved.

42. IAAM, *The Teaching of Mathematics in Secondary Schools* (Cambridge Universit Press, 1973), p.12.

43. Cambridge Syndicate, op.cit. (38), p.ii. Douglas Quadling (interview 24 Oct. 1989 has suggested that the provision of alternative syllabuses in the 1940s was importan for the subsequent development of modern mathematics syllabuses: 'If there had no been alternative syllabus B then it would have been much more difficult for there t be alternative syllabus C in the 1960s.'

44. Parr, H.E., *School Mathematics. A Unified Course*, part 3 (G. Bell and Sons, 1948) p.v. Parr, of Whitgift School, was very successful with his unified course in thre parts.

45. Durell, C.V., *General Mathematics*, vol.3 (G. Bell and Sons, 1947), p.v. Durell' publisher felt that in the post-war market general mathematics textbooks would hav two advantages: novelty and even distribution of cost, i.e. one textbook per yea Durell was at first not sympathetic to the idea but he was gradually won over an produced a highly successful course in four volumes. I am grateful to R.J.B. Glanvill for this note.

46. Talbot, W.M., 'An account of the history of the teaching of mathematics in Englis schools during the last hundred years' (MEd thesis, University of Durham), p.113 Montgomery, R.J., *Examinations* (Longmans, 1965), p.180.

47. Following Mary Cartwright of Girton College, Cambridge, MA President 1951–2, Mi L.D. Adams, who became an HMI, was the first woman President (1959–60) with schoolteaching background. For obituary tributes to Miss Adams, who died in 196(see *MG*, 50 (1966), 255–8.

48. Snell, K.S., 'School mathematics today and tomorrow', *MG*, 37 (1953), 161–7; p.165.

49. Parsons, G.L., '"Teaching the Teacher"', *MG*, 4 (1957), 1–8, p.3.

50. Ibid., p.3. As an examiner, Parsons also drew attention to a decline in standards c manipulative skill in arithmetic and algebra, which 'sounds a warning that the proces of extension of the syllabus has dangers which need to be closely watched' (p.5).

51. Langford, W.J., 'Secondary school mathematics: an international survey', *MG*, 4 (1958), 177–93, p.177. The longevity of Euclid's hold on geometry in education is eve more remarkable in Greece, where ethnic arguments have also played a significant role See Toumasis, C., 'The epos of Euclidean geometry in Greek secondary educatio (1836–1985): pressure for change and resistance', *Educational Studies in Mathematic* 21 (1990), 491–508.

52. Brookes, B., 'The authority of the teacher', in Howson, A.G. (ed.), *Challenges an Responses in Mathematics* (Cambridge University Press, 1987), 75–85, p.77. Brooke suggests that there was a stronger initial response to alternative syllabuses from girl schools. Certainly the very successful, and at the time very fresh, *Mathematics Toda* course, in five parts, by E.E. Biggs and H.E. Vidal, was based on experimentatio in a girls' grammar school.

53. Interview with Ronald Fielding, 29 May 1990. Fielding also made a wry commen

on the tendency of the alternative *papers* to become stereotyped: 'You could always reckon on number seven being on the world; and I haven't taught [the course] for thirty years.'

4. Jeffery, G.B., in MA, 'Mathematics in school examinations, 1950', *MG*, 32 (1948), 240–61, p.252.

5. Langford, W.J., in MA, op.cit. (54), p.241.

56. MA, 'Report of the Council for the year 1948', *MG*, 33 (1949), 14–18, pp.16–17.

57. Dent, op.cit. (20), p.120.

58. MA, *The Rules of the MA* (June 1946).

59. For an obituary of Riley see Tobias, R.K., *MG*, 68 (1984), 270–3.

50. MA, 'Joint report of the Council and the Executive Committee for the period 1939–1944', *MG*, 28 (1944), 86–9, pp.87–8.

51. Institute of Physics and the Mathematical Association, *The Teaching of Mathematics to Physicists* (Institute of Physics, 1944).

52. MA, 'Mathematical Association Teaching Committee', *MG*, 30 (1946), 299–300.

63. Ibid., p.300.

64. Quadling, D.A., to Price, M.H., personal correspondence, 1 Jan. 1988.

65. Durell, C.V., 'Alan Robson', *MG*, 42 (1958), 203–4.

66. A Council report paid tribute to Combridge's chairmanship of the Teaching Committee in the following terms: 'But while he encouraged all possible speed, his tactful insistence on high standards of general production prevented any premature plunge into print.' (*MG*, 41 (1957), inset i–iii, p.ii).

67. Parsons, G.L., in MA, 'Trigonometry in the main school', *MG*, 35 (1951), 228–35, p.232.

68. MA, *The Teaching of Trigonometry in Schools* (G. Bell and Sons, 1950), p.vi.

69. Broadbent, T.A.A., 'Professor Eric Harold Neville', *MG*, 47 (1964), 136–9, p.137.

70. Tuckey, C.O., in MA, op.cit. (67), p.228.

71. MA, *The Teaching of Calculus in Schools* (G. Bell and Sons, 1951); MA, *Analysis Course* (G. Bell and Sons, 1957); MA, *Analysis Course 2* (G. Bell and Sons, 1962).

72. For an obituary of Maxwell, MA President for the year 1960–1, see Quadling, D.A., in *MG*, 72 (1988), 51–2.

73. For an analysis of the occupational locations of members of the MA's subcommittees who worked on the mathematical branches from the 1930s to the 1950s, see Cooper, B., *Renegotiating Secondary School Mathematics* (Falmer Press, 1985), p.38. He fairly points to the public school and university domination, but the policy shift to reports on more advanced work, in the 1950s, reduces the force of this conclusion, for the post-war period.

74. MA, *The Teaching of Higher Geometry in Schools* (G. Bell and Sons, 1953), p.ix.

75. Ibid.

76. Parsons, op.cit. (49), p.8.

77. Interview with Douglas Quadling, 24 Oct. 1989; MA, *The Teaching of Algebra in Sixth Forms* (G. Bell and Sons, 1957). According to Quadling (Quadling, D.A., to Price, M.H., personal correspondence, 30 July 1992), several of Robson's friends and pupils worked with Newman at Bletchley Park during the Second World War.

78. Newman, M.H.A., '"The Teaching of Algebra in Sixth Forms"', *MG*, 42 (1958), 205–9, p.205.

79. Newman, M.H.A., in MA, 'The unification of algebra', *MG*, 21 (1937), 325–9. Newman suggested some introductory work in linear algebra, involving two-by-two matrices, and Robson took up this very early challenge with some success. The possibilities are only touched on in MA, op.cit. (77), pp.34–6.

80. Newman, op.cit. (78), p.208.

81. Newman provided an important early contribution to the new debate in his MA Presidential address of 1959: see his obituary by Quadling, D.A., in *MG*, 68 (1984), 269–70.

82. MA, 'Report of the Council for the year 1961', *MG*, 46 (1962), inset i–iv, p.iii.

83. Combridge, J.T., '"The Teaching of Mechanics in Schools" and other reports', *MG*, 34 (1950), 198–9.

84. MA, *A Second Report on the Teaching of Mechanics in Schools* (G. Bell and Sons, 1965), p.80.

85. Fletcher, T.J., 'Applications of mathematics in English secondary schools', in Institut für Didaktik der Mathematik, *Comparative Studies of Mathematics Curricula – Change and Stability 1960–1980* (IDM, Bielefeld, 1980), 662–706, p.670.
86. MA, *A Second Report on the Teaching of Arithmetic in Schools* (G. Bell and Sons 1964). The efforts to produce a separate report on statistics teaching will be discussed in chapter seven.
87. MA, 'Discussions at the annual general meeting, Oxford, 1965', *MG*, 49 (1965) 361–70, pp.361–5. The mechanics report was also discussed, with less polemic and more points of detail (pp.365–70).
88. Quadling, op.cit. (64).
89. See, for example, the writings of Correlli Barnett and Martin Wiener, cited by McCulloch, G., 'Pioneers of an "alternative road"? The Association of Heads of Secondary Technical Schools, 1951–64', in Goodson, I.F. (ed.), *Social Histories of the Secondary Curriculum: Subjects for Study* (Falmer Press, 1985), 313–42, pp.328–9.
90. Bickley, W.G., 'Mathematics and the engineering student: some general considerations', *MG*, 23 (1939), 434–42, p.435.
91. Ibid., pp.436–7.
92. Bickley, W.G., 'The training of teachers of mathematics to technical students', *MG*, 27 (1943), 127–9.
93. MA, *The Training of Teachers of Mathematics in Technical Schools and Colleges* (G. Bell and Sons, 1949).
94. McLachlan, N.W., in MA, 'Technical mathematics', *MG*, 29 (1945), 145–60, p.159.
95. Kellaway, F.W., 'The teacher of mathematics and society', *MG*, 51 (1967), 193–204, p.203. Kellaway was educated at Reading University, in the 1930s, where he first came under the influence of Neville and the young Broadbent. His professional links with the latter continued through the 1940s, when he moved from educational work for the Admiralty to technical education in Hertfordshire and various principalships. Kellaway assisted Broadbent in the production of the *Gazette*.
96. MA, *Mathematics in the Secondary Technical School* (G. Bell and Sons, 1949), p.15.
97. MA, 'Report of the Council for the year 1948', *MG*, 33 (1949), 14–18, p.16.
98. MA, *The Teaching of Mathematics in Technical Colleges* (G. Bell and Sons, 1954; reprint 1964), p.v.
99. Ibid., p.3.
100. Ibid., p.vii.
101. Dent, op.cit. (20), pp.171–4. National diplomas, for full-time students, have never attracted many students, by comparison with the certificates.
102. MA, op.cit. (98), p.vi.
103. MA, op.cit. (62), p.300.
104. Price, op.cit. (27), pp.21–3, 302–5.
105. Carson, G.St L., 'England', in National Council of Teachers of Mathematics, *Significant Changes and Trends in the Teaching of Mathematics throughout the World since 1910*, 4th yearbook (Columbia University, 1929), 21–31, p.30.
106. Board of Education, *Senior School Mathematics*, educational pamphlet no.101 (HMSO, 1935), p.4.
107. Ibid., p.3.
108. MA, Minute Book of Boys' Schools Committee, 8 March 1930, 5 April 1930, 21 May 1932, 19 Nov. 1932, 5 Jan. 1933, MA archives.
109. MA, 'Mathematics in central schools', *MG*, 18 (1934), 80–94, p.94.
110. Adams, L.D., 'Full cycle', *MG*, 44 (1960), 161–72, p.169.
111. Ibid., p.170.
112. MA, 'The place of mathematics in secondary (modern) schools', *MG*, 30 (1946), 250–71.
113. MA, *The Teaching of Mathematics in Secondary Modern Schools*, interim report (G. Bell and Sons, 1949), p.2. Apart from Mrs Williams, the subcommittee included five other teacher trainers, one from a university department and one from an emergency training college. Emergency colleges helped to boost the number of qualified teachers required to cope with the growing school population after the war.
114. Bushell, W.F., in MA, op.cit. (112), p.263.
115. MA, op.cit. (113), p.3.

116. Ibid., footnote, p.9.
117. MA, *Mathematics in Secondary Modern Schools* (G. Bell and Sons, 1959), p.iii.
118. MA, op.cit. (113), p.12.
119. Williams, E.M., in MA, 'Non-certificate mathematics', *MG*, 33 (1949), 180–6, p.182.
120. Swan, F.J., in MA, 'Mathematics in the comprehensive school', *MG*, 34 (1950), 182–97, p.182.
121. Burdon, J.H., in MA, op.cit. (120) pp.195–6.
122. MA, 'Report of the Council for the year 1946', *MG*, 31 (1947), 66–8.
123. MA, 'Report of the Council for the year 1950', *MG*, 35 (1951), 75–6, p.75. Developments in the branches are detailed in the Council's annual reports.
124. MA, op.cit. (122), p.66.
125. Sowden, K., 'Louise Doris Adams', *MG*, 50 (1966), 256–8, pp.257–8.
126. James, E.J., in MA, 'Work from modern schools', *MG*, 35 (1951), 165–72, p.169.
127. MA, op.cit. (117). James produced his own book before the report was published: *The Teaching of Modern School Mathematics* (Oxford University Press, 1958).
128. MA, 'Report of the Council for the year 1951', *MG*, 36 (1952), 2–4, p.3.
129. Williams, E.M., 'Louise Doris Adams', *MG*, 50 (1966), 255–6.
130. MA, 'Report of the Council for the year 1954', *MG*, 39 (1955), 185–6, p.186.
131. MA, 'Annual general meeting 1959', *MG*, 43 (1959), inset xii.
132. Selleck, R.J.W., *English Primary Education and the Progressives 1914–1939* (Routledge and Kegan Paul, 1972).
133. Adams, op.cit. (110), p.168.
134. Board of Education, *Suggestions for the Consideration of Teachers and Others Concerned in the Work of Public Elementary Schools* (HMSO, 1905); this was renamed the *Handbook of Suggestions for Teachers*, from 1927. The principal authors were members of HMI, who also called on the support of leading educationists for specialist inputs: see Gordon, op.cit. (9), p.281.
135. Board of Education (1931 and 1933), op.cit. (19).
136. Board of Education (1931; revised edn 1948), op.cit. (19), p.75.
137. Ibid., front cover note.
138. Ibid.
139. Adams, op.cit. (110), p.167.
140. Special supplement, op.cit. (8), p.21.
141. Williams, E.M., 'The geometrical notions of young children', *MG*, 18 (1934), 112–18.
142. Quoted in Howson, op.cit. (30), p.181.
143. Ibid., pp.180–3, 187–190, where Howson locates Mrs Williams's higher degree work in the context of the limited research relating to mathematics education in England up to the 1930s. Like Susan Isaacs, she gained her formative teaching experience in the 1920s in a private school, which provided considerable opportunities for educational experimentation.
144. Williams, op.cit. (141), p.113.
145. Ibid., p.114.
146. There is only one passing reference to Piaget in Selleck, op.cit. (132), p.112.
147. MA, op.cit. (14), 21 March 1936, when it was suggested that the Board of Education's *Suggestions* 'might be a basis for this work'.
148. MA, Minute Book of Teaching Committee, 3 Jan. 1939, MA archives.
149. MA, *The Teaching of Mathematics in Primary Schools* (G. Bell and Sons, 1956), p.v. The report was distributed late in 1955, but the publishers gave 1956 as the year of publication.
150. Williams, op.cit. (129), p.255.
151. Williams, E.M., quoted in Howson, op.cit. (30), p.195.
152. Tahta, D., 'Caleb Gattegno 1911–1988', *Mathematics Teaching*, 125 (1988), 9. Tahta has since produced an unpublished bibliography of all Gattegno's writings.
153. Gattegno, C., 'Mathematics and the child', *MG*, 31 (1947), 219–23.
154. Ibid., p.222.
155. Gattegno, C., 'Mathematics and the child', part 2, *MG*, 33 (1949), 108–12; 'Mathematics and the child', part 3, *MG*, 38 (1954), 11–14; 'The idea of dynamic patterns in geometry', *MG*, 38 (1954), 207–9.

156. MA, op.cit. (149).
157. MA, op.cit. (148), 11 April 1953.
158. Ibid., 6 Jan. 1954.
159. MA, 'Report of the Council for the year 1955', *MG*, 40 (1956), xiii-xv, p.xiv.
160. MA, op.cit. (149), pp.v-vi.
161. The reference to coloured rods (ibid., p.99) is likely to have come from Gattegno, who started to disseminate the use of Cuisenaire rods in England around this time.
162. Ibid., p.107.
163. Tahta, op.cit. (152), and Tahta, D., 'Caleb Gattegno', *Mathematics Teaching*, 127 (1989), 59.
164. Ministry of Education, *Primary Education* (HMSO, 1959), p.179.
165. Central Advisory Council, *[Plowden Report] Children and their Primary Schools* (HMSO, 1967), p.235.
166. Interview with Hilary Shuard, 30 April 1990.
167. Interview with Bill Brookes, 14 May 1990; interview with Wilf Flemming, 7 Dec. 1987.
168. Interview with Roland Collins, 29 May 1990.
169. National Council of Teachers of Mathematics, *Multi-Sensory Aids in the Teaching of Mathematics*, 18th yearbook (Columbia University, 1945), p.vii.
170. MA, op.cit. (14), 21 March 1936, 16 Oct. 1937. The report was published in *MG*, 21 (1937), 149–51.
171. MA, 'The place of visual aids in the teaching of mathematics', *MG*, 31 (1947), 193–205, p.205. In 1951, under the auspices of the London branch, the MA contributed to a 'Mathematics Week', including displays, demonstrations, lectures, films and filmstrips, as part of the College of Preceptors' involvement in the Festival of Britain (1851–1951). See MA, 'Mathematics at the Festival', *MG*, 35 (1951), 74.
172. As early as 1945, Rollett gave a talk on 'mathematical models and constructions' at the MA's annual meeting: see *MG*, 29 (1945), 181–92. He admitted, 'The few exhibits I have brought along are nearly all several years old, or recently repaired, as I have not had the opportunity for this kind of work since war began.' (p.191). In the case of polyhedral models, Rollett drew inspiration from G.C. Young and W.H. Young, *The First Book of Geometry* (J.M. Dent, 1905).
173. Sawyer was head of mathematics at Leicester Technical College from 1945 to 1947, and he then moved abroad. With colleagues at Leicester he developed apparatus for teaching mathematics to industrial students. See Sawyer, W.W., *The Search for Pattern* (Penguin Books, 1970), for a description of a range of apparatus and experiments for teaching 'mathematics through the hand'; and 'Mathematics, emotions and things', *Mathematics Teaching*, 142 (1993), 16–19, where Sawyer looks back on his early teaching career in the 1940s.
174. IAAM, *The Teaching of Mathematics* (Cambridge University Press, 1957), p.131.
175. MA, Minute Book of Teaching Committee, 13 March 1948, MA archives.
176. Grattan-Guinness, G.H., to Combridge, J.T., personal correspondence, 14 Jan. 1952, MA archives.
177. MA, op.cit. (175), 5 Jan. 1952.
178. MA, *The Use of Visual Methods in Teaching Mathematics* (G. Bell and Sons, 1954).
179. Ibid., pp.6–8, 9–10. Nicolet had made over a hundred mathematical films and Gattegno was involved in the preparation of accompanying notes for English teachers.
180. Ibid., p.2.
181. Fletcher, T.J., 'Caleb Gattegno', *Mathematics Teaching*, 127 (1989), 59.
182. Interview with Roland Collins, 29 May 1990.
183. On the progress of *Mathematical Pie* see Fowler, G., 'Forty years of savoury pie', *Mathematics in School*, 19 (2) (1990), 13. Production of *Pie* was taken over by the MA in 1985.
184. Interview with Ronald Fielding, 29 May 1990.
185. Collins, R.H., 'Multi-sensory aids for the teaching of mathematics', circular (Feb. 1952), MA archives. Collins also attached advertisements for a demonstration model of the formula for the area of a circle, the Gateway filmstrips and the animated geometry films of Nicolet.
186. Gattegno, C., testimonial (25 Jan. 1952), MA archives.

87. Collins was not a full member of the MA, but his activities came under the close scrutiny of the visual aids subcommittee: see Vesselo, I.R., confidential memorandum (2 June 1952), MA archives.
88. Collins, R.H., 'Association for Teaching Aids in Mathematics', circular (July, 1952), photocopy, MA archives. I am grateful to Bill Brookes for lending me a copy of this circular.
89. ATAM, Minute Book of Committee, 28 June 1952. I am grateful to Bill Brookes and Laurinda Brown for tracking down and lending me this minute book.
90. Interview with Bill Brookes, 14 May 1990.
91. Interview with Trevor Fletcher, 14 Nov. 1989.
92. Interview with Wilf Flemming, 7 Dec. 1987.
93. Tahta, D., to Price, M.H., personal correspondence, 12 Jan. 1990; interview with Geoffrey Howson, 18 Dec. 1989. The tension between Gattegno and Rollett may partly be explained by the former's general suspicion of inspectors, based on his unfavourable continental experiences.
94. See Cooper, op.cit. (73), who sharply contrasts the occupational locations of the ATAM's Central Committee, in 1958 (p.71), and the subcommittees responsible for MA reports on the separate branches (p.38). Roland Collins (interview, 29 May 1990) has emphasized the differences of social class: 'We all [*sic*] came from the classroom and we came from the tough classrooms, not the Charterhouses, not the Etons.'
95. Interview with Trevor Fletcher, 14 Nov. 1989, who has contrasted the ATAM's welcome, in the 1950s, with an image of the MA as 'a remote body of elderly, august people'.
96. ATAM, op.cit. (189). In connection with demonstration lessons, Combridge couldn't resist pointing to the initiative of Mrs Bryant at the AIGT's meeting in 1893, which 'forestalled some of our activist contemporaries by some sixty or seventy years': see Combridge, J.T., typescript of unpublished lecture given at the University of Nottingham, 20 March 1971, MA archives.
97. ATAM, *Bulletin*, 1 (Jan. 1953).
98. Gattegno, C., to ATAM, personal correspondence, 9 Feb. 1958, in ATAM, op.cit. (189). Gattegno gave his last talk in England at the ATM's Easter conference in 1988. He died in July of that year.

Notes and References – Chapter Seven

1. Thwaites, B. (ed.), *On Teaching Mathematics* (Pergamon Press, 1961), foreword, p.ix.
2. Broadbent, T.A.A., 'Institute; Joint Council; Association', *MG*, 49 (1965), 262–5, p.265.
3. Hughes, M.G., *Modernising School Mathematics* (G. Bell and Sons, 1962), p.26.
4. Board of Education, 'The training of mathematics teachers', *MG*, 16 (1932), 331–6, p.332. This report was prepared for the ICMI and presented at Zurich in 1932, following the reconstitution of the ICMI, at Bologna in 1928.
5. MA, *The Supply and Training of Teachers of Mathematics* (G. Bell and Sons, 1963), p.3.
6. Difficulties concerning the supply and calibre of mathematics teachers during the Perry movement were discussed in chapter four. For a detailed discussion of twentieth-century developments in the supply of science (including mathematics) teachers see Jenkins, E.W., *From Armstrong to Nuffield* (John Murray, 1979), ch.6.
7. NCTM, *The Training of Mathematics Teachers for Secondary Schools in England and Wales and in the United States*, 14th yearbook (Columbia University, 1939), p.166.
8. Nunn, T.P., 'The training of the teacher', *MG*, 35 (1951), 41–3.
9. NCTM, op. cit. (7), pp.145–52.
10. Land, F.W., 'The Mathematics Section: TCA – ATCDE – NATFHE', unpublished and undated paper. I am grateful to Frank Land (1911–90) for sending me a copy of this informative paper. For a tribute to Land see Bishop, A., in *Mathematics Teaching*, 132 (1990), 14–16.

11. Simon, B., *Education and the Social Order 1940–1990* (Lawrence and Wishart, 1991) p.575.
12. Dent, H.C., *The Educational System of England and Wales* (University of London Press, 1961; 3rd edn 1965), pp.34–5.
13. Ibid., pp.207–8.
14. Special supplement to celebrate three quarters of a century of *The Times Educational Supplement*, first published 6 September 1910 (1985), p.37.
15. Dent, op. cit. (12), pp.187–8.
16. The parallel expansion of further education was briefly considered in chapter six.
17. Land, op. cit. (10), pp.20–3; see ATCDE, *The Supply of Mathematics and Science Teachers* (Methuen, 1956).
18. MA, op. cit. (5), p.46; and Cambridge, J.T., in MA, *Newsletter*, 15 (Dec. 1969), 5–7 p.6.
19. MA, op. cit. (5), p.46.
20. Interview with Wilf Flemming, 7 Dec. 1987. For a personal view of mathematics teacher education in the 1950s see Flemming, W., 'Thoughts on the training of the mathematics teacher', *MG*, 39 (1955), 20–30.
21. Williams, E.M., 'The changing role of mathematics in education', *MG*, 50 (1966), 243–54, p.251.
22. Interview with Wilf Flemming, 7 Dec. 1987; and Association of University Mathematics Education Teachers, *Mathematics Teacher Education in Universities of the United Kingdom* (AUMET, 1984). The UDEMSG changed its name to AUMET in 1984.
23. Williams, op. cit. (21), p.250.
24. Morris, M., 'A chronic condition', *Times Educational Supplement* (18 Aug. 1989), p.11. For a detailed discussion of post-war trends in science, including mathematics, see Jenkins, op. cit. (6), pp.235–44.
25. Straker, N., 'Mathematics teacher shortages in secondary schools: implications for mathematics departments', *Research Papers in Education*, 2 (2) (1987), 126–52, p.127.
26. Chapman, S., 'University training of mathematicians, *MG*, 30 (1946), 61–70, p.66. For other surveys of early post-war career opportunities for mathematics graduates see Walls, N., 'Careers for graduates in mathematics', *MG*, 31 (1947), 93–7; and Busbridge, I.W., 'Careers for women graduates in mathematics', *MG*, 42 (1958), 109–10. Busbridge drew attention to the early impact of electronic computers, but also to some major inequalities of opportunity for women: '*Industry* is, in general, reluctant to employ women mathematicians for anything except routine work . . .' (p.109); 'It is now possible for women to take up *Actuarial Work* and *Accountancy*, but the prospects are much less good for a woman than for a man.' (p.110).
27. Morris, op. cit. (24).
28. MA, 'Report of the meeting of the Teaching Committee 6th January 1954', *MG*, 38 (May 1954), inset p.v.
29. Langford, W.J., 'Secondary school mathematics: an international survey', *MG*, 42 (1958), 177–93, p.189.
30. Ibid., p.190.
31. Cooper, B., *Renegotiating Secondary School Mathematics* (Falmer Press, 1985), pp.129–30.
32. See ibid., chapters 5, 6 and 8, for a detailed discussion of the three conferences.
33. I am grateful to Douglas Quadling for some of the major points concerning the nature of these conferences.
34. Cooper, op. cit. (31), p.98.
35. Thwaites, op. cit. (1), p. xiii.
36. Ibid., p.x.
37. Quoted in Cooper, op. cit. (31), p.174.
38. Thwaites, B., *The School Mathematics Project: The First Ten Years* (Cambridge University Press, 1972).
39. Cooper, op. cit. (31), pp.92–4. As Jenkins, op. cit. (6), p.234, points out, further education colleges made a growing contribution to O- and A-level work, and also made further demands on the supply of science and mathematics teachers.

40. MA, op. cit. (5), p.43. Passes in two mathematics A-level subjects are counted twice. Degrees from Scottish universities, and mathematics and physics degrees, are included in the totals.
41. Cooper, op. cit. (31), pp.94–5.
42. Maxwell, E.A., 'Pastors and masters', *MG*, 45 (1961), 167–180; Rosenhead, L., 'The teaching of mathematics in schools: a criticism of the English educational system', *MG*, 45 (1961), 279–87.
43. Rollett, A.P., *Honours Courses in Mathematics in the Universities of Great Britain and Ireland, and the Colleges of Advanced Technology* (IAHM, 1964), p.1.
44. Hughes, op. cit. (3), pp.33–5. In her MA Presidential address (1965), Busbridge pointed to the serious dropout from undergraduate single-subject mathematics courses, with just under a third of students failing at some stage; and she was cautious about the prospects for mathematics through expansion in the post-Robbins (1963) era: see 'Robbins – and all that', *MG*, 49 (1965), 241–52. Williams, op. cit. (21), p.250, was less pessimistic in the following year, given the prospect that the total output of mathematics graduates would almost treble between 1960 and 1970.
45. Rollett, op. cit. (43).
46. MA, op. cit. (5).
47. MA, 'Report of the Council for the year 1962', duplicated draft (1963), p.2.
48. Riley, A.W., in MA, *Newsletter*, 4 (July 1963), p.4.
49. Daltry was also a member of the subcommittee and Geoffrey Matthews took over as secretary later in 1962. Flemming (interview, 7 Dec. 1987) has pointed to some antipathy between leading MA members, particularly from the public schools, and teacher trainers. Prior to the Stockholm memorandum, efforts to get collaboration between the ATCDE Mathematics Section and the MA had proved unsuccessful.
50. Riley, op. cit. (48), p.4.
51. Ibid.
52. Williams, E.M., quoted in Riley, op. cit. (48), p.4. There are some striking comparisons here with secondary teacher training in the 1990s under Circular 9/92.
53. Morgan, J.B., 'The thirteenth grade', *MG*, 48 (1964)), 253–67, pp.256–7.
54. Cooper, op. cit. (31), p.117.
55. Cooper, op. cit. (31), p.140.
56. MA, 'Report of the Council for the year 1960', *MG*, 45 (1961), inset pp.xi- xii.
57. Dorrington, B.J.F., to Price, M.H., personal correspondence, undated.
58. MA, 'Report of the Council for the year 1961', *MG*, 46 (1962), inset pp. iii-iv.
59. Dorrington, B.J.F., to Land, F.W., personal correspondence, 20 Sept. 1961.
60. Combridge, J.T., in MA, *Newsletter*, 3 (Feb. 1963), pp.1–2.
61. Ibid., p.1.
62. MA, 'Report of the Council for the year 1963', *Newsletter*, 6 (Sept. 1964), p.3.
63. Combridge, J.T., in MA, *Newsletter* 7 (Feb. 1965), p.4.
64. MA, 'Report of the Council for the year 1967', attached to AGM agenda (1968).
65. Busbridge, I.W., in MA, *Newsletter*, 9 (Feb. 1966), p.6.
66. Girling, B., in MA, *Newsletter*, 15 (Dec. 1969), p.7.
67. MA, 'Report of the Council for the year 1974', attached to AGM agenda (1975), p.11.
68. Dorrington, B.J.F., in MA, *Newsletter*, 33 (Dec. 1975/ Jan. 1976), p.3.
69. MA, 'Report of Council, 1979', draft copy (1980), p.2.
70. Woolnough, B.E., *Physics Teaching in Schools, 1960–85* (Falmer Press, 1988).
71. MA, Minute Book of Council, 29 Oct. 1932, MA archives.
72. MA, Minute Book of Council, 22 Oct. 1949, MA archives.
73. Howson, A.G., 'Seventy-five years of the International Commission on Mathematical Instruction', *Educational Studies in Mathematics*, 15 (1984), 75–93, pp.79–80; IAAM, *Teaching Mathematics in Secondary Schools* (Cambridge University Press, 1973), pp.13–14.
74. Combridge, op. cit. (18), p.7.
75. Combridge, J.T., 'Mathematics – slave, servant or sovereign?', *MG*, 46 (1962), 179–96, p.184.
76. Hodge, W., 'Joint Mathematical Council for the United Kingdom', *MG*, 47 (1963), 130–1; Combridge, J.T., in MA, *Newsletter*, 5 (Jan. 1964), p.2.

77. The Institute of Biology was not set up until 1950, almost three-quarters of a century after the foundation of the Institute of Chemistry. On the biological sciences in education see Jenkins, op. cit. (6), ch.4.
78. Fundamental questions of status in mathematics were raised by the investigations of the Geary Committee: 'It is a regrettable fact . . . that the London Mathematical Society does not at present enjoy the confidence of the average mathematician in colleges of technology or in industry; and conversely the Society does not adequately recognise the work done by industrial mathematicians – as a member of the Council of the Society put it in conversation: "What these people in industry do may be all very well in its own way; but I wish they wouldn't call it mathematics!"': see 'Proposal for an Institute of Mathematics', unpublished and undated paper, MA archives, pp.1–2. Some early papers concerning the history of the JMC and the IMA were deposited in the MA archives by Combridge.
79. Combridge, J.T., in MA, *Newsletter*, 4 (July 1963), p.2.
80. IMA, *General Information* (1986).
81. Kilmister, C.W., in *Bulletin of the London Mathematical Society*, 20 (1988), 156–8, p.157.
82. Combridge, J.T., 'The Mathematical Association and the users of mathematics', unpublished memorandum (1961), MA archives, p.4.
83. Combridge, op. cit. (75), p.186
84. Combridge, op. cit. (82), p.5.
85. Combridge, J.T., in MA, *Newsletter*, 7 (Feb. 1965), p.4.
86. Combridge, J.T., in MA, *Newsletter*, 9 (Feb. 1966), p.2.
87. Woolnough, op. cit. (70), p.124.
88. A number of interviewees spontaneously commented on the tensions caused by the IMA's activism in the educational arena, as personified by its registrar, Clarke.
89. JMC, *Report on the In-Service Training of Teachers of Mathematics* (1965): see Combridge, op. cit. (86), pp.1–2; and MA, *Newsletter*, 10 (Sept. 1966), pp.12–24, for a discussion of the report at the MA's annual meeting (Keele, 1966).
90. IMA, *The First Report on the Shortage of Teachers of Mathematics* (1969).
91. Combridge, op. cit. (18), p.7.
92. Ibid.
93. MA, 'Report of the Council for the year 1966', *Newsletter*, 12 (Sept. 1967), pp.9–12.
94. Lighthill, M.J., 'From the President', in MA, *Newsletter*, 18 (March 1971), p.1.
95. Interview with Trevor Fletcher, 14 Nov. 1989. The pupil-centred emphasis within the ICSITM was, for Fletcher, reflected in the group's acronym: "excite 'em". There are a number of references to the ICSITM's links with the ATAM's membership in Cooper, op. cit. (31).
96. Hughes, op. cit. (3), p.12.
97. Wooton, W., *SMSG: The Making of a Curriculum* (Yale University Press, 1965), p.125.
98. Organization for European Economic Co-operation, *New Thinking in School Mathematics* (OEEC, 1961); Organization for European Economic Co-operation, *Synopses for Modern Secondary School Mathematics* (OEEC, 1961).
99. Interview with Trevor Fletcher, 14 Nov. 1989.
100. Fletcher, T.J. (ed.), *Some Lessons in Mathematics* (Cambridge University Press, 1964).
101. Quadling, D.A., 'Obituary. Edwin Arthur Maxwell', *MG*, 72 (1988), 51–2.
102. Goodstein, R.L., Reviews of OEEC, op. cit. (98), *MG*, 46 (1962), 69–72, p.72. Fletcher responded to Goodstein's critique in a letter published in *MG*, 46 (1962), pp.177–8, where he pointed out that the OEEC publications were informed by psychological and pedagogical as well as mathematical considerations: 'The case for expanding school instruction in the direction of modern algebra . . . rests on recent psychological work by Piaget and on pedagogical research in the classroom.' (p.178).
103. Maxwell, op. cit. (42), p.173.
104. Ibid., p.174.
105. Howson, op. cit. (73), p.84.
106. Hughes, op. cit. (3), pp.29–30. From a university standpoint, Newman outlined his position in a paper: 'Modern mathematics and the school curriculum', *MG*, 45 (1961),

288–92.
107. Howson, op. cit. (73), p.85.
108. MA, 'The use of the axiomatic method in secondary teaching', *MG*, 50 (1966), 259–75.
109. Hughes, M.G., 'Accurate reasoning in sixth form pure mathematics', *MG*, 49 (1965), 265–71, p.267.
110. ATM, *The Development of Mathematical Activity in Children; The Place of the Problem in this Development* (ATM, 1966). According to Bill Brookes, who edited the report (interview 14 May 1991), it was modelled on the 1912 Board of Education reports for the first ICMI; all the contributors were named in their sections.
111. MA, 'Report of the Council for the year 1967', attached to AGM agenda (1968), p.9.
112. Howson, op. cit. (73), p.86.
113. Howson, A.G., 'The First International Congress on Mathematical Education', in MA, *Newsletter*, 15 (Dec. 1969), 3.
114. MA, 'Report of the Council – 1970', printed with AGM agenda (1971), p.9.
115. *MG*, 55 (1972), footnote, p.87.
116. Interview with Wilf Flemming, 7 Dec. 1987.
117. Watson, F.R., *Developments in Mathematics Teaching* (Open Books, 1976), ch.9. For a personal view of the Nuffield Project see Matthews, G., *Mainly on the Bright Side* (Jumpix Books, 1989), 108–28. Early in the life of the project Matthews married Julia Comber, an infant school headteacher, who became a member of the MA's Policy Committee.
118. Central Advisory Council, *[Plowden Report] Children and their Primary Schools* (HMSO, 1967), p.238.
119. MA, *Newsletter*, 8 (Sept. 1965), p.17.
120. Thurston, J.A., 'The annual conference, 1970', in MA, *Newsletter*, 16 (May 1970), 1–2, p.1.
121. MA, *Primary Mathematics: A Further Report* (MA, 1970), p.1.
122. Rollett, A.P., 'A history of teaching modern mathematics in England', *MG*, 47 (1963), 299–306, p.302.
123. Cockcroft, W.H. and Land, F.W., 'The principles of teaching modern mathematics', *MG*, 47 (1963), 307–22, p.310.
124. For a study of the contrasts between the SMP and MME see Cooper, op. cit. (31), ch.10.
125. Howson, A.G., 'Change in mathematics education since the late 1950's – ideas and realisation. Great Britain', *Educational Studies in Mathematics*, 9 (1978), 183–223, pp.187–9; MA, *Mathematics Projects in British Secondary Schools* (G. Bell and Sons, 1968).
126. Tammadge, A., 'SMP: the first ten years', *Mathematics in School* 1 (4) (1972), 6–8.
127. For a range of views on the SMP's first twenty-five years, from 1961, see Howson, A.G. (ed.), *Challenges and Responses in Mathematics* (Cambridge University Press, 1987).
128. Cooper, op.cit. (31), p.174, quotes Thwaites's judgement that the MA had become an 'extremely "trad" organization'.
129. Langford (interview, 10 Dec. 1987) recalls 'meeting Thwaites off the train at Waterloo; and we went into a refreshment room and we sat down and had a committee of two . . . He . . . made his case and I accepted that it was the right thing to do.'
130. Cundy, H.M., 'The School Mathematics Project', *MG*, 47 (1963), 20–1. This was the second number of the *Gazette* to be edited by Maxwell and it included a much higher profile for *teaching* modern mathematics in schools than hitherto, with articles by Matthews on matrices, G.S. Smithers on sets and logic, and Alan Tammadge on links with primary school developments. Tammadge, the head of mathematics at Abingdon School, had early links with the ATAM and also became closely involved with the MA and the SMP: see Tammadge, A.R., 'A mathematics master in the 1960s', in Howson, op.cit. (127), 21–33. He was elected President of the MA for the year 1978–9.
131. MA, op.cit. (125).
132. Interviews with Douglas Quadling, 24 Oct. 1989, and Geoffrey Howson, 18 Dec. 1989. Rollett actively promoted and disseminated experimental work, and had close links

with Matthews: see Matthews, op.cit. (117).

133. Interview with Peter Coaker, 12 April 1990. Coaker worked for BP and contributed to the 1961 conference. He became BP's Educational Affairs Manager and a prominent member of the MA, providing a much-needed industrial perspective. He was elected President of the MA for the year 1984–5.

134. Combridge, J.T., 'Recent developments', in MA, *Mathematics in Education and Industry*, supplement to *Newsletter*, 11 (1967), 6–12, p.8. Cooper, op.cit. (31), uses the evidence of the BP conference proceedings to point to 'inter-associational conflict' between the MA and the ATM.

135. MA, 'Report of the Council for the year 1963', *Newsletter*, 6 (Sept. 1964), pp.11–12.

136. Combridge, J.T., 'The Schools and Industry Committee', in MA, *Newsletter*, 12 (Sept. 1967), 2–3, p.2.

137. MA, *A Revised Guide to Mathematics Projects in British Secondary Schools* (G. Bell and Sons, 1976), pp.18–20.

138. Interview with Peter Coaker, 12 April 1990.

139. MA, *Computers and the Teaching of Numerical Mathematics in the Upper Secondary School* (G. Bell and Sons, 1971).

140. MA, *Applications of Elementary Mathematics* (G. Bell and Sons, 1964); MA, *Applications of Sixth Form Mathematics* (G. Bell and Sons, 1967).

141. Combridge, op.cit. (134), p.11. The Crowther Report, *15–18* (HMSO, 1959), first coined the term 'numeracy' and gave it a broad interpretation.

142. MA, *Mathematics in Education and Industry: A Survey of Regional Reports* (July, 1969), p.5. With support from BP, Combridge edited a wide-ranging collection of papers under the title *Count Me In: Numeracy in Education* (Queen Anne Press, 1968). Combridge and Mullaly headed the list of contributors.

143. MA, *Mathematics in Education and Industry: The Aims and Work of the Schools and Industry Committee* (1975), p.1.

144. MA, *Newsletter*, 47 (Dec. 1979 – Jan. 1980), p.6.

145. Bailey, D.E., *A Survey of Mathematics Projects Involving Education and Employment* (University of Bath, 1978).

146. Combridge, J.T., typescript of unpublished lecture given at the Shell Centre for Mathematical Education, University of Nottingham, 20 March 1971, p.16, MA archives.

147. MA, *Newsletter*, 6 (Sept. 1964), pp.1, 8.

148. Busbridge, I., 'Robbins – and all that', *MG*, 49 (1965), 241–52, p.249.

149. MA, *Suggestions for Sixth-Form Work in Pure Mathematics* (G. Bell and Sons, 1967); MA, *A Suggested Core Syllabus in Pure Mathematics for Sixth Forms* (G. Bell and Sons, 1968).

150. MA, 'The Report of Council – 1968', attached to AGM agenda (1969), p.6.

151. MA, 'Comparison of First Year University Mathematics Syllabuses', *MG*, 56 (1972), 2–4.

152. MA, 'Mathematics at the University', reprint from *MG*, 59 (1975), 221–8.

153. Williams, op.cit. (21), p.252.

154. Cooper, op.cit. (31), pp.165–6. Exceptionally, the *Gazette* included the following short article: Hall, J.A.P., '"N. Bourbaki"', *MG*, 44 (1960), 250–3.

155. Combridge, op.cit. (75), pp.181–3.

156. See note 130 and *MG*, 47 (1963), 277–366, including survey articles by Smithies, Rollett, and Cockcroft and Land, and articles covering different sectors of education: primary, secondary, sixth form, technical and teacher education.

157. Hughes, op.cit. (3).

158. Maxwell, E.A., in MA, *Newsletter*, 9 (Feb. 1966), p.5.

159. MA, 'The Mathematical Association Teaching Committee 1958–1962', *MG*, 43 (1959), inset pp.iv-v.

160. MA, 'Members of the Teaching Committee', *Newsletter*, 4 (July 1963), p.12.

161. Matthews, op.cit. (117), p.97; 'Matrices for the million', *MG*, 47 (1963), 2–8. In 1968 he became Shell Professor of Mathematics Education at the Centre for Science Education, Chelsea College: 'the first occupant of the very first chair of Mathematics Education to be set up in this country' (Matthews, op.cit. (117), p.142). He was elected President of the MA for the year 1977–8 and gave a typically lively address with a

surprising title: 'Sausages and bananas', *MG*, 62 (1978), 145–56. The title was inspired by his former teacher at Marlborough College, Robson, who was aptly nicknamed 'hemispherical boss' by Matthews and his contemporaries.

162. Morgan, op.cit. (53), p.266.
163. Tammadge, A.R., 'Stage A topology in the main school', *MG*, 48 (1964), 365–72.
164. MA, op.cit. (137). Lindsay was an undergraduate and teacher in Reading, before moving into teacher education in 1965. Ruth Tobias was convener and Lindsay was chairman and editor for the MA's work on mathematics laboratories. The pair became the first full-time lecturers appointed to the Shell Centre for Mathematical Education in the University of Nottingham. Here Lindsay specialized in work on the schools and industry interface, and numeracy in the broad sense, including the SLAPONS project. For an obituary of Lindsay, who died in 1985, see Tobias, R., 'Robert Leslie Lindsay', *MG*, 70 (1986), 47–51.
165. MA, *School Library Mathematics List* (G. Bell and Sons, 1966); MA, *Mathematics Laboratories in Schools* (G. Bell and Sons, 1968); MA, *Introduction of SI Units in Schools* (MA 1969); MA, *A Report on Decimal Currency* (MA 1969).
166. IAAM, *The Teaching of Mathematics* (Cambridge University Press, 1957), p.201. This report details the various syllabus options for statistics (pp.201–3); see also Cooper, op.cit. (31), pp.112–13.
167. Bibby, J., *Notes towards a History of Teaching Statistics* (John Bibby (Books), 1986).
168. Hope-Jones, W., 'A plea for teaching probability in schools', *MG*, 12 (1924), 139–57; 'The study of statistics in a school course', *MG*, 17 (1933), 158–76.
169. Brookes, B.C., 'The incorporation of statistics into a school course', *MG*, 31 (1947), 211–18, p.211.
170. Brookes, B.C., *Notes on the Teaching of Statistics in Schools* (Heinemann, 1952), quote from *Nature*, inside back cover. The *Notes* provided further detailed support for teachers seeking to implement new syllabuses in statistics up to A-level.
171. MA, op.cit. (140).
172. See the syllabus analysis in MA, op.cit. (125), p.33.
173. MA, Minute Book of Teaching Committee, 1 Jan. 1957, MA archives.
174. IAAM, op.cit. (166), p.216.
175. For an obituary tribute to Penfold, who died in 1992, see Brown, M., in MA, *Newsletter*, 88 (June 1992), p.16.
176. MA, op.cit. (173), 5 Jan. 1952, 12 April 1958.
177. Penfold, A.P., to Price, M.H., personal correspondence, 1 March 1990.
178. MA, op.cit. (173), 5 Jan. 1960.
179. Penfold, op.cit. (177).
180. MA, op.cit. (173), 11 Nov. 1961.
181. Ibid., 20 April 1963.
182. Ibid., 13 April 1966.
183. Ibid., 29 March 1967.
184. Ibid., 1 April 1970.
185. MA, Council minutes, 30 Oct. 1970, MA archives.
186. MA, op.cit. (114), p.4.
187. Interviews with Peter Reynolds, 31 Jan. 1990, and John Hersee, 13 Sept. 1991.
188. The materials produced by the subcommittee were assigned to its chairman, Daisy Penfold: see MA, 'The Report of Council – 1972', printed with AGM agenda (1973), p.7. The Penfolds subsequently destroyed almost all of their files and notes, 'motivated by disgust at the thoughtlessness of the hold-up in publication' (Penfold, op.cit. (177)). Copies of all the draft chapters, from 1966, have been deposited in the MA archives.
189. MA, 'The Report of Council – 1973', printed with AGM agenda (1974), p.6.
190. MA, 'Report of Council: 1975', A4 duplicated pamphlet (1976), p.4; MA, *An Approach to A Level Probability and Statistics* (G. Bell and Sons, 1975).
191. Barnett, V., 'Teaching statistics in schools in England and Wales', in Institut für Didaktik der Mathematik, *Comparative Studies of Mathematics Curricula – Change and Stability 1960 – 1980* (IDM, Bielefeld, 1980), 444–63, p.449.
192. Committee of Inquiry into the Teaching of Mathematics in Schools, [Cockcroft Report] *Mathematics Counts* (HMSO, 1982), p.234.

193. MA, *Newsletter*, 23 (Nov. 1972), pp.1–2, details the establishment of an independently constituted Committee on Statistical Education supported in principle by the MA, the IMA and the Royal Statistical Society. The Cockcroft Report makes no reference to such a committee.
194. Cockcroft Report, op.cit. (192), p.235.
195. Barnett, op.cit. (191), pp.458–9.
196. Bibby, op.cit. (167), pp.87–9.
197. Barnett, op.cit. (191), p.462.
198. MA, *Transfer from Primary to Secondary Schools* (G. Bell and Sons, 1964).
199. Simon, op.cit. (11), pp.342–50.
200. Simon, B., '10/65 and all that', *Times Educational Supplement* (13 July 1990), p.16.
201. Simon, op.cit. (11), pp.271–82.
202. Ibid., pp.586–9.
203. Ibid., pp.308–11.
204. Ibid., p.304.
205. Special supplement, op.cit. (14), p.48.
206. Cooper, B., 'Secondary school mathematics since 1950: reconstructing differentiation', in Goodson, I.F. (ed.), *Social Histories of the Secondary Curriculum: Subjects for Study* (Falmer Press, 1985), 89–119, pp.96–100.
207. Interview with Geoffrey Howson, 18 Dec. 1989.
208. Cooper, op.cit. (206), pp.98–9.
209. MA, op.cit. (137).
210. Cockcroft Report, op.cit. (192), p.130.
211. MA, op.cit. (173), 31 March 1964.
212. MA, *A Report on Mathematics Syllabuses for the Certificate of Secondary Education* (G. Bell and Sons, 1968).
213. MA, op.cit. (173), 29 March 1967, 16 April 1968.
214. Matthews, G., in MA, *Newsletter*, 8 (Sept. 1965), p.6.
215. Discussion reported in MA, *Newsletter*, 12 (Sept. 1967), p.16.
216. MA, op.cit. (121).
217. MA, op.cit. (215), p.19.
218. MA, *Mathematics Eleven to Sixteen* (G. Bell and Sons, 1974). In Douglas Quadling's judgement (interview 24 Oct. 1989), 'That was the last report we tried to produce in a consensus fashion.'
219. Interview with Trevor Fletcher, 14 Nov. 1989. John Hersee took over from Bailey as chairman of the Teaching Committee in 1973. They both had a major hand in pulling together the various drafts for the 1974 report (interview with John Hersee, 13 Sept. 1991). Hersee was also closely involved with the INSET course initiative: see MA, op.cit. (173), 9 April 1973, 8 April 1974.

Notes and References – Chapter Eight

1. Jeffreys, B., 'From the President', in MA, *Newsletter*, 15 (Dec. 1969), 1.
2. Reynolds, P., 'Full circle', *MG*, 74 (1990), 211–23, p.219.
3. See, for example, from the Falmer Studies in Curriculum History Series: McCulloch, G., Jenkins, E. and Layton, D., *Technological Revolution? The Politics of School Science and Technology in England and Wales since 1945* (Falmer Press, 1985); Moon, B., *The 'New Maths' Curriculum Controversy: An International Story* (Falmer Press, 1986); and Woolnough, B.E., *Physics Teaching in Schools 1960–85: Of People, Policy and Power* (Falmer Press, 1987).
4. Howson, A.G., *A History of Mathematics Education in England* (Cambridge University Press, 1982); Cooper, B., *Renegotiating Secondary School Mathematics* (Falmer Press, 1985).
5. The official text of Margaret Thatcher's speech is reproduced in *MG*, 55 (1971), p.271.
6. The striking impressions of Baker's address are based on personal notes and recollections from the Birmingham Conference.

7. MA, Minutes of the Policy Committees, 21 March 1968, MA archives.
8. MA, Report of the Policy Committee to Council, Sept. 1969, appendix, MA archives, p.4.
9. MA, 'Subscriptions and the future of the Association', *Newsletter*, 16 (May 1970), p.3.
10. Thurston, J.A., 'The Policy Committee', in MA, *Newsletter*, 16 (May 1970), p.4.
11. MA, op.cit. (8), appendix, p.5.
12. MA, op.cit. (7), 13 Sept. 1968.
13. Combridge, J.T., 'The Mathematical Association reaches its first century', *Mathematics in School*, 1 (2) (1972), 6–8, p.8; Combridge, J.T., *The Mathematical Association Records and Sources*, unpublished and undated, MA archives, p.17.
14. MA, op.cit. (8), appendix, p.3.
15. Committee of Inquiry into the Teaching of Mathematics in Schools, [Cockcroft Report] *Mathematics Counts* (HMSO, 1982), p.221.
16. Layton, D., *Interpreters of Science* (John Murray/ASE, 1984), p.116.
17. MA, *Annual Report 1992/3* (1993); ATM, *Annual Report of Activities Year Ended 1992* (1993), p.4.
18. Some issues of the MA's *Newsletter* included sketches of particular branches. For the Oxford and District branch see *Newsletter*, 31 (June 1975), p.9.
19. MA, 'Report of the Council for the year 1962', draft duplicated sheets (1963), p.2.
20. MA, *Newsletter* 16 (May 1970), p.8.
21. MA, 'The Report of Council – 1970', printed with AGM agenda (1971), p.4.
22. MA, op.cit. (7), 14 June 1968, appendix 2.
23. MA, 'Report of Council: 1975', duplicated sheets (1976), p.6.
24. Interview with John Thurston, 30 Oct. 1989.
25. Thurston, J.A., 'Branching out', in MA, *Newsletter*, 38 (Sept.–Oct. 1977), p.4.
26. MA, *News*, 1 (Sept. – Oct. 1984), pp.8–9.
27. MA, *Newsletter*, 88 (June 1992), pp.11–12; MA, Branches Committee Minutes, 6 April 1993.
28. MA, op.cit. (7), 9 May 1968, appendix 1.
29. MA, op.cit. (7), 25 Nov. 1968, appendix 1.
30. Layton, op.cit. (16), pp.112–4. Brian Atwood (interview 16 June 1988), who succeeded Tapper as general secretary of the ASE in 1972, has emphasized his role as a 'managing director' of a business, which in 1988 involved twenty full-time equivalent staff. Around a quarter of the ASE's income came from commercial profits, associated with its bookselling side. Expanding activity in the 1970s led to a renewed appeal for funds, from 1977, which yielded more than £20,000 towards the cost of a major extension to the ASE's headquarters.
31. MA, op.cit. (21), p.3.
32. MA, *Centenary Appeal*, publicity pamphlet (1971).
33. A copy of the trust deed is held in the MA archives, box 37.
34. Morgan, J.B., 'The thirteenth grade', *MG*, 48 (1964), 253–67, p.256.
35. MA, 'Report of the Council for the year 1957', *MG*, 42 (1958), inset iii-vi, pp.iii-iv.
36. MA, 'Report of the Council for the year 1953', *MG*, 38 (1954), 2–4, p.2.
37. MA, 'Report of the Council for the year 1959', *MG*, 44 (1960), inset xxiv-xxvi, p.xxiv.
38. Interview with Geoffrey Howson, 18 Dec. 1989.
39. MA, 'The Report of Council – 1968', printed with AGM agenda (1969), p.1.
40. MA, 'The Report of Council – 1972', printed with AGM agenda (1973), p.1.
41. MA, op.cit. (7), 28 June 1969.
42. Lighthill, M.J., 'The art of teaching the art of applying mathematics', *MG*, 55 (1971), 249–70, p.252.
43. MA, op.cit. (32).
44. Combridge, W.A., 'Centenary appeal', in MA, *Newsletter*, 24 (June 1973), 8–10. In 1972 Winifred Cooke became J.T. Combridge's second wife; in 1986 they both died.
45. MA, 'Report of Council, 1979', duplicated sheets (1980), p.1.
46. MA, 'Report of Council – 1974', printed with AGM agenda (1975), p.9; MA, op.cit. (23), pp.1, 6–7.
47. Gray, J.A., 'Headquarters', in MA, *Newsletter*, 39 (Dec. 1977 – Jan. 1978), 1–2.

48. MA, *Annual Report 1990–1991* (1991), p.18.
49. Hersee, J., Letter from the President to members, 13 July 1992. Happily, Anne Thomas, the new treasurer, reported an operating surplus in her April 1993 report: see MA, op.cit. (17), p.2.
50. MA, *The Rules of the Mathematical Association* (1946).
51. The proposal for a standing subcommittee of Council was put by Broadbent in 1949 and carried through by a small subcommittee under Langford: see MA, Minute Book of Council, 3 Jan. 1950, MA archives.
52. MA, *The Rules of the Mathematical Association* (1962), p.10. Oddly, there is no mention of the Standing Committee of Council in the published rules of 1951 and 1957.
53. Combridge, J.T., in MA, *Newsletter*, 15 (Dec. 1969), 5–7, p.7.
54. MA, op.cit. (7), 9 May 1968, appendix 2.
55. MA, op.cit. (7), 25 Nov. 1968, appendix 2.
56. MA, *Rules of the Mathematical Association* (1972), p.6.
57. MA, *Rules and Regulations* (1980), pp.11–12.
58. The Council for 1990–1 consisted of sixty-six members, including sixteen Vice-Presidents (MA, op.cit. (48), p.20).
59. The proposals failed to secure the necessary three-quarters majority at the 1992 annual general meeting: see MA, *Newsletter*, 88 (June 1992), pp.2–3. All the major proposals were adopted at the 1993 meeting: see MA, *Newsletter*, 91 (June 1993), pp.1–2.
60. Bishop, A., 'Structural alterations', in MA, *Newsletter*, 87 (Feb. 1992), 3–6, where the MA President, 1991–2, explains the rationale for organizational change.
61. MA, op.cit. (7), 13 Sept. 1968, appendix.
62. Thurston, op.cit. (10), p.4.
63. MA, op.cit. (7), 14 June 1968.
64. MA, op.cit. (7), 27 June 1968.
65. MA, op.cit. (9), p.3.
66. Quadling, D.A., 'The new magazine', in MA, *Newsletter*, 17 (Oct. 1970), p.1.
67. MA, *Newsletter*, 19 (June 1971), p.5.
68. Interview with Geoffrey Howson, 18 Dec. 1989.
69. MA, op.cit. (23), p.5.
70. Interview with Peter Reynolds, 31 Jan. 1990.
71. MA, op.cit. (40), pp.3–5.
72. Reynolds, P., '*Mathematics in School*', in MA, *Newsletter*, 26 (Feb./March 1974), 1–2, p.2.
73. Kilpatrick, J., 'A history of research in mathematics education', in Grouws, D.A. (ed.), *Handbook of Research on Mathematics Teaching and Learning* (Macmillan, 1992), 3–38.
74. Ibid., p.30.
75. On the seminal contribution of Freudenthal to mathematics education see Goffree, F., *Hans Freudenthal: Working on Mathematics Education* (University of Amsterdam, 1992).
76. Kilpatrick, op.cit. (73), p.26.
77. Carter, D.C. and Wain, G.T., *References of Use to Teachers of Mathematics* (University of Leeds, 1974).
78. Graphs of the (predominantly American) output of research studies, theses and dissertations on mathematics education over the twentieth century also show the 'take off' in the 1960s (Kilpatrick, op.cit. (73), p.28).
79. Howson, A.G., 'Research in mathematics education', *MG*, 72 (1988), 265–71.
80. Interview with Bill Brookes, 14 May 1991.
81. Interview with Peter Reynolds, 31 Jan. 1990.
82. Interview with John Hersee, 13 Sept. 1991.
83. MA, op.cit. (67), p.2.
84. MA, *Newsletter*, 31 (June/July 1975), p.4; MA, *Newsletter*, 42 (Sept.–Oct., 1978), pp.2–3; MA, 'Report of Council 1980', A5 pamphlet (1981), pp.5–7.
85. MA, 'Report of Council, 1977', duplicated sheets (1978), pp.6–7.
86. MA, *Computers in the Mathematics Curriculum* (MA,1992). MA, *Teaching Committee News 1992*, A5 pamphlet (1992), includes reports from eighteen subcommittees; and

the numbering system for subcommittees runs to 95.
87. Reynolds, op.cit. (2), p.219.
88. MA, op.cit. (23), p.2.
89. MA, op.cit. (85), p.2.
90. MA, *Newsletter*, 38 (Sept.–Oct. 1977), p.5.
91. According to Reynolds (interview 31 Jan. 1990), it was Quadling who 'had the vision of a diploma in maths education', and he persuaded Reynolds to play a leading part, as he had also done in the case of the editorship of *Mathematics in School*.
92. The CNAA link provided a base for the early planning meetings, which were chaired by Kerr, whose expertise and efficiency proved invaluable (interview with Douglas Quadling, 24 Oct. 1989).
93. Reynolds, P., 'In-service education of teachers of mathematics', *British Journal of In-Service Education*, 8 (1) (1981), 51–5.
94. MA, op.cit. (90), p.5.
95. Interview with Geoffrey Howson, 18 Dec. 1989.
96. Layton, op.cit. (16), pp.280–1.
97. Thomas, A., 'End of an era or another beginning?', *Mathematics in School*, 19 (5) (Nov. 1990), 40–2, p.40.
98. Interview with Peter Reynolds, 31 Jan. 1990.
99. Thomas, op.cit. (97), p.40.
100. Ibid.
101. Combridge (1972), op.cit. (13), p.8.
102. Hayman, M., 'The British Mathematical Olympiad', in MA, *Newsletter*, 8 (Sept. 1965), 9.
103. Watson, F.R., 'XIth International Mathematical Olympiad', in MA, *Newsletter*, 15 (Dec. 1969), 8.
104. MA, 'Report of Council – 1969', printed with AGM agenda (1970), p.4; MA, op.cit. (21), pp.7–8.
105. MA, op.cit. (23), pp.10–11.
106. MA, op.cit. (48), p.13; MA, op.cit. (17), p.2.
107. Quadling, D.A., 'Four hundred up', *MG*, 57 (1973), 85–6, p.85.
108. MA, *Centenary Conference Programme* (1971).
109. Interview with John Thurston, 30 Oct. 1989. For his impressions of the MA's Edinburgh conference see MA, *Newsletter*, 22 (June 1972), pp.1–4.
110. MA, op.cit. (45), p.18.
111. The MA's work on mathematics in technical education was considered in chapter six.
112. Special supplement to celebrate three quarters of a century of *The Times Educational Supplement*, first published 6 September 1910 (1985), p.44. Polytechnics, with their vocational orientation, were intended to be 'separate but equal' to universities. The ideal of equality was taken a stage further forward in 1992, with polytechnics changing their names to universities.
113. Interview with John Thurston, 30 Oct. 1989.
114. MA, 'The Report of Council – 1971', printed with AGM agenda (1972), p.3.
115. MA, *Teaching Committee News 1990*, A5 pamphlet (1990), p.4.
116. In Thurston's view (interview 30 Oct. 1989), Appleton remains 'the father figure in our work', a sentiment echoed by the industrialist Peter Coaker (interview 12 April 1990).
117. One leading LEA adviser for further education, Huw Kyffin, first became involved with the MA through the further education subcommittee. He became the business manager of the Teaching Committee (interview with John Thurston, 30 Oct. 1989). Kyffin has since become involved in a proposal to establish a new National Association for Numeracy and Mathematics in Colleges: see *Times Educational Supplement* (12 March 1993), extra, p.vii.
118. MA, *Teaching Committee News 1992*, A5 pamphlet (1992), p.4.
119. Interview with Hilary Shuard, 30 April 1990. She died in December 1992. For an obituary tribute to Shuard see Cross, K., in *Mathematics Teaching*, 142 (1993), 4.
120. MA, op.cit. (48), pp.2–4; MA, *Newsletter*, 88 (June 1992), p.4.
121. Reynolds, op.cit. (93), p.51.

122. Winkley, D., *Diplomats and Detectives: LEA Advisers at Work* (Robert Royce, 1985), ch.2.
123. Kent, D., 'NAMA: initiatives', *Times Educational Supplement* (10 Oct. 1986).
124. AUMET, *Mathematics Teacher Education in Universities of the United Kingdom* (1984), p.22.
125. Interviews with Bill Brookes, 14 May 1991, and Douglas Quadling, 24 Oct. 1989. According to Brookes, it was the meeting of moderators for the MA's Diploma in Mathematical Education which helped to establish SCAMES.
126. Howson, A.G., 'Change in mathematics education since the late 1950's – ideas and realisation. Great Britain', *Educational Studies in Mathematics*, 9 (1978), 183–223, p.212.
127. Simon, B., *Education and the Social Order 1940–1990* (Lawrence and Wishart, 1991), ch.9.
128. Kerr, E., 'Some thoughts on the educational system and mathematics teaching', *MG*, 61 (1977), 157–73, p.160.
129. Cockcroft Report, op.cit. (15), p.ix.
130. Ibid.
131. Freddy Mann also shared in the editing of the MA's most recent major report, *Computers in the Mathematics Curriculum* (1992). This report is broken down into numbered paragraphs throughout, along the lines of the Cockcroft Report.
132. Cooper refers to the reaction to reform in mathematics education around the mid-1970s as a 'crisis'; ironically, a different 'crisis' had also contributed in large measure to the modern mathematics reforms of the early 1960s: see Cooper, B., 'Secondary school mathematics since 1950: reconstructing differentiation', in Goodson, I.F. (ed.), *Social Histories of the Secondary Curriculum: Subjects for Study* (Falmer Press, 1985), 89–119, pp.106–12.
133. Hayman, M., 'To each according to his needs', *MG*, 59 (1975), 137–53.
134. Cockcroft Report, op.cit. (15), pp.13–14.
135. Cockcroft Report, op.cit. (15), appendix 3.
136. For a history of the British Society for the History of Mathematics see Fauvel, J., Gowing, R., Grattan-Guinness, I. and Rogers, L., *The First Twenty-One Years 1971–1992*, special issue of BSHM, *Newsletter*, 21 (1992).
137. Kilpatrick, J., op.cit. (73), pp.25–6.
138. Cockcroft Report, op.cit. (15), pp.62–4 and appendix 2.
139. Layton, op.cit. (16), pp.289–90. The ASE held COSTA together until 1977, when administrative responsibility was handed over to the Historical Association.
140. MA (1981), op.cit. (84), p.11. Howson served a three-year term on the Joint Committee of the IMA and the Royal Society. During the period of the Great Debate he raised serious questions about the influence of the Joint Committee, the JMC and Royal Society itself, in shaping educational policy for school mathematics: 'Unfortunately all the committees consist of mathematicians without power; educational administrators and, in particular, the Department of Education and Science are not represented (other than through the presence of a mathematics inspector).' (Howson, op.cit. (126), p.212.) Further questioning from Howson has proved to be particularly pertinent in the light of subsequent developments: '...are [these committees] all necessary? Do they enable "our collective voice" to be heard at DES, or does the Department still depend for its information and advice on individuals who have "the ear" of the Minister or one of her more influential servants?' (Howson, in MA, op.cit. (85), p.15.)
141. Cockcroft Report, op.cit. (15), p.iii.
142. Ibid., p.133.
143. Ibid., p.130.
144. Cooper, op.cit. (132).
145. Cockcroft Report, op.cit. (15), p.134.
146. Ibid., p.159.
147. Quadling, D.A., 'Pressures and priorities', *MG*, 65 (1981), 157–66, p.165.
148. Brooks, R., *Contemporary Debates in Education: An Historical Perspective* (Longman, 1991), pp.20–3.
149. Simon, op.cit. (127), p.306; and Gordon, P., Aldrich, R. and Dean, D., *Education and Policy in England in the Twentieth Century* (Woburn Press, 1991), pp.305–9.

150. Simon, op.cit. (127), pp.492–4.
151. Gordon, op.cit. (149), pp.287–8.
152. Simon, op.cit. (127), p.508.
153. Aldrich, R., 'Educational legislation of the 1980s in England: an historical analysis', *History of Education*, 21 (1) (1992), 57–69, p.60.
154. Brooks, op.cit. (148), pp.4–48.
155. Simon, op.cit. (127), p.457.
156. MA, *Newsletter*, 36 (March 1977), p.1.
157. MA, op.cit. (85), pp.1–5.
158. Chitty, C., 'Central control of the school curriculum, 1944–87', *History of Education*, 17 (4) (1988), 321–34, p.331.
159. Gordon, op.cit. (149), pp.289–91.
160. Ibid., pp.260–1.
161. Ibid., pp.315, 317.
162. Aldrich, op.cit. (153).
163. Chitty, op.cit. (158), pp.333–4.
164. Brown, M., 'Teachers as workers and teachers as learners', survey paper for Theme Group 1, ICME 6, Budapest (1988).
165. Howson, A.G., 'New challenges', *MG*, 73 (1989), 175–86, p.176. See also Simon, op.cit. (127), ch.11 on 'consultation' during Baker's term of office.
166. Howson, A.G., *National Curricula in Mathematics* (MA, 1991).
167. Brown, M., 'The second iteration', *MG*, 75 (1991), 263–74, p.269.
168. Howson, op.cit. (165), p.183.
169. Ibid., p.184.
170. Ibid., p.185.
171. Ibid., p.185.
172. Hilary Shuard, MA President 1985–6, and Anita Straker, an LEA inspector and MA President 1986–7, also became involved with the National Curriculum Mathematics Working Group. Since 1980 the MA has elected only two university mathematicians as Presidents: Michael Atiyah and Margaret Rayner.
173. Interview with John Hersee, 13 Sept. 1991.
174. The conclusion concerning the potential of professional subversion is based on confidential oral evidence.
175. Black, P., 'Prejudice, tradition and death of a dream', *Times Educational Supplement* (28 Aug. 1992), 8. Black chose the education section of the British Association as his platform. Bolton, E., 'Eric Bolton's apocalypse', *Education*, 180 (4) (1992), 67–8. Bolton chose the annual conference of the Council of Local Education Authorities. For a collection of critical professional responses, including Black, Bolton and Graham, see Chitty, C. and Simon, B. (eds), *Education Answers Back: Critical Responses to Government Policy* (Lawrence and Wishart, 1993).
176. Interview with Trevor Fletcher, 14 Nov. 1989.
177. Dodd, W.A., in MA, *Newsletter*, 17 (Oct. 1970), p.3.
178. Dodd, W.A., to Price, M.H., personal correspondence, 22 April 1985.
179. Interview with Trevor Fletcher, 14 Nov. 1989.
180. Tammadge, A., in MA, *Newsletter*, 46 (Sept./Oct. 1979), p.1.
181. Ibid., pp.1–2.
182. ATM, *Annual Report on Activities Year Ended 1991* (1992), p.2; and see *Reports* for preceding years.
183. Woolnough, op.cit. (3), p.137.
184. Hill, G., 'Influential voice', *Times Educational Supplement* (1 Jan. 1988), p.15.
185. Rudduck, J., 'The National Association for the Teaching of English', in Stenhouse, L., *Curriculum Research and Development in Action* (Heinemann, 1980), 8–22.
186. Joint Council of Language Associations, leaflet (1990).
187. Bibby, N., 'The relationship of the MA and the ATM', *Mathematics Teaching*, 126 (1988), 22–3.
188. Bishop, A., '1993 and beyond', *Mathematics Teaching*, 132 (1990), 53–6.
189. Bishop, A., 'Visions, mechanisms and professionals', *MG*, 76 (1992), 438–45.
190. Kilpatrick, J., 'Ties that bind: professional associations in mathematics education', unpublished paper (1992). I am grateful to Jeremy Kilpatrick for letting me have a

copy of this paper and discussing it with me.
191. Ibid., p.15.
192. Interviews with Douglas Quadling, 24 Oct. 1989, Hilary Shuard, 30 April 1990, and John Hersee, 13 Sept. 1991. According to Hersee, 'It used to be said that the ATM was interested in means and the MA was interested in ends.'
193. Reynolds, P., 'The future of the Association: discussion document' (Jan. 1990).
194. Interview with John Hersee, 13 Sept. 1991.
195. Kilpatrick, op.cit. (190), p.10.
196. Bishop, op.cit. (189), p.445.
197. Ibid., p.438. In the case of resources, collaboration between the ATM, MA and NAMA has yielded a recent policy document: *Teaching Mathematics: The Resource Implications* (MA and ATM, 1991).
198. See, for example, AMET, *Newsletter*, special edition (Feb. 1992), which includes correspondence with Kenneth Clarke and related press coverage.
199. Bishop, op.cit. (189), p.445.
200. Briggs, A., 'The history man', *Times Educational Supplement* (12 July 1991), p.22.

NAME INDEX

SUBJECT INDEX